Great-heart
"The Interpreter then called for a Man-Servant of his, one Great-heart"
—page 214

THE HARVARD CLASSICS

EDITED BY CHARLES W ELIOT LL D

THE PILGRIM'S PROGRESS

BY JOHN BUNYAN

THE LIVES OF JOHN DONNE AND GEORGE HERBERT

BY IZAAK WALTON

WITH INTRODUCTIONS AND NOTES

VOLUME 15

P F COLLIER & SON
NEW YORK

Designed, Printed, and Bound at
The Collier Press, New York

CONTENTS

INTRODUCTORY NOTE

JOHN BUNYAN *was born at Elstow, Bedfordshire, England, in November, 1628. His father was a maker and mender of pots and kettles, and the son followed the same trade. Though he is usually called a tinker, Bunyan had a settled home and place of business. He had little schooling, and he describes his early surroundings as poor and mean. When he was not yet sixteen his mother died; in two months his father married again; and the son enlisted as a soldier in the Civil War in November, 1644, though whether on the Parliamentary or Royalist side is not certain. The armies were disbanded in 1646, and about two years later Bunyan married a wife whose piety redeemed him from his delight in rural sport and the habit of profane swearing. He became much interested in religion, but it was only after a tremendous spiritual conflict, lasting three or four years, that he found peace. His struggles are related with extraordinary vividness and intensity in his "Grace Abounding to the Chief of Sinners." In 1655, the year in which he lost his wife, he began to exhort, and two years later he became a regular Non-conformist preacher, continuing, however, to practise his trade. His success as a preacher roused opposition among the regular clergy, and in 1658 he was indicted at the assizes. His writing began with a controversy against the Quakers, and shows from the first the command of a homely but vigorous style.*

With the reenactment of the laws against non-conformity at the Restoration, Bunyan became subject to more severe persecution, and with a short intermission he was confined to prison from 1660 till 1672. Again and again he might have been released, but he refused to promise to desist from preaching, and there was no alternative for the justices but to keep him in confinement. Sometimes lax jailers permitted him to preach at church meetings; he frequently ministered to his fellow-prisoners; and he supported his family, now looked after by a second wife, by making laces. He had apparently abundant leisure, for he wrote in prison a large number of books, the first one of importance being that already mentioned, "Grace Abounding"

(1666). "The Pilgrim's Progress" was also written in jail, but probably during a later confinement of six months in 1675.

In 1672 Charles II suspended the laws against Non-conformists and Roman Catholics, and Bunyan was released. He was called to be minister to a Non-conformist congregation in Bedford, and preached in the barn which served them as a church. But his ministrations were not confined to Bedford. He made preaching tours over a wide district, and even to London, and attracted great crowds of listeners. Meanwhile he continued to write. The first edition of "The Pilgrim's Progress" in 1678 was followed by others with additions, and in 1684 by the second part. "The Life and Death of Mr. Badman" appeared in 1680; "The Holy War made by Shaddai upon Diabolus" in 1682. If the works left in manuscript at his death be included, the total of his books amounts to nearly sixty. He died in 1688, leaving a widow and six children, and a personal estate of less than £100. "The Pilgrim's Progress" became at once popular, and has continued to be by far the most widely read of all his works, and one of the most universally known of English books. Though in the form of an allegory, the narrative interest is so powerful, the drawing of permanent types of human character is so vigorous, and the style is so simple and direct that it takes rank as a great work of fiction. The best sides of English Puritanism have here their most adequate and characteristic expression, while the intensity of Bunyan's religious fervor and the universality of the spiritual problems with which he deals, raise the work to a place among the great religious classics of the world.

THE AUTHOR'S APOLOGY

FOR HIS BOOK

WHEN at the first I took my Pen in hand
Thus for to write; I did not understand
That I at all should make a little Book
In such a mode; Nay, I had undertook
To make another, which when almost done,
Before I was aware I this begun.
And thus it was: I writing of the Way
And Race of Saints, in this our Gospel-day,
Fell suddenly into an Allegory
About their Journey, and the way to Glory,
In more than twenty things which I set down:
This done, I twenty more had in my Crown,
And they again began to multiply,
Like sparks that from the coals of fire do fly.
Nay then, thought I, if that you breed so fast,
I'll put you by yourselves, lest you at last
Should prove ad infinitum, *and eat out*
The Book that I already am about.
Well, so I did; but yet I did not think
To shew to all this World my Pen and Ink
In such a mode; I only thought to make
I knew not what: nor did I undertake
Thereby to please my Neighbor; no not I;
I did it mine own self to gratifie.
Neither did I but vacant seasons spend
In this my Scribble; nor did I intend
But to divert myself in doing this
From worser thoughts which make me do amiss.
Thus I set Pen to Paper with delight,
And quickly had my thoughts in black and white.

For having now my Method by the end,
Still as I pull'd, it came; and so I penn'd
It down, until it came at last to be
For length and breadth the bigness which you see.
Well, when I had thus put mine ends together,
I shew'd them others, that I might see whether
They would condemn them, or them justifie:
And some said, Let them live; some, Let them die;
Some said, John, *print it; others said, Not so:*
Some said, It might do good; others said, No.
Now was I in a straight, and did not see
Which was the best thing to be done by me:
At last I thought, Since you are thus divided,
I print it will, and so the case decided.
For, thought I, some I see would have it done,
Though others in that Channel do not run.
To prove then who advised for the best,
Thus I thought fit to put it to the test.
I further thought, if now I did deny
Those that would have it thus, to gratifie,
I did not know but hinder them I might
Of that which would to them be great delight.
For those which were not for its coming forth
I said to them, Offend you I am loth,
Yet since your Brethren pleased with it be,
Forbear to judge till you do further see.
If that thou wilt not read, let it alone;
Some love the meat, some love to pick the bone:
Yea, that I might them better palliate,
I did too with them thus Expostulate:
May I not write in such a stile as this?
In such a method too, and yet not miss
Mine end, thy good? why may it not be done?
Dark Clouds bring Waters, when the bright bring none.
Yea, dark or bright, if they their Silver drops
Cause to descend, the Earth, by yielding Crops,
Gives praise to both, and carpeth not at either,
But treasures up the Fruit they yield together;
Yea, so commixes both, that in her Fruit
None can distinguish this from that: they suit

Her well, when hungry; but, if she be full,
She spues out both, and makes their blessings null.
You see the ways the Fisher-man doth take
To catch the Fish; what Engines doth he make?
Behold how he engageth all his Wits,
Also his Snares, Lines, Angles, Hooks, and Nets.
Yet Fish there be, that neither Hook, nor Line,
Nor Snare, nor Net, nor Engine can make thine;
They must be grop'd for, and be tickled too,
Or they will not be catch'd, whate'er you do.
How doth the Fowler seek to catch his Game
By divers means, all which one cannot name?
His Gun, his Nets, his Lime-twigs, Light, and Bell;
He creeps, he goes, he stands; yea who can tell
Of all his postures? Yet there's none of these
Will make him master of what Fowls he please.
Yea, he must Pipe and Whistle to catch this;
Yet if he does so, that *Bird he will miss.*
If that a Pearl may in a Toad's head dwell,
And may be found too in an Oyster-shell;
If things that promise nothing do contain
What better is than Gold; who will disdain,
That have an inkling of it, there to look,
That they may find it? Now my little Book
(Though void of all those Paintings that may make
It with this or the other man to take)
Is not without those things that do excel
What do in brave, but empty notions dwell.
Well, yet I am not fully satisfied,
That this your Book will stand, when soundly try'd.
Why, what's the matter? It is dark. What tho?
But it is feigned: What of that I tro?
Some men, by feigning words as dark as mine,
Make truth to spangle, and its rays to shine.
But they want solidness. Speak man thy mind.
They drownd the weak; Metaphors make us blind.
Solidity indeed becomes the Pen
Of him that writeth things Divine to men;
But must I needs want solidness, because
By Metaphors I speak? Were not God's Laws,

His Gospel-Laws, in olden time held forth
By Types, Shadows, and Metaphors? Yet loth
Will any sober man be to find fault
With them, lest he be found for to assault
The highest Wisdom. No, he rather stoops,
And seeks to find out what by Pins and Loops,
By Calves, and Sheep, by Heifers, and by Rams,
By Birds, and Herbs, and by the blood of Lambs,
God speaketh to him. And happy is he
That finds the light and grace that in them be.
Be not too forward therefore to conclude
That I want solidness, that I am rude:
All things solid in shew not solid be;
All things in Parables despise not we;
Lest things most hurtful lightly we receive,
And things that good are, of our souls bereave.
My dark and cloudy words they do but hold
The Truth, as Cabinets inclose the Gold.
The Prophets used much by Metaphors
To set forth Truth; yea, whoso considers
Christ, his Apostles too, shall plainly see,
That Truths to this day in such Mantles be.
Am I afraid to say that Holy Writ,
Which for its Stile and Phrase puts down all Wit,
Is everywhere so full of all these things,
Dark Figures, Allegories? Yet there springs
From that same Book that lustre, and those rays
Of light, that turns our darkest nights to days.
Come, let my Carper to his Life now look,
And find there darker lines than in my Book
He findeth any; Yea, and let him know,
That in his best things there are worse lines too.
May we but stand before impartial men,
To his poor One I dare adventure Ten,
That they will take my meaning in these lines
Far better than his lies in Silver Shrines.
Come, Truth, although in Swaddling-clouts, I find,
Informs the Judgment, rectifies the Mind,
Pleases the Understanding, makes the Will
Submit; the Memory too it doth fill

With what doth our Imagination please;
Likewise it tends our troubles to appease.
Sound words I know Timothy *is to use,*
And old Wives' Fables he is to refuse;
But yet grave Paul *him nowhere doth forbid*
The use of Parables; in which lay hid
That Gold, those Pearls, and precious stones that were
Worth digging for, and that with greatest care.
Let me add one word more. O man of God,
Art thou offended? Dost thou wish I had
Put forth my matter in another dress,
Or that I had in things been more express?
Three things let me propound, then I submit
To those that are my betters, as is fit.
1. *I find not that I am denied the use*
Of this my method, so I no abuse
Put on the Words, Things, Readers; or be rude
In handling Figure or Similitude,
In application; but, all that I may,
Seek the advance of Truth this or that way.
Denied, did I say? Nay, I have leave,
(Example too, and that from them that have
God better pleased, by their words or ways,
Than any man that breatheth now a-days)
Thus to express my mind, thus to declare
Things unto thee, that excellentest are.
2. *I find that men (as high as Trees) will write*
Dialogue-wise; yet no man doth them slight
For writing so; Indeed if they abuse
Truth, cursed be they, and the craft they use
To that intent; but yet let Truth be free
To make her sallies upon thee and me,
Which way it pleases God. For who knows how,
Better than he that taught us first to Plow,
To guide our Mind and Pens for his Design?
And he makes base things usher in Divine.
3. *I find that Holy Writ in many places*
Hath semblance with this method, where the cases
Do call for one thing, to set forth another;
Use it I may then, and yet nothing smother

Truth's golden Beams: nay, by this method may
Make it cast forth its rays as light as day.
And now, before I do put up my Pen,
I'll shew the profit of my Book, and then
Commit both thee and it unto that hand
That pulls the strong down, and makes weak ones stand.
This Book it chalketh out before thine eyes
The man that seeks the everlasting Prize;
It shews you whence he comes, whither he goes,
What he leaves undone, also what he does;
It also shews you how he runs and runs,
Till he unto the Gate of Glory comes.
It shews too, who set out for life amain,
As if the lasting Crown they would obtain;
Here also you may see the reason why
They lose their labour, and like Fools do die.
This Book will make a Traveller of thee,
If by its Counsel thou wilt ruled be;
It will direct thee to the Holy Land,
If thou wilt its directions understand:
Yea, it will make the slothful active be;
The blind also delightful things to see.
Art thou for something rare and profitable?
Wouldest thou see a Truth within a Fable?
Art thou forgetful? Wouldest thou remember
From New-year's-day *to the last of* December?
Then read my Fancies, they will stick like Burrs,
And may be to the Helpless, Comforters.
This Book is writ in such a Dialect
As may the minds of listless men affect:
It seems a novelty, and yet contains
Nothing but sound and honest Gospel strains.
Would'st thou divert thyself from Melancholy?
Would'st thou be pleasant, yet be far from folly?
Would'st thou read Riddles, and their Explanation?
Or else be drowned in thy Contemplation?
Dost thou love picking meat? Or would'st thou see
A man i' th' Clouds, and hear him speak to thee?
Would'st thou be in a Dream, and yet not sleep?
Or would'st thou in a moment laugh and weep?

Wouldest thou lose thyself, and catch no harm,
And find thyself again without a charm?
Would'st read thyself, and read thou know'st not what,
And yet know whether thou art blest or not,
By reading the same lines? O then come hither,
And lay my Book, thy Head, and Heart together.

JOHN BUNYAN.

THE PILGRIM'S PROGRESS

IN THE SIMILITUDE OF A DREAM.

As I walk'd through the wilderness of this world, I lighted on a certain place where was a Den, and I laid me down in that place to sleep; and as I slept, I dreamed a Dream. I dreamed, and behold I saw a Man cloathed with Rags, standing in a certain place, with his face from his own house, a Book in his hand, and a great Burden upon his back. I looked, and saw him open the Book, and read therein; and as he read, he wept and trembled; and not being able longer to contain, he brake out with a lamentable cry, saying *What shall I do?*

The Jail

His outcry

In this plight therefore he went home, and refrained himself as long as he could, that his Wife and Children should not perceive his distress, but he could not be silent long, because that his trouble increased: Wherefore at length he brake his mind to his Wife and Children; and thus he began to talk to them: *O my dear Wife,* said he, *and you the Children of my bowels, I your dear friend, am in myself undone by reason of a Burden that lieth hard upon me; moreover, I am for certain informed that this our City will be burned with fire from Heaven; in which fearful overthrow, both myself, with thee my Wife, and you my sweet Babes, shall miserably come to ruine, except* (*the which yet I see not*) *some way of escape can be found, whereby we may be delivered.* At this his Relations were sore amazed; not for that they believed that what he had said to them was true, but because they thought that some frenzy

This world

He knows no way of escape as yet

distemper had got into his head; therefore, it drawing towards night, and they hoping that sleep might settle his brains, with all haste they got him to bed: But the night was as troublesome to him as the day; wherefore, instead of sleeping, he spent it in sighs and tears. So, when the morning was come, they would know how he did; He told them, *Worse and worse:* he also set to talking to them again, but they began to be hardened: they also thought to drive away his distemper by harsh and surly carriages to him; sometimes they would deride, sometimes they would chide, and sometimes they would quite neglect him: Wherefore he began to retire himself to his chamber, to pray for and pity them, and also to condole his own misery; he would also walk solitarily in the fields, sometimes reading, and sometimes praying: and thus for some days he spent his time.

Carnal physic for a sick soul

Now, I saw upon a time, when he was walking in the fields, that he was, as he was wont, reading in his Book, and greatly distressed in his mind; and as he read, he burst out, as he had done before, crying, *What shall I do to be saved?*

I saw also that he looked this way and that way, as if he would run; yet he stood still, because, as I perceived, he could not tell which way to go. I looked then, and saw a man named *Evangelist,* coming to him, and asked, *Wherefore dost thou cry?*

He answered, Sir, I perceive by the Book in my hand, that I am condemned to die, and after that to come to Judgment, and I find that I am not willing to do the first, nor able to do the second.

> *Christian* no sooner leaves the World but meets
> *Evangelist,* who lovingly him greets
> With tidings of another: and doth shew
> Him how to mount to that from this below.

Then said *Evangelist,* Why not willing to die, since this life is attended with so many evils? The Man answered, Because I fear that this burden that is upon my back will sink me lower than the Grave, and I shall fall into *Tophet.* And, Sir, if I be not fit to go to Prison, I am not fit to go to Judgment, and from thence to Execution; and the thoughts of these things make me cry.

Then said *Evangelist,* If this be thy condition, why standest thou still? He answered, Because I know not whither to go. Then he gave him a *Parchment-roll,* and there was written within, *Fly from the wrath to come.*

Conviction of the necessity of flying

The Man therefore read it, and looking upon *Evangelist* very carefully, said, Whither must I fly? Then said *Evangelist,* pointing with his finger over a very wide field, Do you see yonder *Wicket-gate?* The Man said, No. Then said the other, Do you see yonder shining Light? He said, I think I do. Then said *Evangelist,* Keep that Light in your eye, and go up directly thereto: so shalt thou see the Gate; at which, when thou knockest, it shall be told thee what thou shalt do.

Christ, and the way to him cannot be found without the Word

So I saw in my Dream that the Man began to run. Now he had not run far from his own door, but his Wife and Children, perceiving it, began to cry after him to return; but the Man put his fingers in his ears, and ran on, crying, *Life! Life! Eternal Life!* So he looked not behind him, but fled towards the middle of the Plain.

They that fly from the wrath to come, are a gazing-stock to the world

The Neighbors also came out to see him run; and as he ran, some mocked, others threatened, and some cried after him to return; and among those that did so, there were two that resolved to fetch him back by force. The name of the one was *Obstinate,* and the name of the other *Pliable.* Now by this time the Man was got a good distance from them; but however they were resolved to pursue him, which they did, and in a little time they overtook him. Then said the Man, Neighbors, wherefore are you come? They said, To persuade you to go back with us. But he said, That can by no means be; you dwell, said he, in the City of *Destruction,* the place also where I was born, I see it to be so; and dying there, sooner or later, you will sink lower than the Grave, into a

Obstinate and Pliable follow him

place that burns with Fire and Brimstone: be content, good Neighbors, and go along with me.

OBST. What, said *Obstinate,* and leave our friends and our comforts behind us!

CHR. Yes, said *Christian,* for that was his name, because that *all* which you shall forsake is not worthy to be compared with a *little* of that that I am seeking to enjoy; and if you will go along with me and hold it, you shall fare as I myself; for there where I go, is enough and to spare: Come away, and prove my words.

OBST. What are the things you seek, since you leave all the world to find them?

CHR. I seek an *Inheritance incorruptible, undefiled, and that fadeth not away,* and it is laid up in Heaven, and safe there, to be bestowed at the time appointed, on them that diligently seek it. Read it so, if you will, in my Book.

OBST. Tush, said *Obstinate,* away with your Book; will you go back with us or no?

CHR. No, not I, said the other, because I have laid my hand to the Plow.

OBST. Come then, Neighbor *Pliable,* let us turn again, and go home without him; there is a company of these craz'd-headed coxcombs, that, when they take a fancy by the end, are wiser in their own eyes than seven men that can render a reason.

PLI. Then said *Pliable,* Don't revile; if what the good *Christian* says is true, the things he looks after are better than ours; my heart inclines to go with my Neighbor.

OBST. What! more fools still? Be ruled by me, and go back; who knows whither such a brain-sick fellow will lead you? Go back, go back, and be wise.

Christian and Obstinate pull for Pliable's soul

CHR. Come with me, Neighbor *Pliable;* there are such things to be had which I spoke of, and many more Glories besides. If you believe not me, read here in this Book; and for the truth of what is exprest therein, behold, all is confirmed by the blood of Him that made it.

PLI. Well, Neighbor *Obstinate,* said *Pliable,* I begin to come to a point: I intend to go along with this good man, and to cast in my lot with him: but, my good companion, do you know the way to this desired place?

Pliable contented to go with Christian

CHR. I am directed by a man, whose name is *Evangelist,* to speed me to a little Gate that is before us, where we shall receive instructions about the way.

PLI. Come then, good Neighbor, let us be going. Then they went both together.

OBST. And I will go back to my place, said *Obstinate;* I will be no companion of such mis-led, fantastical fellows.

Obstinate goes railing back

Now I saw in my Dream, that when *Obstinate* was gone back, *Christian* and *Pliable* went talking over the Plain; and thus they began their discourse.

Talk between Christian and Pliable

CHR. Come Neighbor *Pliable,* how do you do? I am glad you are persuaded to go along with me: Had even *Obstinate* himself but felt what I have felt of the powers and terrors of what is yet unseen, he would not thus lightly have given us the back.

PLI. Come, Neighbor *Christian,* since there are none but us two here, tell me now further what the things are, and how to be enjoyed, whither we are going?

CHR. I can better conceive of them with my Mind, than speak of them with my Tongue: but yet, since you are desirous to know, I will read of them in my Book.

God's things unspeakable

PLI. And do you think that the words of your Book are certainly true?

CHR. Yes, verily; for it was made by him that cannot lye.

PLI. Well said; what things are they?

CHR. There is an endless Kingdom to be inhabited,

and everlasting Life to be given us, that we may inhabit that Kingdom for ever.

PLI. Well said; and what else?

CHR. There are Crowns of glory to be given us, and Garments that will make us shine like the Sun in the firmament of Heaven.

PLI. This is excellent; and what else?

CHR. There shall be no more crying, nor sorrow, for He that is owner of the place will wipe all tears from our eyes.

PLI. And what company shall we have there?

CHR. There we shall be with *Seraphims* and *Cherubins,* creatures that will dazzle your eyes to look on them: There also you shall meet with thousands and ten thousands that have gone before us to that place; none of them are hurtful, but loving and holy; every one walking in the sight of God, and standing in his presence with acceptance for ever. In a word, there we shall see the Elders with their golden Crowns, there we shall see the Holy Virgins with their golden Harps, there we shall see men that by the World were cut in pieces, burnt in flames, eaten of beasts, drowned in the seas, for the love that they bare to the Lord of the place, all well, and cloathed with Immortality as with a garment.

PLI. The hearing of this is enough to ravish one's heart; but are these things to be enjoyed? How shall we get to be sharers hereof?

CHR. The Lord, the Governor of the country, hath recorded *that* in this Book; the substance of which is, If we be truly willing to have it, he will bestow it upon us freely.

PLI. Well, my good companion, glad am I to hear of these things; come on, let us mend our pace.

CHR. I cannot go so fast as I would, by reason of this Burden that is upon my back.

Now I saw in my Dream, that just as they had ended this talk, they drew near to a very miry *Slough,* that was in the midst of the plain; and they, being heedless, did both fall suddenly into the bog.

The name of the slough was *Dispond.* Here therefore they wallowed for a time, being grievously bedaubed with the dirt; and *Christian,* because of the Burden that was on his back, began to sink in the mire.

The Slough of Dispond

PLI. Then said *Pliable,* Ah Neighbor *Christian,* where are you now?

CHR. Truly, said *Christian,* I do not know.

PLI. At that *Pliable* began to be offended, and angerly said to his fellow, Is this the happiness you have told me all this while of? If we have such ill speed at our first setting out, what may we expect 'twixt this and our Journey's end? May I get out again with my life, you shall possess the brave Country alone for me. And with that he gave a desperate struggle or two, and got out of the mire on that side of the Slough which was next to his own house: so away he went, and *Christian* saw him no more.

It is not enough to be pliable

Wherefore *Christian* was left to tumble in the Slough of *Dispond* alone; but still he endeavoured to struggle to that side of the Slough that was still further from his own house, and next to the Wicket-gate; the which he did, but could not get out, because of the Burden that was upon his back: But I beheld in my Dream, that a man came to him, whose name was *Help,* and asked him, *What he did there?*

Christian in trouble seeks still to get further from his own house

CHR. Sir, said *Christian,* I was bid go this way by a man called *Evangelist,* who directed me also to yonder Gate, that I might escape the wrath to come; and as I was going thither, I fell in here.

HELP. But why did you not look for the steps?

CHR. Fear followed me so hard, that I fled the next way, and fell in.

The promises.

HELP. Then said he, *Give me thy hand:* so he gave him his hand, and he drew him out, and set him upon sound ground, and bid him go on his way.

Help lifts him up

Then I stepped to him that pluckt him out, and said, Sir, wherefore, since over this place is the way from the City of *Destruction* to yonder Gate, is it that this plat is not mended, that poor travellers might go thither with more security? And he said unto me, This miry Slough is such a place as cannot be mended; it is the descent whither the scum and filth that attends conviction for sin doth continually run, and therefore it is called the Slough of *Dispond;* for still as the sinner is awakened about his lost condition, there ariseth in his soul many fears and doubts, and discouraging apprehensions, which all of them get together, and settle in this place: And this is the reason of the badness of this ground.

What makes the Slough of Dispond

It is not the pleasure of the King that this place should remain so bad. His labourers also have, by the direction of His Majesties Surveyors, been for above these sixteen hundred years imployed about this patch of ground, if perhaps it might have been mended: yea, and to my knowledge, said he, *here* hath been swallowed up at least twenty thousand cart-loads, yea, millions of wholesome instructions, that have at all seasons been brought from all places of the King's dominions (and they that can tell say they are the best materials to make good ground of the place), if so be it might have been mended, but it is the Slough of *Dispond* still, and so will be when they have done what they can.

The promises of forgiveness and acceptance to life by faith in Christ

True, there are by the direction of the Lawgiver, certain good and substantial steps, placed even through the very midst of this Slough; but at such time as this place doth much spue out its filth, as it doth against change of weather, these steps are hardly seen; or if they be, men through the dizziness of their heads, step besides; and then they are bemired to purpose, notwithstanding the steps be there; but the ground is good when they are once got in at the Gate.

Pliable got home, and is visited of his neighbors

Now I saw in my Dream, that by this time *Pliable* was got home to his house again. So his Neighbors came to visit him: and some of them called him wise man for coming back, and some called him fool for hazarding himself with *Christian:* others again did mock at his cowardliness; saying, Surely since you began to venture, I would not have been so base to have given out for a few difficulties. So *Pliable* sat sneaking among them. But at last he got more confidence, and then they all turned their tales, and began to deride poor *Christian* behind his back. And thus much concerning *Pliable.*

His entertainment by them at his return

Now as *Christian* was walking solitary by himself, he espied one afar off come crossing over the field to meet him; and their hap was to meet just as they were crossing the way of each other. The gentleman's name that met him was Mr. *Worldly Wiseman:* he dwelt in the Town of *Carnal Policy,* a very great Town, and also hard by from whence *Christian* came. This man then meeting with *Christian,* and having some inkling of him,—for *Christian's* setting forth from the City of *Destruction* was much noised abroad, not only in the Town where he dwelt, but also it began to be the town-talk in some other places,—Master *Worldly Wiseman* therefore, having some guess of him, by beholding his laborious going, by observing his sighs and groans, and the like, began thus to enter into some talk with *Christian.*

Mr Worldly Wiseman meets with Christian

Talk betwixt Mr Worldly Wiseman and Christian

World. How now, good fellow, whither away after this burdened manner?

Chr. A burdened manner indeed, as ever I think poor creature had. And whereas you ask me, *Whither away?* I tell you, Sir, I am going to yonder Wicket-gate before me; for there, as I am informed, I shall be put into a way to be rid of my heavy Burden.

World. Hast thou a Wife and Children?

Chr. Yes, but I am so laden with this Burden, that I cannot take that pleasure in them as formerly; methinks I am as if I had none.

World. Wilt thou hearken to me if I give thee counsel?

CHR. If it be good, I will; for I stand in need of good counsel.

Mr Worldly Wiseman's counsel to Christian

WORLD. I would advise thee then, that thou with all speed get thyself rid of thy Burden; for thou wilt never be settled in thy mind till then; nor canst thou enjoy the benefits of the blessing which God hath bestowed upon thee till then.

CHR. That is that which I seek for, even to be rid of this heavy Burden; but get it off myself, I cannot; nor is there any man in our country that can take it off my shoulders; therefore am I going this way, as I told you, that I may be rid of my Burden.

WORLD. Who bid thee go this way to be rid of thy Burden?

CHR. A man that appeared to me to be a very great and honorable person; his name as I remember is *Evangelist*.

Mr Worldly Wiseman condemned Evangelist's counsel

WORLD. I beshrew him for his counsel; there is not a more dangerous and troublesome way in the world than is that unto which he hath directed thee; and that thou shalt find, if thou wilt be ruled by his counsel. Thou hast met with something (as I perceive) already; for I see the dirt of the Slough of *Dispond* is upon thee; but that Slough is the beginning of the sorrows that do attend those that go on in that way: Hear me, I am older than thou; thou art like to meet with, in the way which thou goest, Wearisomeness, Painfulness, Hunger, Perils, Nakedness, Sword, Lions, Dragons, Darkness, and in a word, Death, and what not! These things are certainly true, having been confirmed by many testimonies. And why should a man so carelessly cast away himself, by giving heed to a stranger?

The frame of the heart of a young Christian

CHR. Why, Sir, this Burden upon my back is more terrible to me than are all these things which you have mentioned; nay, methinks I care not what I meet with in the way, so be I can also meet with deliverance from my Burden.

WORLD. How camest thou by thy Burden at first?

CHR. By reading this Book in my hand.

WORLD. I thought so; and it is happened unto thee as to other weak men, who meddling with things too high for them, do suddenly fall into thy distractions; which distractions do not only unman men (as thine I perceive has done thee), but they run them upon desperate ventures, to obtain they know not what.

Worldly Wiseman does not like that men should be serious in reading the Bible

CHR. I know what I would obtain; it is ease for my heavy burden.

WORLD. But why wilt thou seek for ease this way, seeing so many dangers attend it? Especially, since (hadst thou but patience to hear me) I could direct thee to the obtaining of what thou desirest, without the dangers that thou in this way wilt run thyself into; yea, and the remedy is at hand. Besides, I will add, that instead of those dangers, thou shalt meet with much safety, friendship, and content.

Whether Mr Worldly Wiseman prefers morality before the strait gate

CHR. Pray Sir, open this secret to me.

WORLD. Why in yonder Village (the village is named *Morality*) there dwells a Gentleman whose name is *Legality,* a very judicious man, and a man of very good name, that has skill to help men off with such burdens as thine are from their shoulders: yea, to my knowledge he hath done a great deal of good this way; ay, and besides, he hath skill to cure those that are somewhat crazed in their wits with their burdens. To him, as I said, thou mayest go, and be helped presently. His house is not quite a mile from this place, and if he should not be at home himself, he hath a pretty young man to his Son, whose name is *Civility,* that can do it (to speak on) as well as the old Gentleman himself; there, I say, thou mayest be eased of thy Burden; and if thou art not minded to go back to thy former habitation, as indeed I would not wish thee, thou mayest send for thy Wife and Children to thee to this village, where there are houses now stand empty, one of which thou mayest have at reasonable rates; Provision is there also cheap and good; and that which will make thy life the more happy is, to be sure there thou shalt live by honest Neighbors, in credit and good fashion.

Christian snared by Mr Worldly Wiseman's words

Now was *Christian* somewhat at a stand, but presently he concluded, If this be true which this Gentleman hath said, my wisest course is to take his advice; and with that he thus farther spoke.

CHR. Sir, which is my way to this honest man's house?

Mount Sinai

WORLD. Do you see yonder high Hill?

CHR. Yes, very well.

WORLD. By that Hill you must go, and the first house you come at is his.

Christian afraid that Mount Sinai would fall on his head

So *Christian* turned out of his way to go to Mr *Legality's* house for help; but behold, when he was got now hard by the Hill, it seemed so high, and also that side of it that was next the wayside, did hang so much over, that *Christian* was afraid to venture further, lest the Hill should fall on his head; wherefore there he stood still, and he wot not what to do. Also his Burden *now* seemed heavier to him than while he was in his way. There came also flashes of fire out of the Hill, that made *Christian* afraid that he should be burned. Here therefore he sweat and did quake for fear.

When Christians unto Carnal Men give ear,
Out of their way they go, and pay for 't dear;
For Master *Worldly Wiseman* can but shew
A Saint the way to Bondage and to Wo.

Evangelist findeth Christian under Mount Sinai, and looketh severely upon him

And now he began to be sorry that he had taken Mr *Worldly Wiseman's* counsel. And with that he saw *Evangelist* coming to meet him; at the sight also of whom he began to blush for shame. So *Evangelist* drew nearer and nearer; and coming up to him, he looked upon him with a severe and dreadful countenance, and thus began to reason with *Christian*.

EVAN. What doest thou here, *Christian?* said

he: at which words *Christian* knew not what to answer; wherefore at present he stood speechless before him. Then said *Evangelist* farther, Art not thou the man that I found crying without the walls of the City of *Destruction?*

Evangelist reasons afresh with Christian

CHR. Yes, dear Sir, I am the man.

EVAN. Did not I direct thee the way to the little Wicket-gate,

CHR. Yes, dear Sir, said *Christian.*

EVAN. How is it then that thou art so quickly turned aside? for thou art now out of the way.

CHR. I met with a Gentleman so soon as I had got over the Slough of *Dispond,* who persuaded me that I might, in the village before me, find a man that could take off my Burden.

EVAN. What was he?

CHR. He looked like a Gentleman, and talked much to me, and got me at last to yield; so I came hither: but when I beheld this Hill, and how it hangs over the way, I suddenly made a stand, lest it should fall on my head.

EVAN. What said that Gentleman to you?

CHR. Why, he asked me whither I was going; and I told him.

EVAN. And what said he then?

CHR. He asked me if I had a family; and I told him. But, said I, I am so loaden with the Burden that is on my back, that I cannot take pleasure in them as formerly.

EVAN. And what said he then?

CHR. He bid me with speed get rid of my Burden; and I told him 'twas ease that I sought. And, said I, I am therefore going to yonder Gate, to receive further direction how I may get to the place of deliverance. So he said that he would shew me a better way, and short, not so attended with difficulties as the way, Sir, that you set me; which way, said he, will direct you to a Gentleman's house that hath skill to take off these Burdens: So I believed him, and turned out of that way into this, if haply I might be soon eased of my Burden. But when I came to this place, and beheld things as they are, I stopped for fear (as I said) of danger: but I now know not what to do.

EVAN. Then, said *Evangelist,* stand still a little, that I may shew thee the words of God. So he stood trembling. Then said *Evangelist,* See that ye refuse not him that speaketh; for if they escaped not who refused him that spake on Earth, much more shall not we escape, if we turn away from him that speaketh from Heaven. He said moreover, Now the just shall live by faith: but if any man draws back, my soul shall have no pleasure in him. He also did thus apply them, Thou art the man that art running into this misery, thou hast begun to reject the counsel of the Most High, and to draw back thy foot from the way of peace, even almost to the hazarding of thy perdition.

Evangelist convinces Christian of his error

Then *Christian* fell down at his foot as dead, crying, *Wo is me, for I am undone:* At the sight of which, *Evangelist* caught him by the right hand, saying, All manner of sin and blasphemies shall be forgiven unto men; be not faithless, but believing. Then did *Christian* again a little revive, and stood up trembling, as at first, before *Evangelist.*

Mr Worldly Wiseman described by Evangelist

Then *Evangelist* proceeded, saying, Give more earnest heed to the things that I shall tell thee of. I will now shew thee who it was that deluded thee, and who it was also to whom he sent thee. The man that met thee is one *Worldly Wiseman,* and rightly is he so called: partly because he savoureth only the doctrine of this world, (therefore he always goes to the Town of *Morality* to church); and partly because he loveth that doctrine best, for it saveth him from the Cross. And because he is of this carnal temper, therefore he seeketh to prevent my ways, though right. Now there are three things in this man's counsel that thou must utterly abhor.

Evangelist discovers the deceit of Mr Worldly Wiseman

1. His turning thee out of the way.

2. His labouring to render the Cross odious to thee.

3. And his setting thy feet in that way that leadeth unto the administration of Death.

First, Thou must abhor his turning thee out of the way; yea, and thine own consenting thereto, because this is to reject the counsel of God for the sake of the counsel of a *Worldly Wiseman.* The Lord says, *Strive to enter in at the strait gate,* the gate to which I sent thee; *for strait is the gate that leadeth unto life, and few there be that find it.* From this little Wicket-gate, and from the way thereto, hath this wicked man turned thee, to the bringing of thee almost to destruction; hate therefore his turning thee out of the way, and abhor thyself for hearkening to him.

Secondly, Thou must abhor his labouring to render the Cross odious unto thee; for thou art to *prefer it before the treasures of Egypt.* Besides, the King of Glory hath told thee, that *he that will save his life shall lose it:* and He that comes after him, and hates not his father, and mother, and wife, and children, and brethren, and sisters, yea and his own life also, he cannot be my Disciple. I say therefore, for a man to labour to persuade thee, that that shall be thy death, without which, the Truth hath said, thou canst not have eternal life; This doctrine thou must abhor.

Thirdly, Thou must hate his setting of thy feet in the way that leadeth to the ministration of death. And for this thou must consider to whom he sent thee, and also how unable that person was to deliver thee from thy Burden.

He to whom thou was sent for ease, being by name *Legality,* is the Son of the Bond-woman which now is, and is in bondage with her children; and is in a mystery this Mount *Sinai,* which thou hast feared will fall on thy head. Now if she with her children are in bondage, how canst thou expect by them to be made free? This *Legality* therefore

The bond-woman

is not able to set thee free from thy Burden. No man was as yet ever rid of his Burden by him; no, nor ever is like to be: ye cannot be justified by the Works of the Law; for by the deeds of the Law no man living can be rid of his Burden: therefore, Mr *Worldly Wiseman* is an alien, and Mr *Legality* a cheat; and for his son *Civility*, notwithstanding his simpering looks, he is but a hypocrite and cannot help thee. Believe me, there is nothing in all this noise, that thou hast heard of this sottish man, but a design to beguile thee of thy Salvation, by turning thee from the way in which I had set thee. After this *Evangelist* called aloud to the Heavens for confirmation of what he had said; and with that there came words and fire out of the Mountain under which poor *Christian* stood, that made the hair of his flesh stand. The words were thus pronounced, *As many as are the works of the Law are under the curse; for it is written, Cursed is every one that continueth not in all things which are written in the Book of the Law to do them.*

Now *Christian* looked for nothing but death, and began to cry out lamentably, even cursing the time in which he met with Mr *Worldly Wiseman*, still calling himself a thousand fools for hearkening to his counsel: he also was greatly ashamed to think that this Gentleman's arguments, flowing only from the flesh, should have that prevalency with him as to cause him to forsake the right way. This done, he applied himself again to *Evangelist* in words and sense as follows.

Christian inquires if he may yet be happy

CHR. Sir, what think you? Is there hopes? May I now go back and go up to the Wicket-gate? Shall I not be abandoned for this, and sent back from thence ashamed? I am sorry I have hearkened to this man's counsel: But may my sin be forgiven?

Evangelist comforts him

EVAN. Then said *Evangelist* to him, Thy sin is very great, for by it thou hast committed two evils: thou hast forsaken the way that is good, to tread in forbidden paths; yet will the man at the Gate receive thee, for he has good-will for men; only, said he, take heed that thou turn not aside again, lest thou perish from the way, when his wrath is kindled but a little. Then did *Christian* address himself to go back; and *Evangelist,* after he had kissed him, gave him one smile, and bid him God speed. So he went on with haste, neither spake he to any man by the way; nor if any man asked him, would he vouchsafe them an answer. He went like one that was all the while treading on forbidden ground, and could by no means think himself safe, till again he was got into the way which he left to follow Mr *Worldly Wiseman's* counsel. So in process of time *Christian* got up to the Gate. Now over the Gate there was written, *Knock and it shall be opened unto you.*

He that will enter in must first without
Stand knocking at the Gate, nor need he doubt
That is a knocker but to enter in,
For God can love him, and forgive his sin.

He knocked therefore more than once or twice, saying,

May I now enter here? Will he within
Open to sorry me, though I have been
An undeserving Rebel? Then shall I
Not fail to sing his lasting praise on high.

At last there came a grave person to the gate named *Good-will,* who asked Who was there? and whence he came? and what he would have?

CHR. Here is a poor burdened sinner. I come from the City of *Destruction,* but am going to Mount *Zion,* that I may be delivered from the wrath to come. I would therefore, Sir, since I am informed that by this Gate is the way thither, know if you are willing to let me in.

The gate will be opened to broken-hearted sinners

GOOD-WILL. I am willing with all my heart, said he; and with that he opened the Gate.

So when *Christian* was stepping in, the other

gave him a pull. Then said *Christian,* What means that? The other told him, A little distance from this Gate, there is erected a strong Castle, of which *Beelzebub* is the Captain; from thence both he and they that are with him shoot arrows at those that come up to this Gate, if haply they may die before they can enter in. Then said *Christian,* I rejoice and tremble. So when he was got in, the man of the Gate asked him who directed him thither?

Satan envies those that enter the strait gate

Christian entered the gate with joy and trembling

CHR. *Evangelist* bid me come hither and knock (as I did); and he said that you, Sir, would tell me what I must do.

Talk between Good-will and Christian

GOOD-WILL. An open door is set before thee, and no man can shut it.

CHR. Now I begin to reap the benefits of my hazards.

GOOD-WILL. But how is it that you came alone?

CHR. Because none of my Neighbors saw their danger, as I saw mine.

GOOD-WILL. Did any of them know of your coming?

CHR. Yes, my Wife and Children saw me at the first, and called after me to turn again; also some of my Neighbors stood crying and calling after me to return; but I put my fingers in my ears, and so came on my way.

GOOD-WILL. But did none of them follow you, to persuade you to go back?

CHR. Yes, both *Obstinate* and *Pliable;* but when they saw that they could not prevail, *Obstinate* went railing back, but *Pliable* came with me a little way.

GOOD-WILL. But why did he not come through?

A man may have company when he sets out for heaven, and yet go thither alone

CHR. We indeed came both together, until we came to the Slough of *Dispond,* into the which we also suddenly fell. And then was my Neighbor *Pliable* discouraged, and would not adventure further. Wherefore getting out again on that side next to his own house, he told me I should possess the brave country alone for him; so he went *his* way, and I came *mine:* he after *Obstinate,* and I to this Gate.

GOOD-WILL. Then said *Good-will,* Alas, poor man, is the cœlestial glory of so small esteem with him, that he counteth it not worth running the hazards of a few difficulties to obtain it?

CHR. Truly, said *Christian,* I have said the truth of *Pliable,* and if I should also say all the truth of myself, it will appear there is no betterment 'twixt him and myself. 'Tis true, he went back to his own house, but I also turned aside to go in the way of death, being persuaded thereto by the carnal arguments of one Mr *Worldly Wiseman.*

Christian accuseth himself before the man at the gate

GOOD-WILL. O, did he light upon you? What! he would have had you a sought for ease at the hands of Mr. *Legality.* They are both of them a very cheat: But did you take his counsel?

CHR. Yes, as far as I durst: I went to find out Mr *Legality,* until I thought that the Mountain that stands by his house would have fallen upon my head; wherefore there I was forced to stop.

GOOD-WILL. That Mountain has been the death of many, and will be the death of many more; 'tis well you escaped being by it dashed in pieces.

CHR. Why truly I do not know what had become of me there, had not *Evangelist* happily met me again, as I was musing in the midst of my dumps: but 'twas God's mercy that he came to me again, for else I had never come hither. But now I am come, such a one as I am, more fit indeed for death by that Mountain than thus to stand talking with my Lord; but O, what a favour is this to me, that yet I am admitted entrance here.

GOOD-WILL. We make no objections against any, notwithstanding all that they have done before they come hither, they in no wise are cast out; and therefore, good *Christian,* come a little way with me, and I will teach thee about the way

Christian comforted again

Christian directed yet on his way

thou must go. Look before thee; dost thou see this narrow way? THAT is the way thou must go; it was cast up by the Patriarchs, Prophets, Christ, and his Apostles; and it is as straight as a rule can make it: This is the way thou must go.

Christian afraid of losing his way

CHR. But said *Christian,* Is there no turnings nor windings, by which a Stranger may lose the way?

GOOD-WILL. Yes, there are many ways *butt* down upon this, and they are crooked and wide: But thus thou mayest distinguish the right from the wrong, the right only being straight and narrow.

Christian weary of his burden

Then I saw in my Dream, that *Christian* asked him further If he could not help him off with his Burden that was upon his back; for as yet he had not got rid thereof, nor could he by any means get it off without help.

There is no deliverance from the guilt and burden of sin, but by the death and blood of Christ

He told him, As to thy Burden, be content to bear it, until thou comest to the place of *Deliverance;* for there it will fall from thy back itself.

Then *Christian* began to gird up his loins, and to address himself to his Journey. So the other told him, That by that he was gone some distance from the Gate, he would come at the house of the *Interpreter,* at whose door he should knock, and he would shew him excellent things. Then *Christian* took his leave of his Friend, and he again bid him God speed.

Christian comes to the house of the Interpreter

Then he went on till he came at the house of the *Interpreter,* where he knocked over and over; at last one came to the door, and asked Who was there?

CHR. Sir, here is a Traveller, who was bid by an acquaintance of the good man of this house to call here for my profit; I would therefore speak with the Master of the house. So he called for the Master of the house, who after a little time came to *Christian,* and asked him what he would have?

CHR. Sir, said *Christian,* I am a man that am

come from the City of *Destruction,* and am going to the Mount *Zion;* and I was told by the Man that stands at the Gate at the head of this way, that if I called here, you would shew me excellent things, such as would be a help to me in my Journey.

He is entertained

INTER. Then said the *Interpreter,* Come in, I will shew thee that which will be profitable to thee. So he commanded his man to light the Candle, and bid *Christian* follow him, so he had him into a private room, and bid his man open a door; the which when he had done, *Christian* saw the Picture of a very grave Person hang up against the wall; and this was the fashion of it. It had eyes lifted up to Heaven, the best of Books in his hand, the Law of Truth was written upon his lips, the World was behind his back. It stood as if it pleaded with men, and a Crown of Gold did hang over his head.

Illumination

Christian sees a grave picture

The fashion of the picture

CHR. Then said *Christian,* What means this?

INTER. The Man whose Picture this is, is one of a thousand; he can beget children, travel in birth with children, and nurse them himself when they are born. And whereas thou seest him with his eyes lift up to Heaven, the best of Books in his hand, and the Law of Truth writ on his lips, it is to shew thee that his work is to know and unfold dark things to sinners; even as also thou seest him stand as if he pleaded with men; and whereas thou seest the World as cast behind him, and that a Crown hangs over his head, that is to shew thee that slighting and despising the things that are present, for the love that he hath to his Master's service, he is sure in the world that comes next to have Glory for his reward. Now, said the *Interpreter,* I have shewed thee this Picture first, because the Man whose Picture this is, is the only man whom the Lord of the place whither thou art going, hath authorized to be thy guide in all difficult places thou mayest meet with in the way;

The meaning of the picture

Why he showed him the picture first

wherefore take good heed to what I have shewed thee, and bear well in thy mind what thou hast seen, lest in thy Journey thou meet with some that pretend to lead thee right, but their way goes down to death.

Then he took him by the hand, and led him into a very large *Parlour* that was full of dust, because never swept; the which after he had reviewed a little while, the *Interpreter* called for a man to sweep. Now when he began to sweep, the dust began so abundantly to fly about, that *Christian* had almost therewith been choaked. Then said the *Interpreter* to a *Damsel* that stood by, Bring hither the Water, and sprinkle the Room; the which when she had done, it was swept and cleansed with pleasure.

Chr. Then said *Christian,* What means this?

Inter. The *Interpreter* answered, This *parlour* is the heart of a man that was never sanctified by the sweet Grace of the Gospel: the *dust* is his Original Sin and inward Corruptions, that have defiled the whole man. He that began to sweep at first, is the Law; but she that brought water, and did sprinkle it, is the Gospel. Now, whereas thou sawest that so soon as the first began to sweep, the dust did so fly about that the Room by him could not be cleansed, but that thou wast almost choaked therewith; this is to shew thee, that the Law, instead of cleansing the heart (by its working) from sin, doth revive, put strength into, and increase it in the soul, even as it doth discover and forbid it, for it doth not give power to subdue.

Again, as thou sawest the *Damsel* sprinkle the room with Water, upon which it was cleansed with pleasure; this is to shew thee, that when the Gospel comes in the sweet and precious influences thereof to the heart, then I say, even as thou sawest the Damsel lay the dust by sprinkling the floor with Water, so is sin vanquished and subdued, and the soul made clean, through the faith of it, and consequently fit for the King of Glory to inhabit.

I saw moreover in my Dream, that the *Interpreter* took him by the hand, and had him into a little room, where sat two little Children, each one in his chair. The name of the eldest was *Passion,* and the name of the other *Patience. Passion* seemed to be much discontent; but *Patience* was very quiet. Then *Christian* asked, What is the reason of the discontent of *Passion?* The *Interpreter* answered, The Governor of them would have him stay for his best things till the beginning of the next year; but he will have all now; but *Patience* is willing to wait.

He showed him Passion and Patience

Passion will have all now. Patience is for waiting

Then I saw that one came to *Passion,* and brought him a bag of treasure, and poured it down at his feet, the which he took up and rejoiced therein; and withal, laughed *Patience* to scorn. But I beheld but a while, and he had lavished all away, and had nothing left him but Rags.

Passion has his desire

And quickly lavishes all away

CHR. Then said *Christian* to the *Interpreter,* Expound this matter more fully to me.

INTER. So he said, These two Lads are figures: *Passion,* of the men of *this* world; and *Patience,* of the men of *that* which is to come; for as here thou seest, *Passion* will have all now this year, that is to say, in this world; so are the men of this world: they must have all their good things now, they cannot stay till next year, that is, until the next world, for their portion of good. That proverb, *A Bird in the Hand is worth two in the Bush,* is of more authority with them than are all the Divine testimonies of the good of the world to come. But as thou sawest that he had quickly lavished all away, and had presently left him nothing but Rags; so will it be with all such men at the end of this world.

The matter expounded

The worldly man for a bird in the hand

CHR. Then said *Christian,* Now I see that *Patience* has the best wisdom, and that upon many accounts. 1. Because he stays for the best things.

Patience has the best wisdom

2. And also because he will have the Glory of his, when the other has nothing but Rags.

Things that are first must give place; but things that are last are lasting

INTER. Nay, you may add another, to wit, the glory of the *next* world will never wear out; but *these* are suddenly gone, Therefore Passion had not so much reason to laugh at *Patience,* because he had his good things first, as *Patience* will have to laugh at *Passion,* because he had his best things last; for *first* must give place to *last,* because *last* must have his time to come: but last gives place to nothing; for there is not another to succeed. He therefore that hath his portion *first,* must needs have a time to spend it; but he that hath his portion *last,* must have it lastingly; therefore it is said of *Dives, In thy lifetime thou receivedst thy good things, and likewise* Lazarus *evil things; but now he is comforted, and thou art tormented.*

Dives had his good things first

CHR. Then I perceive 'tis not best to covet things that are now, but to wait for things to come.

The first things are but temporal

INTER. You say truth: *For the things which are seen are* Temporal; *but the things that are not seen are* Eternal. But though this be so, yet since things present and our fleshly appetite are such near neighbors one to another; and, again, because things to come and carnal sense are such strangers one to another; therefore it is that the first of these so suddenly fell into *amity,* and that *distance* is so continued between the second.

Then I saw in my Dream that the *Interpreter* took *Christian* by the hand, and led him into a place where was a Fire burning against a wall, and one standing by it, always casting much Water upon it, to quench it; yet did the Fire burn higher and hotter.

Then said *Christian,* What means this?

The *Interpreter answered,* This Fire is the work of Grace that is wrought in the heart; he that casts Water upon it, to extinguish and put it out, is the *Devil;* but in that thou seest the Fire notwithstanding burn higher and hotter, thou shalt also see the reason of that. So he had him about to the backside of the wall, where he saw a man with a Vessel of Oil in his hand, of the which he did also continually cast (but secretly) into the Fire.

Then said *Christian,* What means this?

The *Interpreter answered,* This is Christ, who continually, with the Oil of his Grace, maintains the work already begun in the heart: by the means of which notwithstanding what the Devil can do, the souls of his people prove gracious still. And in that thou sawest that the man stood behind the wall to maintain the Fire, that is to teach thee that it is hard for the tempted to see how this work of Grace is maintained in the soul.

I saw also that the *Interpreter* took him again by the hand, and led him into a pleasant place, where was builded a stately Palace, beautiful to behold; at the sight of which *Christian* was greatly delighted: He saw also upon the top thereof, certain persons walking, who were cloathed all in gold.

Then said *Christian,* May we go in thither?

Then the *Interpreter* took him, and led him up toward the door of the Palace; and behold, at the door stood a great company of men, as desirous to go in, but durst not. There also sat a man at a little distance from the door, at a table-side, with a Book and his Inkhorn before him, to take the name of him that should enter therein; He saw also, that in the door-way stood many men in armour to keep it, being resolved to do the men that would enter what hurt and mischief they could. Now was *Christian* somewhat in a maze. At last, when every man started back for fear of the armed men, *Christian* saw a man of a very stout countenance come up to the man that sat there to write, saying, *Set down my name, Sir:* the which when he had done, he saw the man draw his Sword, and put an Helmet upon his head, and rush toward the door upon the armed men, who laid upon him with deadly force; but the man, not at all discouraged,

The valiant man

fell to cutting and hacking most fiercely. So after he had received and given many wounds to those that attempted to keep him out, he cut his way through them all, and pressed forward into the Palace, at which there was a pleasant voice heard from those that were within, even of those that walked upon the top of the Palace, saying,

Come in, Come in;
Eternal Glory thou shalt win.

So he went in, and was cloathed with such garments as they. Then *Christian* smiled, and said, I think verily I know the meaning of this.

Despair like an iron cage

Now, said *Christian,* let me go hence. Nay, stay, said the *Interpreter,* till I have shewed thee a little more, and after that thou shalt go on thy way. So he took him by the hand again, and led him into a very dark room, where there sat a man in an Iron Cage.

Now the Man, to look on, seemed very sad; he sat with his eyes looking down to the ground, his hands folded together; and he sighed as if he would break his heart. Then said *Christian, What means this?* At which the *Interpreter* bid him talk with the Man.

Then said *Christian* to the Man, *What art thou?* The Man answered, *I am what I was not once.*

CHR. What wast thou once?

MAN. The Man said, I was once a fair and flourishing Professor, both in mine own eyes, and also in the eyes of others; I once was, as I thought, fair for the Cœlestial City, and had then even joy at the thoughts that I should get thither.

CHR. Well, but what art thou now?

MAN. I am now a man of *Despair,* and am shut up in it, as in this Iron Cage. I cannot get out; O *now* I cannot.

CHR. But how camest thou in this condition?

MAN. I left off to watch and be sober; I laid the reins upon the neck of my lusts; I sinned against the light of the Word and the goodness of God; I have grieved the Spirit, and he is gone; I tempted the Devil, and he is come to me; I have provoked God to anger, and he has left me; I have so hardened my heart, that I *cannot* repent.

Then said *Christian* to the *Interpreter,* But are there no hopes for such a man as this? Ask him, said the *Interpreter.*

CHR. Then said the *Christian,* Is there no hope, but you must be kept in the Iron Cage of Despair?

MAN. No, none at all.

CHR. Why? the Son of the Blessed is very pitiful.

MAN. I have crucified him to myself afresh, I have despised his Person, I have despised his Righteousness, I have counted his Blood an unholy thing; I have done despite to the Spirit of Grace: Therefore I have shut myself out of all the Promises, and there now remains to me nothing but threatnings, dreadful threatnings, fearful threatnings of certain Judgment and fiery Indignation, which shall devour me as an Adversary.

CHR. For what did you bring yourself into this condition?

MAN. For the Lusts, Pleasures, and Profits of this World; in the enjoyment of which I did then promise myself much delight; but now every one of those things also bite me, and gnaw me like a burning worm.

CHR. But canst thou not now repent and turn?

MAN. God hath denied me repentance: his Word gives me no encouragement to believe; yea, himself hath shut me up in this Iron Cage; nor can all the men in the world let me out. O Eternity! Eternity! how shall I grapple with the misery that I must meet with in Eternity!

INTER. Then said the *Interpreter* to *Christian,* Let this man's misery be remembred by thee, and be an everlasting caution to thee.

CHR. Well, said *Christian,* this is fearful; God help me to watch and be sober, and to pray that I may shun the cause of this man's misery. Sir, is it not time for me to go on my way now?

INTER. Tarry till I shall shew thee one thing more, and then thou shalt go thy way.

So he took *Christian* by the hand again, and led him into a Chamber, where there was one rising out of bed; and as he put on his raiment, he shook and trembled. Then said *Christian,* Why doth this man thus tremble? The *Interpreter* then bid him tell to *Christian* the reason of his so doing. So he began and said, This night, as I was in my sleep, I dreamed, and behold the Heavens grew exceeding black; also it thundred and lightned in most fearful wise, that it put me into an agony; so I looked up in my Dream, and saw the Clouds rack at an unusual rate, upon which I heard a great sound of a Trumpet, and saw also a Man sit upon a Cloud, attended with the thousands of Heaven; they were all in flaming fire, also the Heavens were in a burning flame. I heard then a Voice saying, *Arise ye dead, and come to Judgment;* and with that the Rocks rent, the Graves opened, and the Dead that were therein came forth. Some of them were exceeding glad, and looked upward; and some sought to hide themselves under the Mountains. Then I saw the Man that sat upon the Cloud open the Book, and bid the World draw near. Yet there was, by reason of a fierce flame which issued out and came from before him, a convenient distance betwixt him and them, as betwixt the Judge and the Prisoners at the bar. I heard it also proclaimed to them that attended on the Man that sat on the Cloud, *Gather together the Tares, the Chaff, and Stubble, and cast them into the burning Lake.* And with that, the bottomless pit opened, just whereabout I stood; out of the mouth of which there came in an abundant manner, smoke and coals of fire, with hideous noises. It was also said to the same persons, *Gather my Wheat into the Garner.* And with that I saw many catch'd up and carried away into the Clouds, but I was left behind. I also sought to hide myself, but I could not, for the Man that sat upon the Cloud still kept his eye upon me: my sins also came into my mind; and my Conscience did accuse me on every side. Upon this I awaked from my sleep.

CHR. But what was it that made you so afraid of this sight?

MAN. Why, I thought that the day of Judgment was come, and that I was not ready for it: but this frighted me most, that the Angels gathered up several, and left me behind; also the pit of Hell opened her mouth just where I stood: my Conscience too afflicted me; and as I thought, the Judge had always his eye upon me, shewing indignation in his countenance.

Then said the *Interpreter* to *Christian, Hast thou considered all these things?*

CHR. Yes, and they put me in *hope* and *fear.*

INTER. Well, keep all things so in thy mind that they may be as a Goad in thy sides, to prick thee forward in the way thou must go. Then *Christian* began to gird up his loins, and address himself to his Journey. Then said the *Interpreter,* The Comforter be always with thee, good *Christian,* to guide thee in the way that leads to the City. So *Christian* went on his way saying,

> Here I have seen things rare and profitable;
> Things pleasant, dreadful, things to make me stable
> In what I have begun to take in hand;
> Then let me think on them, and understand
> Wherefore they shew'd me was, and let me be
> Thankful, O good Interpreter, to thee.

Now I saw in my Dream, that the highway up which *Christian* was to go, was fenced on either side with a Wall, and that Wall is called *Salvation.* Up this way therefore did burdened *Christian* run, but not without great difficulty, because of the load on his back.

He ran thus till he came at a place somewhat ascending, and upon that place stood a Cross, and a little below in the bottom, a Sepulchre. So I saw in my Dream, that just as *Christian* came up with the *Cross,* his Burden loosed from off his shoulders, and fell from off his back, and began to tumble, and so continued to do, till it came to the mouth of the Sepulchre, where it fell in, and I saw it no more.

When God releases us of our guilt and burden we are as those that leap for joy

Then was *Christian* glad and lightsome, and said with a merry heart, *He hath given me rest by his sorrow, and life by his death.* Then he stood still awhile to look and wonder; for it was very surprising to him, that the sight of the Cross should thus ease him of his Burden. He looked therefore, and looked again, even till the springs that were in his head sent the waters down his cheeks. Now as he stood looking and weeping, behold three Shining Ones came to him and saluted him with *Peace be to thee;* so the first said to him, *Thy sins be forgiven:* the second stript him of his Rags, and clothed him with Change of Raiment; the third also set a mark in his forehead, and gave him a Roll with a Seal upon it, which he bid him look on as he ran, and that he should give it in at the Cœlestial Gate. So they went their way.

A Christian can sing though alone, when God doth give him the joy of his heart

Who's this? the Pilgrim. How! 'tis very true,
Old things are past away, all's become new.
Strange! he's another man, upon my word,
They be fine Feathers that make a fine Bird.

Then *Christian* gave three leaps for joy, and went on singing,

Thus far did I come laden with my sin;
Nor could aught ease the grief that I was in
Till I came hither: What a place is this!
Must here be the beginning of my bliss?
Must here the Burden fall from off my back?
Must here the strings that bound it to me crack?
Blest Cross! blest Sepulchre! blest rather be
The Man that there was put to shame for me.

Simple, Sloth, and Presumption

I saw then in my Dream that he went on thus, even until he came at a bottom, where he saw, a little out of the way, three men fast asleep, with fetters upon their heels. The name of the one was *Simple,* another *Sloth,* and the third *Presumption.*

Christian then seeing them lie in this case, went to them, if peradventure he might awake them, and cried, You are like them that sleep on the top of a mast, for the Dead Sea is under you, a gulf that hath no bottom. Awake therefore and come away; be willing also, and I will help you off with your Irons. He also told them, If he that goeth about like a *roaring lion* comes by, you will certainly become a prey to his teeth. With that they looked upon him, and began to reply in his sort: *Simple* said, *I see no danger; Sloth* said, *Yet a little more sleep;* and *Presumption* said, *Every Fat*[1] *must stand upon his own bottom.* And so they lay down to sleep again and *Christian* went on his way.

There is no persuasion will do, if God openeth not the eyes

Yet was he troubled to think that men in that danger should so little esteem the kindness of him that so freely offered to help them, both by awakening of them, counselling of them, and proffering to help them off with their Irons. And as he was troubled thereabout he espied two men come tumbling over the Wall, on the left hand of the narrow way; and they made up apace to him. The name of the one was *Formalist,* and the name of the other *Hypocrisy.* So, as I said, they drew up unto him, who thus entered with them into discourse.

Christian talked with them

CHR. Gentlemen, Whence came you, and whither do you go?

FORM. and HYP. We were born in the land of *Vain-glory,* and are going for praise to Mount *Sion.*

CHR. Why came you not in at the Gate which standeth at the beginning of the Way? Know you not that it is written, That *he that cometh not in by the Door, but climbeth up some other way, the same is a Thief and a Robber?*

FORM. and HYP. They said, That to go to the Gate for entrance was by all their countrymen

[1] *I. e.,* Vat or tub.

counted too far about; and that therefore their usual way was to make a short cut of it, and to climb over the wall, as they had done.

CHR. But will it not be counted a Trespass against the Lord of the City whither we are bound, thus to violate his revealed will?

They that come into the way, but not by the door, think that they can say something in vindication of their own practice

FORM. and HYP. They told him, That as for that, he needed not to trouble his head thereabout; for what they did they had custom for; and could produce, if need were, Testimony that would witness it for more than a thousand years.

CHR. But, said *Christian,* will your practice stand a Trial at Law?

FORM. and HYP. They told him, That custom, it being of so long a standing as above a thousand years, would doubtless now be admitted as a thing legal by an impartial Judge; and besides, said they, if we get into the way, what's matter which way we get in? if we are in, we are in; thou art but in the way, who, as we perceive, came in at the Gate; and we are also in the way, that came tumbling over the wall; wherein now is thy condition beter than ours?

CHR. I walk by the Rule of my Master; you walk by the rude working of your fancies. You are counted thieves already, by the Lord of the way; therefore I doubt you will not be found true men at the end of the way. You come in by yourselves, without his direction; and shall go out by yourselves, without his mercy.

To this they made him but little answer; only they bid him look to himself. Then I saw that they went on every man in his way, without much conference one with another; save that these two men told *Christian,* that as to *Laws* and *Ordinances,* they doubted not but they should as conscientiously do them as he; therefore, said they, we see not wherein thou differest from us but by the *Coat* that is on thy back, which was, as we trow, given thee by some of thy Neighbors, to hide the shame of thy nakedness.

CHR. By Laws and Ordinances you will not be saved, since you came not in by the door. And as for this *Coat* that is on my back, it was given me by the Lord of the place whither I go; and that, as you say, to cover my nakedness with. And I take it as a token of his kindness to me, for I had nothing but rags before. And besides, thus I comfort myself as I go: Surely think I, when I come to the gate of the City, the Lord thereof will know me for good, since I have this Coat on my back; a Coat that he gave me freely in the day that he stript me of my rags. I have moreover a Mark in my forehead, of which perhaps you have taken no notice, which one of my Lord's most intimate associates fixed there in the day that my Burden fell off my shoulders. I will tell you moreover, that I had then given me a Roll sealed, to comfort me by reading as I go in the way; I was also bid to give it in at the Cœlestial Gate, in token of my certain going in after it; all which things I doubt you want, and want them because you came not in at the Gate.

Christian has got his Lord's coat on his back, and is comforted therewith; he is comforted, also, with his mark and his roll

To these things they gave him no answer; only they looked upon each other and laughed. Then I saw that they went on all, save that *Christian* kept before, who had no more talk but with himself, and that sometimes sighingly, and sometimes comfortably; also he would be often reading in the Roll that one of the Shining Ones gave him, by which he was refreshed.

Christian has talk himself

I beheld then, that they all went on till they came to the foot of the Hill *Difficulty,* at the bottom of which was a Spring. There was also in the same place two other ways besides that which came straight from the Gate; one turned to the left hand and the other to the right, at the bottom of the Hill; but the narrow way lay right up the Hill, and the name of the going up the side of the Hill is called *Difficulty*. *Christian* now went to the Spring, and drank thereof to refresh himself, and then began to go up the Hill, saying,

He comes to the Hill Difficulty

The Hill, tho' high, I covet to ascend,
The difficulty will not me offend;
For I perceive the way to life lies here:
Come, pluck up, Heart, let's neither faint nor fear;
Better, tho' difficult, the right way to go,
Than wrong, though easy, where the end is wo.

The danger of turning out of the way

The other two also came to the foot of the Hill; but when they saw that the Hill was steep and high, and that there was two other ways to go; and supposing also that these two ways might meet again with that up which *Christian* went, on the other side of the Hill; therefore they were resolved to go in those ways. Now the name of one of those ways was *Danger,* and the name of the other *Destruction.* So the one took the way which is called *Danger,* which led him into a great Wood; and the other took directly up the way to *Destruction,* which led him into a wide field, full of dark Mountains, where he stumbled and fell, and rose no more.

Shall they who wrong begin yet rightly end?
Shall they at all have Safety for their friend?
No, no; in headstrong manner they set out,
And headlong will they fall at last no doubt.

A word of grace

I looked then after *Christian* to see him go up the Hill, where I perceived he fell from running to going, and from going to clambering upon his hands and his knees, because of the steepness of the place. Now about the mid-way to the top of the Hill was a pleasant *Arbor,* made by the Lord of the Hill for the refreshing of weary travellers; thither therefore *Christian* got, where also he sat down to rest him. Then he pulled his Roll out of his bosom, and read therein to his comfort; he also now began afresh to take a review of the Coat or Garment that was given him as he stood by the Cross. Thus pleasing himself awhile, he at last fell into a slumber, and thence into a fast sleep, which detained him in that place until it was almost night; and in his sleep his Roll fell out of his hand. Now as he was sleeping, there came one to him and awaked him, saying, *Go to the Ant, thou sluggard; consider her ways, and be wise.* And with that *Christian* suddenly started up, and sped on his way, and went apace till he came to the top of the Hill.

He that sleeps is a loser

Now when he was got up to the top of the Hill, there came two men running against him amain; the name of the one was *Timorous*, and the other, *Mistrust;* to whom *Christian* said, Sirs, what's the matter you run the wrong way? *Timorous* answered, that they were going to the City of *Zion*, and had got up that difficult place; but, said he, the further we go, the more danger we meet with; wherefore we turned, and are going back again.

Christian meets with Mistrust and Timorous

Yes, said *Mistrust*, for just before us lie a couple of Lions in the way, (whether sleeping or waking we know not) and we could not think, if we came within reach, but they would presently pull us in pieces.

CHR. Then said *Christian*, You make me afraid, but whither shall I fly to be safe? If I go back to mine own country, *that* is prepared for Fire and Brimstone, and I shall certainly perish there. If I can get to the Cœlestial City, I am sure to be in safety there. I must venture: To go back is nothing but death; to go forward is fear of death, and life everlasting beyond it. I will yet go forward. So *Mistrust* and *Timorous* ran down the Hill, and *Christian* went on his way. But thinking again of what he heard from the men, he felt in his bosom for his Roll, that he might read therein and be comforted; but he felt, and found it not. Then was *Christian* in great distress, and knew not what to do; for he wanted that which used to relieve him, and that which should have been his pass into the Cœlestial City. Here therefore he began to be much perplexed, and knew not what to do. At last he bethought himself that he had slept in the *Arbor* that is on the side of the Hill; and falling down upon his knees he asked God's forgiveness for that

Christian shakes off fear

Christian missed his roll wherein he used to take comfort

He is perplexed for his roll

his foolish fact[1] and then went back to look for his Roll. But all the way he went back, who can sufficiently set forth the sorrow of *Christian's* heart? Sometimes he sighed, sometimes he wept, and oftentimes he chid himself for being so foolish to fall asleep in that place, which was erected only for a little refreshment for his weariness. Thus therefore he went back, carefully looking on this side and on that, all the way as he went, if happily he might find his Roll, that had been his comfort so many times in his Journey. He went thus till he came again within sight of the *Arbor* where he sat and slept; but that sight renewed his sorrow the more, by bringing again, even afresh, his evil of sleeping into his mind. Thus therefore he now went on bewailing his sinful sleep, saying, *O wretched man that I am,* that I should sleep in the daytime! that I should sleep in the midst of difficulty! that I should so indulge the flesh, as to use that rest for ease to my flesh, which the Lord of the Hill hath erected only for the relief of the spirits of Pilgrims? How many steps have I took in vain! (Thus it happened to *Israel* for their sin, they were sent back again by the way of the Red Sea), and I am made to tread those steps with sorrow, which I might have trod with delight, had it not been for this sinful sleep. How far might I have been on my way by this time! I am made to tread those steps thrice over, which I needed not to have trod but once; yea now also I am like to be benighted, for the day is almost spent. O that I had not slept!

Christian bewails his foolish sleeping

Now by this time he was come to the *Arbor* again, where for a while he sat down and wept; but at last, as *Christian* would have it, looking sorrowfully down under the settle, there he espied his Roll; the which he with trembling and haste catched up, and put it into his bosom. But who can tell how joyful this man was when he had gotten his Roll again! for this Roll was the assurance of his life

Christian findeth his roll where he lost it

[1] Deed.

and acceptance at the desired Haven. Therefore he laid it up in his bosom, gave thanks to God for directing his eye to the place where it lay, and with joy and tears betook himself again to his Journey. But Oh how nimbly now did he go up the rest of the Hill! Yet before he got up, the Sun went down upon *Christian;* and this made him again recall the vanity of his sleeping to his remembrance; and thus he again began to condole with himself. *O thou sinful sleep: how for thy sake am I like to be benighted in my Journey! I must walk without the Sun, darkness must cover the path of my feet, and I must hear the noise of doleful creatures, because of my sinful sleep.* Now also he remembered the story that *Mistrust* and *Timorous* told him of, how they were frighted with the sight of the Lions. Then said *Christian* to himself again, These beasts range in the night for their prey; and if they should meet with me in the dark, how should I shift them? How should I escape being by them torn in pieces? Thus he went on his way. But while he was thus bewailing his unhappy miscarriage, he lift up his eyes, and behold there was a very stately Palace before him, the name of which was *Beautiful;* and it stood just by the High-way side.

So I saw in my Dream that he made haste and went forward, that if possible he might get Lodging there. Now before he had gone far, he entered into a very narrow passage, which was about a furlong off of the Porter's Lodge; and looking very narrowly before him as he went, he espied two Lions in the way. Now, thought he, I see the dangers that *Mistrust* and *Timorous* were driven back by. (The Lions were chained, but he saw not the chains.) Then he was afraid, and thought also himself to go back after them, for he thought nothing but death was before him: But the Porter at the lodge, whose name is *Watchful,* perceiving that *Christian* made a halt as if he would go back, cried unto him, saying, **Is thy strength so small? Fear not the Lions, for** they are chained, and are placed there for trial of faith where it is, and for discovery of those that have none. Keep in the midst of the Path, and no hurt shall come unto thee.

> Difficulty is behind, Fear is before,
> Though he's got on the Hill, the Lions roar;
> A Christian man is never long at ease,
> When one fright's gone, another doth him seize.

Then I saw that he went on, trembling for fear of the Lions, but taking good heed to the directions of the Porter; he heard them roar, but they did him no harm. Then he clapt his hands, and went on till he came and stood before the Gate where the Porter was. Then said *Christian* to the Porter, Sir, what house is this? and may I lodge here to-night? The Porter answered, This house was built by the Lord of the Hill, and he built it for the relief and security of Pilgrims. The Porter also asked whence he was, and whither he was going?

CHR. I am come from the City of *Destruction,* and am going to Mount *Zion;* but because the Sun is now set, I desire, if I may, to lodge here to-night.

POR. What is your name?

CHR. My name is now *Christian,* but my name at the first was *Graceless;* I came of the race of *Japheth,* whom God will persuade to dwell in the Tents of *Shem.*

POR. But how doth it happen that you come so late? The Sun is set.

CHR. I had been here sooner, but that, wretched man that I am! I slept in the *Arbor* that stands on the Hill-side; nay, I had notwithstanding that, been here much sooner, but that in my sleep I lost my evidence, and came without it to the brow of the Hill; and then feeling for it, and finding it not, I was forced with sorrow of heart to go back to the place where I had slept my sleep, where I found it, and now I am come.

POR. Well, I will call out one of the Virgins of

this place, who will, if she likes your talk, bring you in to the rest of the Family, according to the rules of the house. So *Watchful* the Porter, rang a bell, at the sound of which came out at the door of the house, a grave and beautiful damsel named *Discretion*, and asked why she was called.

The Porter answered, This man is in a Journey from the City of *Destruction* to Mount *Zion*, but being weary and benighted, he asked me if he might lodge here to-night; so I told him I would call for thee, who, after discourse had with him, mayest do as seemeth thee good, even according to the Law of the house.

Then she asked him whence he was, and whither he was going; and he told her. She asked him also, how he got into the way; and he told her. Then she asked him, what he had seen and met with in the way; and he told her. And last she asked his name; so he said, It is *Christian*, and I have so much the more a desire to lodge here to-night, because, by what I perceive, this place was built by the Lord of the Hill, for the relief and security of Pilgrims. So she smiled, but the water stood in her eyes; and after a little pause, she said, I will call forth two or three more of the Family. So she ran to the door, and called out *Prudence, Piety,* and *Charity,* who after a little more discourse with him, led him in to the Family; and many of them, meeting him at the threshold of the house, said, Come in thou blessed of the Lord: this house was built by the Lord of the Hill, on purpose to entertain such Pilgrims in. Then he bowed his head, and followed them into the house. So when he was come in and set down, they gave him something to drink, and consented together, that until supper was ready, some of them should have some particular discourse with *Christian,* for the best improvement of time; and they appointed *Piety,* and *Prudence,* and *Charity* to discourse with him; and thus they began:

Piety discourses him

PIETY. Come good *Christian,* since we have been so loving to you, to receive you into our house this night, let us, if perhaps we may better ourselves thereby, talk with you of all things that have happened to you in your Pilgrimage.

CHR. With a very good will, and I am glad that you are so well disposed.

PIETY. What moved you at first to betake yourself to a Pilgrim's life?

How Christian was driven out of his own country

CHR. I was driven out of my Native Country, by a dreadful sound that was in mine ears: to wit, that unavoidable destruction did attend me, if I abode in that place where I was.

PIETY. But how did it happen that you came out of your Country this way?

How he got into the way to Zion

CHR. It was as God would have it; for when I was under the fears of destruction, I did not know whither to go; but by chance there came a man, even to me, as I was trembling and weeping, whose name is *Evangelist,* and he directed me to the Wicket-gate, which else I should never have found, and so set me into the way that hath led me directly to this house.

PIETY. But did you not come by the house of the *Interpreter?*

A rehearsal of what he saw in the way

CHR. Yes, and did see such things there, the remembrance of which will stick by me as long as I live; specially three things: to wit, How Christ, in despite of Satan, maintains his work of Grace in the heart; how the man had sinned himself quite out of hopes of God's mercy; and also the Dream of him that thought in his sleep the day of Judgment was come.

PIETY. Why, Did you hear him tell his dream?

CHR. Yes, and a dreadful one it was. I thought it made my heart ake as he was telling of it; but yet I am glad I heard it.

PIETY. Was that all that you saw at the house of the *Interpreter?*

CHR. No: he took me and had me where he

shewed me a stately Palace, and how the people were clad in Gold that were in it; and how there came a venturous man and cut his way through the armed men that stood in the door to keep him out, and how he was bid to come in, and win eternal Glory. Methought those things did ravish my heart; I would have stayed at that good man's house a twelve-month, but that I knew I had further to go.

PIETY. And what saw you else in the way?

CHR. Saw! Why, I went but a little further, and I saw one, as I thought in my mind, hang bleeding upon the Tree; and the very sight of him made my Burden fall off my back (for I groaned under a very heavy Burden), but then it fell down from off me. 'Twas a strange thing to me, for I never saw such a thing before; yea, and while I stood looking up (for then I could not forbear looking) three Shining Ones came to me. One of them testified that my sins were forgiven me; another stript me of my Rags, and gave me this broidered Coat which you see; and the third set the Mark which you see in my forehead, and gave me this sealed Roll: (and with that he plucked it out of his bosom.)

PIETY. But you saw more than this, did you not?

CHR. The things that I have told you were the best; yet some other matters I saw, as namely I saw three men, *Simple, Sloth,* and *Presumption,* lie asleep a little out of the way as I came, with Irons upon their heels; but do you think I could awake them? I also saw *Formalist* and *Hypocrisy* come tumbling over the wall, to go, as they pretended, to *Zion;* but they were quickly lost; even as I myself did tell them, but they would not believe. But, above all, I found it hard work to get up this Hill, and as hard to come by the Lions' mouths; and truly if it had not been for the good man, the Porter that stands at the Gate, I do not know but that after all I might have gone back again; but now I thank God I am here, and I thank you for receiving of me.

Prudence discourses him

Then *Prudence* thought good to ask him a few questions, and desired his answer to them.

PRUD. Do you not think sometimes of the Country from whence you came?

Christian's thoughts of his native country

CHR. Yes, but with much shame and detestation: Truly, if I had been mindful of that Country from whence I came out, I might have had opportunity to have returned; but now I desire a better Country, that is, a Heavenly.

PRUD. Do you not yet bear away with you some of the things that then you were conversant withal?

Christian distasted with carnal cogitations

CHR. Yes, but greatly against my will; especially my inward and carnal cogitations, with which all my countrymen, as well as myself, were delighted; but now all those things are my grief; and might I but chuse mine own things, I would chuse never to think of those things more; but when I would be doing of that which is best, that which is worst is with me.

Christian's choice

PRUD. Do you not find sometimes, as if those things were vanquished, which at other times are your perplexity?

Christian's golden hours

CHR. Yes, but that is seldom; but they are to me golden hours in which such things happen to me.

PRUD. Can you remember by what means you find your annoyances at times, as if they were vanquished?

How Christian gets power against his corruptions

CHR. Yes, when I think what I saw at the Cross, that will do it; and when I look upon my broidered Coat, that will do it; also when I look into the Roll that I carry in my bosom, that will do it; and when my thoughts wax warm about whither I am going, that will do it.

PRUD. And what is it that makes you so desirous to go to Mount *Zion?*

Why Christian would be at Mount Zion

CHR. Why, there I hope to see him *alive* that did hang *dead* on the Cross; and there I hope to be rid of all those things that to this day are in me an annoyance to me; there, they say, there is no death; and there I shall dwell with such Company as I like best. For to tell you truth, I love him, because I was by him eased of my Burden, and I am weary of my inward sickness; I would fain be where I shall die no more, and with the Company that shall continually cry, *Holy, Holy, Holy.*

Then said *Charity* to *Christian,* Have you a family? Are you a married man?

Charity discourses him

CHR. I have a Wife and four small Children.

CHAR. And why did you not bring them along with you?

CHR. Then *Christian* wept, and said, Oh how willingly would I have done it, but they were all of them utterly averse to my going on Pilgrimage.

Christian's love to his wife and children

CHAR. But you should have talked to them, and have endeavoured to have shewn them the danger of being behind.

CHR. So I did, and told them also what God had shewed to me of the destruction of our City; but I seemed to them as one that mocked, and they believed me not.

CHAR. And did you pray to God that he would bless your counsel to them?

CHR. Yes, and that with much affection; for you must think that my Wife and poor Children were very dear unto me.

CHAR. But did you tell them of your own sorrow, and fear of destruction? for I suppose that destruction was visible enough to you.

CHR. Yes, over, and over, and over. They might also see my fears in my countenance, in my tears, and also in my trembling under the apprehension of the Judgment that did hang over our heads; but all was not sufficient to prevail with them to come with me.

Christian's fears of perishing might be read in his very countenance

CHAR. But what could they say for themselves, why they came not?

CHR. Why, my Wife was afraid of losing this World, and my Children were given to the foolish Delights of youth: so what by one thing, and what by another, they left me to wander in this manner alone.

The cause why his wife and children did not go with him

CHAR. But did you not with your vain life, damp all that you by words used by way of persuasion to bring them away with you?

Christian's good conversation before his wife and children

CHR. Indeed I cannot commend my life; for I am conscious to myself of many failings therein: I know also, that a man by his conversation may soon overthrow, what by argument or persuasion he doth labour to fasten upon others for their good. Yet, this I can say, I was very wary of giving them occasion, by any unseemly action, to make them averse to going on Pilgrimage. Yea, for this very thing they would tell me I was too precise, and that I denied myself of things (for their sakes) in which they saw no evil. Nay, I think I may say, that if what they saw in me did hinder them, it was my great tenderness in sinning against God, or of doing any wrong to my Neighbor.

Christian clear of their blood if they perish

CHAR. Indeed *Cain* hated his Brother, because his own works were evil, and his Brother's righteous; and if thy Wife and Children have been offended with thee for this, they thereby shew themselves to be implacable to good, and thou hast delivered thy soul from their blood.

What Christian had to his supper

Their talk at supper-time

Now I saw in my Dream, that thus they sat talking together until supper was ready. So when they had made ready, they sat down to meat. Now the Table was furnished with fat things, and with Wine that was well refined: and all their talk at the Table was about the LORD of the Hill; as namely, about what HE had done, and wherefore HE did what He did, and why HE had builded that House: and by what they said, I perceived that he had been a *great Warriour,* and had fought with and slain him that had the power of Death, but not without great danger to himself, which made me love him the more.

For, as they said, and as I believe (said *Christian*) he did it with the loss of much blood; but that which put Glory of Grace into all he did, was, that he did it out of pure love to his Country. And besides, there were some of them of the household that said they had seen and spoke with him since he did die on the Cross; and they have attested that they had it from his own lips, that he is such a lover of poor Pilgrims, that the like is not to be found from the East to the West.

Christ makes princes of beggars

They moreover gave an instance of what they affirmed, and that was, He had stript himself of his glory, that he might do this for the Poor; and that they heard him say and affirm, *That he would not dwell in the Mountain of* Zion *alone.* They said moreover, that he had made many Pilgrims Princes, though by nature they were Beggars born, and their original had been the dunghill.

Christian's bed-chamber

Thus they discoursed together till late at night; and after they had committed themselves to their Lord for protection, they betook themselves to rest: the Pilgrim they laid in a large upper chamber, whose window opened towards the Sun rising: the name of the chamber was *Peace,* where he slept till break of day, and then he awoke and sang,

> Where am I now? Is this the love and care
> Of Jesus for the men that Pilgrims are
> Thus to provide! That I should be forgiven
> And dwell already the next door to Heaven!

Christian had into the study, and what he saw there

So in the morning they all got up, and after some more discourse, they told him that he should not depart till they had shewed him the *Rarities* of that place. And first they had him into the Study, where they shewed him Records of the greatest antiquity; in which, as I remember my Dream, they shewed him first the *Pedigree* of the Lord of the Hill, that he was the Son of the Antient of Days, and came by an Eternal Generation. Here also was more fully recorded the Acts that he had done, and the names of many hundreds that he had taken into his service; and how he had placed them in such Habitations that could neither by length of Days, nor decays of Nature, be dissolved.

Then they read to him some of the worthy Acts that some of his servants had done: as, how they had subdued Kingdoms, wrought Righteousness, obtained Promises, stopped the mouths of Lions, quenched the violence of Fire, escaped the edge of the Sword; out of weakness were made strong, waxed valiant in fight, and turned to flight the Armies of the *Aliens*.

Then they read again in another part of the Records of the house, where it was shewed how willing their Lord was to receive into his favour any, even any, though they in time past had offered great affronts to his Person and proceedings. Here also were several other Histories of many other famous things, of all which *Christian* had a view; as of things both Antient and Modern: together with Prophecies and Predictions of things that have their certain accomplishment, both to the dread and amazement of Enemies, and the comfort and solace of Pilgrims.

Christian had into the armoury

The next day they took him and had him into the Armory, where they shewed him all manner of Furniture, which their Lord had provided for Pilgrims, as Sword, Shield, Helmet, Breastplate, *All-prayer,* and Shoes that would not wear out. And there was here enough of this to harness out as many men for the service of their Lord as there be Stars in the Heaven for multitude.

Christian is made to see ancient things

They also shewed him some of the Engines with which some of his Servants had done wonderful things. They shewed him *Moses'* Rod; the Hammer and Nail with which *Jael* slew *Sisera;* the Pitchers, Trumpets and Lamps too, with which *Gideon* put to flight the Armies of *Midian:* Then they shewed him the Ox's goad wherewith *Shamgar* slew six hundred men: They shewed him also the Jaw-bone with which *Samson* did such mighty feats: They shewed him moreover the Sling and Stone with which *David* slew *Goliah* of *Gath;* and the Sword also with which their Lord will kill the Man of

Sin, in the day that he shall rise up to the prey. They shewed him besides many excellent things, with which *Christian* was much delighted. This done, they went to their rest again.

Christian showed the Delectable Mountains

Then I saw in my Dream, that on the morrow he got up to go forwards, but they desired him to stay till the next day also; and then, said they, we will (if the day be clear) shew you the Delectable Mountains, which, they said, would yet further add to his comfort, because they were nearer the desired Haven than the place where at present he was: so he consented and stayed. When the morning was up, they had him to the top of the House, and bid him look South; so he did: and behold at a great distance he saw a most pleasant Mountainous Country, beautified with Woods, Vineyards, Fruits of all sorts, Flowers also, with Springs and Fountains, very delectable to behold. Then he asked the name of the Country:

They said it was *Immanuel's Land;* and it is as common, they said, as this *Hill* is, to and for all the Pilgrims. And when thou comest there, from thence, said they, thou mayest see to the gate of the Cœlestial City, as the Shepherds that live there will make appear.

Christian sets forward

Now he bethought himself of setting forward, and they were willing he should: but first, said they, let us go again into the Armory: So they did; and when they came there, they harnessed him from head to foot with what was of proof, lest perhaps he should meet with assaults in the way. He being therefore thus accoutred, walketh out with his friends to the Gate, and there he asked the Porter if he saw any Pilgrims pass by: Then the Porter answered, Yes.

Christian sent away armed

CHR. Pray, did you know him? said he.

POR. I asked his name, and he told me it was *Faithful.*

CHR. O, said *Christian,* I know him; he is my Townsman, my near Neighbor, he comes from the place where I was born: How far do you think he may be before?

POR. He is got by this time below the Hill.

How Christian and the Porter greet at parting

CHR. Well, said *Christian,* good Porter, the Lord be with thee, and add to all thy blessings much increase, for the kindness that thou hast shewed to me.

Whilst *Christian* is among his godly friends,
Their golden mouths make him sufficient mends
For all his griefs, and when they let him go,
He's clad with northern Steel from top to toe.

The Valley of Humiliation

Then he began to go forward; but *Discretion, Piety, Charity,* and *Prudence,* would accompany him down to the foot of the Hill. So they went on together, reiterating their former discourses, till they came to go down the Hill. Then said *Christian,* As it was *difficult* coming up, so (so far as I can see) it is *dangerous* going down. Yes, said *Prudence,* so it is, for it is a hard matter for a man to go down into the Valley of *Humiliation,* as thou art now, and to catch no slip by the way; therefore, said they, are we come out to accompany thee down the Hill. So he began to go down, but very warily; yet he caught a slip or two.

Then I saw in my Dream that these good Companions, when *Christian* was gone down to the bottom of the Hill, gave him a loaf of Bread, a bottle of Wine, and a cluster of Raisins; and then he went on his way.

Christian has no armour for his back

But now, in this Valley of *Humiliation,* poor *Christian* was hard put to it; for he had gone but a little way, before he espied a foul *Fiend* coming over the field to meet him; his name is *Apollyon.* Then did *Christian* begin to be afraid, and to cast in his mind whether to go back or to stand his ground: But he considered again that he had no Armor for his back, and therefore thought that to turn the back to him might give him the greater advantage with ease to pierce him with his Darts.

Therefore he resolved to venture and stand his ground; For, thought he, had I no more in mine eye than the saving of my life, 'twould be the best way to stand.

Christian's resolution at the approach of Apollyon

So he went on, and *Apollyon* met him. Now the Monster was hideous to behold; he was cloathed with scales like a Fish (and they are his pride); he had wings like a Dragon, feet like a Bear, and out of his belly came Fire and Smoke; and his mouth was as the mouth of a Lion. When he was come up to *Christian,* be beheld him with a disdainful countenance, and thus began to question with him.

APOL. Whence come you? and whither are you bound?

CHR. I am come from the City of *Destruction,* which is the place of all evil, and am going to the City of *Zion.*

APOL. By this I perceive thou art one of my Subjects, for all that Country is mine, and I am the Prince and God of it. How is it then that thou hast run away from thy King? Were it not that I hope thou mayest do me more service, I would strike thee now at one blow to the ground.

Discourse betwixt Christian and Apollyon

CHR. I was born indeed in your dominions, but your service was hard, and your wages such as a man could not live on, *for the wages of sin is death;* therefore when I was come to years, I did as other considerate persons do, look out, if perhaps I might mend myself.

APOL. There is no Prince that will thus lightly lose his Subjects, neither will I as yet lose thee: but since thou complainest of thy service and wages, be content to go back; what our Country will afford, I do here promise to give thee.

Apollyon's flattery

CHR. But I have let myself to another, even to the King of Princes, and how can I with fairness go back with thee?

APOL. Thou hast done in this, according to the Proverb, changed a bad for a worse; but it is ordi-

Apollyon under-values Christ's service

nary for those that have professed themselves his Servants, after a while to give him the slip, and return again to me: Do thou so too, and all shall be well.

CHR. I have given him my faith, and sworn my allegiance to him; how then can I go back from this, and not be hanged as a Traitor?

Apollyon pretends to be merciful

APOL. Thou didst the same to me, and yet I am willing to pass by all, if now thou wilt yet turn again and go back.

CHR. What I promised thee was in my nonage; and besides, I count that the Prince under whose Banner now I stand is able to absolve me; yea, and to pardon also what I did as to my compliance with thee; and besides, O thou destroying *Apollyon,* to speak truth, I like his Service, his Wages, his Servants, his Government, his Company and Country, better than thine; and therefore leave off to persuade me further; I am his Servant, and I will follow him.

Apollyon pleads the grievous ends of Christians, to dissuade Christian from persisting in his way

APOL. Consider again when thou art in cool blood, what thou art like to meet with in the way that thou goest. Thou knowest that for the most part, his Servants come to an ill end, because they are transgressors against me and my ways: How many of them have been put to shameful deaths; and besides, thou countest his service better than mine, whereas he never came yet from the place where he is to deliver any that served him out of our hands; but as for me, how many times, as all the World very well knows, have I delivered, either by power or fraud, those that have faithfully served me, from him and his, though taken by them; and so I will deliver thee.

CHR. His forbearing at present to deliver them is on purpose to try their love, whether they will cleave to him to the end; and as for the ill end thou sayest they come to, that is most glorious in their account; for for present deliverance, they do not much expect it, for they stay for their Glory, and then they shall have it, when their Prince comes in his and the Glory of the Angels.

APOL. Thou hast already been unfaithful in thy service to him, and how dost thou think to receive wages of him?

CHR. Wherein, O *Apollyon,* have I been unfaithful to him?

Apollyon pleads Christian's infirmities against him

APOL. Thou didst faint at first setting out, when thou wast almost choked in the Gulf of *Dispond;* thou didst attempt wrong ways to be rid of thy Burden, whereas thou shouldest have stayed till thy Prince had taken it off; thou didst sinfully sleep and lose thy choice thing; thou wast also almost persuaded to go back, at the sight of the Lions; and when thou talkest of thy Journey, and of what thou hast heard and seen, thou art inwardly desirous of vain-glory in all that thou sayest or doest.

CHR. All this is true, and much more which thou hast left out; but the Prince whom I serve and honor is merciful, and ready to forgive; but besides, these infirmities possessed me in thy Country, for there I sucked them in, and I have groaned under them, been sorry for them, and have obtained Pardon of my Prince.

Apollyon in a rage falls upon Christian

APOL. Then *Apollyon* broke out into a grievous rage, saying, I am an enemy to this Prince; I hate his Person, his Laws, and People; I am come out on purpose to withstand thee.

CHR. *Apollyon,* beware what you do, for I am in the King's High-way, the way of Holiness, therefore take heed to yourself.

APOL. Then *Apollyon* straddled quite over the whole breadth of the way, and said, I am void of fear in this matter, prepare thyself to die; for I swear by my infernal Den, that thou shalt go no further; here will I spill thy soul.

And with that he threw a flaming Dart at his breast, but *Christian* had a Shield in his hand, with which he caught it, and so prevented the danger of that.

Christian wounded in his understanding, faith, and conversation

Then did *Christian* draw, for he saw 'twas time to bestir him: and *Apollyon* as fast made at him, throwing Darts as thick as Hail; by the which, notwithstanding all that *Christian* could do to avoid it, *Apollyon* wounded him in his *head,* his *hand,* and *foot:* This made *Christian* give a little back; *Apollyon* therefore followed his work amain, and *Christian* again took courage, and resisted as manfully as he could. This sore Combat lasted for above half a day, even till *Christian* was almost quite spent; for you must know that *Christian,* by reason of his wounds, must needs grow weaker and weaker.

Apollyon casteth down to the ground Christian

Then *Apollyon* espying his opportunity, began to gather up close to *Christian,* and wrestling with him, gave him a dreadful fall; and with that *Christian's* Sword flew out of his hand. Then said *Apollyon, I am sure of thee now:* and with that he had almost pressed him to death, so that *Christian* began to despair of life: but as God would have it, while *Apollyon* was fetching of his last blow, thereby to make a full end of this good man, *Christian* nimbly stretched out his hand for his Sword, and caught it, saying, *Rejoice not against me, O mine Enemy! when I fall I shall arise;* and with that gave him a deadly thrust, which made him give back, as one that had received his mortal wound: *Christian,* perceiving that, made at him again, saying, *Nay, in all these things we are more than Conquerors through him that loved us.* And with that *Apollyon* spread forth his Dragon's wings, and sped him away, that *Christian* for a season saw him no more.

Christian's victory over Apollyon

A brief relation of the combat by the spectator

In this Combat no man can imagine, unless he had seen and heard as I did, what yelling and hideous roaring *Apollyon* made all the time of the fight, he spake like a Dragon; and on the other side, what sighs and groans burst from *Christian's* heart. I never saw him all the while give so much as one pleasant look, till he perceived he had wounded

Apollyon with his two-edged Sword; then indeed he did smile, and look upward; but 'twas the dreadfullest sight that ever I saw.

A more unequal match can hardly be:
Christian must fight an Angel; but you see
The Valiant Man by handling Sword and Shield,
Doth make him, tho' a Dragon, quit the field.

So when the Battle was over, *Christian* said, I will here give thanks to him that hath delivered me out of the mouth of the Lion, to him that did help me against *Apollyon*. And so he did, saying,

Christian gives God thanks for deliverance

Great *Beelzebub,* the Captain of this Fiend,
Design'd my ruin; therefore to this end
He sent him harness'd out: and he with rage
That hellish was, did fiercely me engage:
But blessed *Michael* helped me, and I
By dint of Sword did quickly make him fly.
Therefore to him let me give lasting praise,
And thank and bless his holy name always.

Then there came to him a hand, with some of the leaves of the Tree of Life, the which *Christian* took, and applied to the wounds that he had received in the Battle, and was healed immediately. He also sat down in that place to eat Bread, and to drink of the Bottle that was given him a little before; so being refreshed, he addressed himself to his Journey, with his Sword drawn in his hand; for he said, I know not but some other Enemy may be at hand. But he met with no other affront from *Apollyon* quite through this Valley.

Christian goes on his journey with his sword drawn in his hand

Now at the end of this Valley was another, called the Valley of the *Shadow of Death,* and *Christian* must needs go through it, because the way to the Cœlestial City lay through the midst of it. Now, this Valley is a very solitary place. The Prophet *Jeremiah* thus describes it: *A wilderness, a land of desarts and of pits, a land of drought, and of the shadow of death, a land that no man* (but a Christian) *passeth through, and where no man dwelt.*

The Valley of the Shadow of Death

Now here *Christian* was worse put to it than in his fight with *Apollyon,* as by the sequel you shall see.

The children of the spies go back

I saw then in my Dream, that when *Christian* was got to the borders of the *Shadow of Death,* there met him two men, Children of them that brought up an evil report of the good land, making haste to go back; to whom *Christian* spake as follows,

CHR. Whither are you going?

MEN. They said, Back, back; and we would have you to do so too, if either life or peace is prized by you.

CHR. Why, what's the matter? said *Christian.*

MEN. Matter! said they; we were going that way as you are going, and went as far as we durst; and indeed we were almost past coming back; for had we gone a little further, we had not been here to bring the news to thee.

CHR. But what have you met with? said *Christian.*

MEN. Why we were almost in the Valley of the *Shadow of Death;* but that by good hap we looked before us, and saw the danger before we came to it.

CHR. But what have you seen? said *Christian.*

MEN. Seen! Why, the Valley itself, which is as dark as pitch; we also saw there the Hobgoblins, Satyrs, and Dragons of the Pit; we heard also in that Valley a continual howling and yelling, as of a people under unutterable misery, who there sat bound in affliction and irons; and over that Valley hangs the discouraging clouds of Confusion; Death also doth always spread his wings over it. In a word, it is every whit dreadful, being utterly without Order.

CHR. Then said *Christian,* I perceive not yet, by what you have said, but that this is my way to the desired Haven.

MEN. Be it thy way; we will not chuse it for ours. So they parted, and *Christian* went on his way, but still with his Sword drawn in his hand, for fear lest he should be assaulted.

I saw then in my Dream, so far as this Valley reached, there was on the right hand a very deep Ditch; that Ditch is it into which the blind have led the blind in all ages, and have both there miserably perished. Again, behold on the left hand, there was a very dangerous Quag, into which, if even a good man falls, he can find no bottom for his foot to stand on. Into that Quag King *David* once did fall, and had no doubt therein been smothered, had not he that is able pluckt him out.

The path-way was here also exceeding narrow, and therefore good *Christian* was the more put to it; for when he sought in the dark to shun the ditch on the one hand, he was ready to tip over into the mire on the other; also when he sought to escape the mire, without great carefulness he would be ready to fall into the ditch. Thus he went on, and I heard him here sigh bitterly; for, besides the dangers mentioned above, the path-way was here so dark, that ofttimes, when he lift up his foot to set forward, he knew not where, or upon what he should set it next.

Poor man! where art thou now? Thy Day is Night.
Good man be not cast down, thou yet art right:
Thy way to Heaven lies by the gates of Hell;
Chear up, hold out, with thee it shall go well.

About the midst of this Valley, I perceived the mouth of Hell to be, and it stood also hard by the wayside. Now thought *Christian*, what shall I do? And ever and anon the flame and smoke would come out in such abundance, with sparks and hideous noises (things that cared not for *Christian's* Sword, as did *Apollyon* before) that he was forced to put up his Sword, and betake himself to another weapon, called *All-prayer*. So he cried in my hearing, *O Lord I beseech thee deliver my Soul.* Thus he went on a great while, yet still the flames would

Christian put to a stand, but for a while

be reaching towards him: Also he heard doleful voices, and rushings to and fro, so that sometimes he thought he should be torn in pieces, or trodden down like mire in the Streets. This frightful sight was seen, and these dreadful noises were heard by him for several miles together; and coming to a place where he thought he heard a company of *Fiends* coming forward to meet him, he stopt, and began to muse what he had best to do. Sometimes he had half a thought to go back; then again he thought he might be half way through the Valley; he remembered also how he had already vanquished many a danger, and that the danger of going back might be much more than for to go forward; so he resolved to go on. Yet the *Fiends* seemed to come nearer and nearer; but when they were come even almost at him, he cried out with a most vehement voice, *I will walk in the strength of the Lord God;* so they gave back, and came no further.

Christian made believe that he spake blasphemies, when it was Satan that suggested them into his mind

One thing I would not let slip; I took notice that now poor *Christian* was so confounded, that he did not know his own voice; and thus I perceived it: Just when he was come over against the mouth of the burning Pit, one of the wicked ones got behind him, and stept up softly to him, and whisperingly suggested many grievous blasphemies to him, which he verily thought had proceeded from his own mind. This put *Christian* more to it than anything that he met with before, even to think that he should now blaspheme him that he loved so much before; yet, if he could have helped it, he would not have done it; but he had not the discretion neither to stop his ears, nor to know from whence those blasphemies came.

When *Christian* had travelled in this disconsolate condition some considerable time, he thought he heard the voice of a man, as going before him, saying, *Though I walk through the Valley of the Shadow of Death, I will fear none ill, for thou art with me.*

Then was he glad, and that for these reasons:

First, Because he gathered from thence, that some who feared God were in this Valley as well as himself.

Secondly, For that he perceived God was with them, though in that dark and dismal state; and why not, thought he, with me? though by reason of the impediment that attends this place, I cannot perceive it.

Thirdly, For that he hoped, could he overtake them, to have company by and by. So he went on, and called to him that was before; but he knew not what to answer, for that he also thought himself to be alone. And by and by the day broke; then said *Christian, He hath turned the Shadow of Death into the morning.*

Christian glad at break of day

Now morning being come, he looked back, not out of desire to return, but to see, by the light of the day, what hazards he had gone through in the dark. So he saw more perfectly the Ditch that was on the one hand, and the Quag that was on the other; also how narrow the way was which led betwixt them both; also now he saw the Hobgoblins, and Satyrs, and Dragons of the Pit, but all afar off; for after break of day, they came not nigh; yet they were discovered to him, according to that which is written, *He discovered deep things out of darkness, and bringeth out to light the Shadow of Death.*

Now was *Christian* much affected with his deliverance from all the dangers of his solitary way; which dangers, though he feared them more before, yet he saw them more clearly now, because the light of the day made them conspicuous to him. And about this time the Sun was rising, and this was another mercy to *Christian;* for you must note, that though the first part of the Valley of the *Shadow of Death* was dangerous, yet this second part which he was yet to go, was, if possible, far more dangerous: for from the place where he now stood, even to the end of the Valley, the way was all along set

The second part of this valley very dangerous

so full of Snares, Traps, Gins, and Nets here, and so full of Pits, Pitfalls, deep Holes, and Shelvings down there, that had it now been dark, as it was when he came the first part of the way, had he had a thousand souls, they had in reason been cast away; but as I said, just now the Sun was rising. Then said he, *His candle shineth on my head, and by his light I go through darkness.*

In this light therefore he came to the end of the Valley. Now I saw in my Dream, that at the end of this Valley lay blood, bones, ashes, and mangled bodies of men, even of Pilgrims that had gone this way formerly; and while I was musing what should be the reason, I espied a little before me a Cave, where two Giants, *Pope* and *Pagan,* dwelt in old time; by whose power and tyranny the men whose bones, blood, ashes, *&c.* lay there, were cruelly put to death. But by this place *Christian* went without much danger, whereat I somewhat wondered; but I have learnt since, that *Pagan* has been dead many a day; and as for the other, though he be yet alive, he is by reason of age, and also of the many shrewd brushes that he met with in his younger days, grown so crazy, and stiff in his joints, that he can now do little more than sit in his Cave's mouth, grinning at Pilgrims as they go by, and biting his nails, because he cannot come to them.

So I saw that *Christian* went on his way; yet at the sight of the *Old Man* that sat in the mouth of the Cave, he could not tell what to think, specially because he spake to him, though he could not go after him, saying, *You will never mend till more of you be burned:* But he held his peace, and set a good face on't, and so went by and catcht no hurt. Then sang *Christian,*

O world of wonders! (I can say no less)
That I should be preserv'd in that distress
That I have met with here! O blessed be
That hand that from it hath delivered me!
Dangers in darkness, Devils, Hell, and Sin.

Did compass me, while I this Vale was in:
Yea, Snares, and Pits, and Traps, and Nets did lie
My path about, that worthless silly I
Might have been catch'd, intangled, and cast down;
But since I live, let JESUS wear the Crown.

Now as *Christian* went on his way, he came to a little ascent, which was cast up on purpose that Pilgrims might see before them. Up there therefore *Christian* went, and looking forward, he saw *Faithful* before him, upon his Journey. Then said *Christian* aloud, Ho, ho, So-ho; stay, and I will be your Companion. At that *Faithful* looked behind him; to whom *Christian* cried again, Stay, stay, till I come up to you: But *Faithful* answered, No, I am upon my life, and the Avenger of Blood is behind me.

Christian overtakes Faithful

At this *Christian* was somewhat moved, and putting to all his strength, he quickly got up with *Faithful*, and did also overrun him, so the *last was first*. Then did *Christian* vain-gloriously smile, because he had gotten the start of his Brother; but not taking good heed to his feet, he suddenly stumbled and fell, and could not rise again, until *Faithful* came up to help him.

Christian's fall makes Faithful and he go lovingly together

Then I saw in my Dream they went very lovingly on together, and had sweet discourse of all things that had happened to them in their Pilgrimage; and thus *Christian* began:

CHR. My honoured and well beloved Brother *Faithful*, I am glad that I have overtaken you; and that God has so tempered our spirits, that we can walk as Companions in this so pleasant a path.

FAITH. I had thought, dear Friend, to have had your company quite from our Town; but you did get the start of me, wherefore I was forced to come thus much of the way alone.

CHR. How long did you stay in the City of *Destruction*, before you set out after me on your Pilgrimage?

FAITH. Till I could stay no longer; for there was

Their talk about the country from whence they came

great talk presently after you were gone out, that our City would in short time with Fire from Heaven be burned down to the ground.

CHR. What, did your Neighbors talk so?

FAITH. Yes, 'twas for a while in everybody's mouth.

CHR. What, and did no more of them but you come out to escape the danger?

FAITH. Though there was, as I said, a great talk thereabout, yet I do not think they did firmly believe it. For in the heat of the discourse, I heard some of them deridingly speak of you and of your desperate Journey, (for so they called this your Pilgrimage) but I did believe, and do still, that the end of our City will be with Fire and Brimstone from above; and therefore I have made mine escape.

CHR. Did you hear no talk of Neighbor *Pliable?*

FAITH. Yes *Christian,* I heard that he followed you till he came at the Slough of *Dispond,* where, as some said, he fell in; but he would not be known to have so done; but I am sure he was soundly bedabbled with that kind of dirt.

CHR. And what said the Neighbors to him?

How Pliable was accounted of, when he got home

FAITH. He hath since his going back been had greatly in derision, and that among all sorts of people; some do mock and despise him; and scarce will any set him on work. He is now seven times worse than if he had never gone out of the City.

CHR. But why should they be so set against him, since they also despise the way that he forsook?

FAITH. Oh, they say, Hang him, he is a Turncoat, he was not true to his profession: I think God has stirred up even his Enemies to hiss at him, and make him a Proverb, because he hath forsaken the way.

CHR. Had you no talk with him before you came out?

FAITH. I met him once in the Streets, but he

leered away on the other side, as one ashamed of what he had done; so I spake not to him.

CHR. Well, at my first setting out, I had hopes of that man; but now I fear he will perish in the overthrow of the City, for it is happened to him according to the true Proverb, *The Dog is turned to his Vomit again, and the Sow that was washed to her wallowing in the Mire.*

The dog and the sow

FAITH. They are my fears of him too; but who can hinder that which will be?

CHR. Well Neighbor *Faithful,* said *Christian,* let us leave him, and talk of things that more immediately concern ourselves. Tell me now, what you have met with in the way as you came; for I know you have met with some things, or else it may be writ for a wonder.

FAITH. I escaped the Slough that I perceive you fell into, and got up to the Gate without that danger; only I met with one whose name was *Wanton,* that had like to have done me a mischief.

Faithful assaulted by Wanton

CHR. 'Twas well you escaped her Net; *Joseph* was hard put to it by her, and he escaped her as you did; but it had like to have cost him his life. But what did she do to you?

FAITH. You cannot think (but that you know something) what a flattering tongue she had; she lay at me hard to turn aside with her, promising me all manner of content.

CHR. Nay, she did not promise you the content of a good conscience.

FAITH. You know what I mean, all carnal and fleshly content.

CHR. Thank God you have escaped her: The abhorred of the Lord shall fall into her Ditch.

FAITH. Nay, I know not whether I did wholly escape her or no.

CHR. Why, I tro you did not consent to her desires.

FAITH. No, not to defile myself; for I remembred an old writing that I had seen, which saith, *Her steps take hold of Hell.* So I shut mine eyes, because I would not be bewitched with her looks: then she railed on me, and I went my way.

CHR. Did you meet with no other assault as you came?

He is assaulted by Adam the First

FAITH. When I came to the foot of the Hill called *Difficulty,* I met with a very aged Man, who asked me, *What I was, and whither bound?* I told him, That I was a Pilgrim, going to the Cœlestial City. Then said the old man, Thou lookest like an honest fellow; wilt thou be content to dwell with me for the wages that I shall give thee? Then I asked him his name, and where he dwelt? He said his name was *Adam the First, and I dwell in the Town of* Deceit. I asked him then, What was his work? and what the wages that he would give? He told me, That his work was *many delights;* and his wages, *that I should be his Heir at last.* I further asked him, What House he kept, and what other Servants he had? So he told me, That his House was maintained with all the dainties in the world; and that his Servants were those of his own begetting. Then I asked how many Children he had? He said that he had but three Daughters: *The Lust of the Flesh, The Lust of the Eyes,* and *The Pride of Life,* and that I should marry them all if I would. Then I asked him how long time he would have me live with him? And he told me, As long as he lived himself.

CHR. Well, and what conclusion came the old man and you to at last?

FAITH. Why, at first, I felt myself somewhat inclinable to go with the man, for I thought he spake very fair; but looking in his forehead, as I talked with him, I saw there written, *Put off the old man with his deeds.*

CHR. And how then?

FAITH. Then it came burning hot into my mind, whatever he said, and however he flattered, when he got me home to his House, he would sell me for a slave. So I bid him forbear to talk, for I would not come near the door of his House. Then he reviled me, and told me that he would send such a one after me, that should make my way bitter to my Soul. So I turned to go away from him; but just as I turned myself to go thence, I felt him take hold of my flesh and give me such a deadly twitch back, that I thought he had pulled part of me after himself. This made me cry, *O wretched Man!* So I went on my way up the Hill.

Now when I had got about halfway up, I looked behind me, and saw one coming after me, swift as the wind; so he overtook me just about the place where the Settle stands.

CHR. Just there, said *Christian,* did I sit down to rest me; but being overcome with sleep, I there lost this Roll out of my bosom.

FAITH. But good Brother hear me out. So soon as the man overtook me, he was but a word and a blow, for down he knocked me, and laid me for dead. But when I was a little come to myself again, I asked him wherefore he served me so? He said, Because of my secret inclining to *Adam the First:* and with that he struck me another deadly blow on the breast, and beat me down backward, so I lay at his foot as dead as before. So when I came to myself again I cried him mercy; but he said, I know not how to shew mercy; and with that knocked me down again. He had doubtless made an end of me, but that one came by, and bid him forbear.

CHR. Who was that that bid him forbear?

FAITH. I did not know him at first, but as he went by, I perceived the holes in his hands and in his side; then I concluded that he was our Lord. So I went up the Hill.

CHR. That man that overtook you was *Moses:* He spareth none, neither knoweth he how to shew mercy to those that transgress his Law.

The temper of Moses

FAITH. I know it very well; it was not the first time that he has met with me. 'Twas he that came to me when I dwelt securely at home, and that told me, He would burn my house over my head if I staid there.

CHR. But did you not see the house that stood there on the top of that Hill, on the side of which *Moses* met you?

FAITH. Yes, and the Lions too, before I came at it: but for the Lions, I think they were asleep, for it was about Noon; and because I had so much of the day before me, I passed by the Porter, and came down the Hill.

CHR. He told me indeed that he saw you go by, but I wish you had called at the house, for they would have shewed you so many Rarities, that you would scarce have forgot them to the day of your death. But pray tell me, Did you meet nobody in the Valley of *Humility?*

Faithful assaulted by Discontent

FAITH. Yes, I met with one *Discontent,* who would willingly have persuaded me to go back again with him; his reason was, for that the Valley was altogether without *honour.* He told me moreover, that there to go was the way to disobey all my friends, as *Pride, Arrogancy, Self-conceit, Worldly-glory,* with others, who he knew, as he said, would be very much offended, if I made such a Fool of myself as to wade through this Valley.

CHR. Well, and how did you answer him?

Faithful's answer to Discontent

FAITH. I told him, That although all these that he had named might claim kindred of me, and that rightly, (for indeed they were my Relations *according to the flesh*) yet since I became a Pilgrim they have disowned me, as I also have rejected them; and therefore they were to me now no more than if they had never been of my lineage. I told him moreover, that as to this Valley, he had quite misrepresented the thing; *for before Honour is Humility, and a haughty spirit before a fall.* Therefore said I, I had rather go through this Valley to the honour that was so accounted by the wisest, than chuse the way which he esteemed most worthy our affections.

CHR. Met you with nothing else in that Valley?

FAITH. Yes, I met with *Shame;* but of all the men that I met with in my Pilgrimage, he I think bears the wrong name. The other would be said nay, after a little argumentation, (and somewhat else) but this boldfaced *Shame* would never have done.

He is assaulted with Shame

CHR. Why, what did he say to you?

FAITH. What! why he objected against Religion itself; he said it was a pitiful low sneaking business for a man to mind Religion; he said that a tender conscience was an unmanly thing; and that for a man to watch over his words and ways, so as to tie up himself from that hectoring liberty that the brave spirits of the times accustom themselves unto, would make him the ridicule of the times. He objected also, that but few of the Mighty, Rich, or Wise, were ever of my opinion; nor any of them neither, before they were persuaded to be Fools, and to be of a voluntary fondness to venture the loss of all, *for nobody else knows what.* He moreover objected the base and low estate and condition of those that were chiefly the Pilgrims of the times in which they lived: also their ignorance, and want of understanding in all Natural Science. Yea, he did hold me to it at that rate also, about a great many more things than here I relate; as, that it was a *shame* to sit whining and mourning under a Sermon, and a *shame* to come sighing and groaning home; that it was a *shame* to ask my Neighbour forgiveness for petty faults, or to make restitution where I had taken from any. He said also that Religion made a man grow strange to the great, because of a few vices (which he called by finer names) and made him own and respect the base, because of the same Religious Fraternity. And is not this, said he, a *shame?*

CHR. And what did you say to him?

FAITH. Say! I could not tell what to say at first. Yea, he put me so to it, that my blood came up in my face; even this *Shame* fetched it up, and had almost beat me quite off. But at last I began to consider, *That that which is highly esteemed among Men, is had in abomination with God.* And I thought again, this *Shame* tells me what *men* are; but it tells me nothing what *God* or the *Word of God* is. And I thought moreover, that at the day of doom, we shall not be doomed to death or life according to the hectoring spirits of the world, but according to the Wisdom and Law of the Highest. Therefore thought I, what God says is best, is best, though all the men in the world are against it. Seeing then that God prefers his Religion, seeing God prefers a tender Conscience, seeing they that make themselves Fools for the Kingdom of Heaven are wisest; and that the poor man that loveth Christ is richer than the greatest man in the world that hates him; *Shame* depart, thou art an enemy to my Salvation: shall I entertain thee against my Sovereign Lord? How then shall I look him in the face at his coming? Should I now be ashamed of his ways and Servants, how can I expect the blessing? But indeed this *Shame* was a bold villain; I could scarce shake him out of my company; yea, he would be haunting of me, and continually whispering me in the ear, with some one or other of the infirmities that attend Religion; but at last I told him, 'Twas but in vain to attempt further in this business; for those things that he disdained, in those did I see most glory; and so at last I got past this importunate one. And when I had shaken him off, then I began to sing:

The tryals that those men do meet withal,
That are obedient to the Heavenly call,
Are manifold, and suited to the flesh,
And come, and come, and come again afresh;
That now, or some time else, we by them may
Be taken, overcome, and cast away.
Oh, let the Pilgrims, let the Pilgrims then,
Be vigilant, and quit themselves like men.

Chr. I am glad, my Brother, that thou didst withstand this Villain so bravely; for of all, as thou sayest, I think he has the wrong name; for he is so bold as to follow us in the Streets, and to attempt to put us to shame before all men; that is, to make us ashamed of that which is good: but if he was not himself audacious, he would never attempt to do as he does; but let us still resist him; for notwithstanding all his bravadoes, he promoteth the Fool and none else. *The Wise shall inherit glory,* said *Solomon, but shame shall be the promotion of Fools.*

Faith. I think we must cry to Him for help against *Shame,* that would have us to be valiant for *Truth* upon the Earth.

Chr. You say true; but did you meet nobody else in that Valley?

Faith. No not I; for I had Sun-shine all the rest of the way through that, and also through the Valley of the Shadow of Death.

Chr. 'Twas well for you; I am sure it fared far otherwise with me; I had for a long season, as soon almost as I entred into that Valley, a dreadful Combat with that foul Fiend *Apollyon;* yea, I thought verily he would have killed me, especially when he got me down and crushed me under him, as if he would have crushed me to pieces; for as he threw he, my Sword flew out of my hand; nay, he told me, *He was sure of me:* but *I cried to God, and he heard me, and delivered me out of all my troubles.* Then I entred into the Valley of the Shadow of Death, and had no light for almost half the way through it. I thought I should have been killed there, over and over; but at last day brake, and the Sun rose, and I went through that which was behind with far more ease and quiet.

Talkative described

Moreover, I saw in my Dream, that as they went on, *Faithful,* as he chanced to look on one side, saw a man whose name is *Talkative,* walking at a distance besides them; (for in this place there was room enough for them all to walk). He was a tall man, and something more comely at a distance than at hand. To this man *Faithful* addressed himself in this manner.

FAITH. Friend, Whither away? Are you going to the Heavenly Country?

TALK. I am going to the same place.

FAITH. That is well; then I hope we may have your good company.

TALK. With a very good will will I be your Companion.

Faithful and Talkative enter discourse

FAITH. Come on then, and let us go together, and let us spend our time in discoursing of things that are profitable.

TALK. To talk of things that are good, to me is very acceptable, with you or with any other; and I am glad that I have met with those that incline to so good a work; for to speak the truth, there are but few that care thus to spend their time (as they are in their travels), but chuse much rather to be speaking of things to no profit; and this hath been a trouble to me.

Talkative's dislike of bad discourse

FAITH. That is indeed a thing to be lamented; for what things so worthy of the use of the tongue and mouth of men on Earth as are the things of the God of Heaven?

TALK. I like you wonderful well, for your saying is full of conviction; and I will add, What thing so pleasant, and what so profitable, as to talk of the things of God? What things so pleasant? (that is, if a man hath any delight in things that are wonderful) for instance, if a man doth delight to talk of the History or the Mystery of things; or if a man doth love to talk of Miracles, Wonders, or Signs, where shall he find things recorded so delightful, and so sweetly penned, as in the Holy Scripture?

FAITH. That's true; but to be profited by such things in our talk should be that which we design.

TALK. That's it that I said; for to *talk* of such

things is most profitable; for by so doing, a man may get knowledge of many things; as of the vanity of earthly things, and the benefit of things above: (Thus in general) but more particularly. By this a man may learn the necessity of the New-birth, the insufficiency of our works, the need of Christ's righteousness, *&c.* Besides, by this a man may learn by *talk,* what it is to repent, to believe, to pray, to suffer, or the like; by this also a man may learn what are the great promises and consolations of the Gospel, to his own comfort. Further, by this a man may learn to refute false opinions, to vindicate the truth, and also to instruct the ignorant. **Talkative's fine discourse**

FAITH. All this is true, and am I glad to hear these things from you.

TALK. Alas! the want of this is the cause that so few understand the need of faith, and the necessity of a work of Grace in their Soul, in order to eternal life; but ignorantly live in the works of the Law, by which a man can by no means obtain the Kingdom of Heaven.

FAITH. But by your leave, Heavenly knowledge of these is the gift of God; no man attaineth to them by human industry, or only by the talk of them.

TALK. All this I know very well; for a man can receive nothing, except it be given him from Heaven: all is of Grace, not of Works: I could give you a hundred Scriptures for the confirmation of this. **O brave Talkative**

FAITH. Well then, said *Faithful,* what is that one thing that we shall at this time found our discourse upon?

TALK. What you will. I will talk of things Heavenly, or things Earthly; things Moral, or things Evangelical; things Sacred or things Prophane; things past or things to come; things foreign or things at home; things more Essential, or things Circumstantial; provided that all be done to our profit. **O brave Talkative**

FAITH. Now did *Faithful* begin to wonder; and

Faithful beguiled by Talkative

stepping to *Christian* (for he walked all this while by himself) he said to him, (but softly) What a brave Companion have we got! Surely this man will make a very excellent Pilgrim.

Christian makes a discovery of Talkative, telling Faithful who he was

CHR. At this *Christian* modestly smiled, and said, This man with whom you are so taken, will beguile with this tongue of his, twenty of them that know him not.

FAITH. Do you know him then?

CHR. Know him! Yes, better than he knows himself.

FAITH. Pray what is he?

CHR. His name is *Talkative;* he dwelleth in our Town: I wonder that you should be a stranger to him, only I consider that our Town is large.

FAITH. Whose Son is he? And whereabout doth he dwell?

CHR. He is the son of one *Say-well;* he dwelt in *Prating Row;* and is known of all that are acquainted with him, by the name of *Talkative* in *Prating Row;* and notwithstanding his fine tongue, he is but a sorry fellow.

FAITH. Well, he seems to be a very pretty man.

CHR. That is, to them who have thorough acquaintance with him, for he is best abroad, near home he is ugly enough: Your saying that he is a *pretty man,* brings to my mind what I have observed in the work of the Painter, whose Pictures shew best at a distance, but very near, more unpleasing.

FAITH. But I am ready to think you do but jest, because you smiled.

CHR. God forbid that I should jest (though I smiled) in this matter, or that I should accuse any falsely: I will give you a further discovery of him: This man is for any company, and for any talk; as he talketh now with you, so he will talk when he is on the Ale-bench; and the more drink he hath in his crown, the more of these things he hath in his mouth; Religion hath no place in his heart, or house, or conversation; all he hath lieth in his tongue, and his Religion is to make a noise therewith.

FAITH. Say you so! Then am I in this man greatly deceived.

CHR. Deceived! you may be sure of it; remember the Proverb, *They say and do not: but the Kingdom of God is not in word, but in power. He talketh* of Prayer, of Repentance, of Faith, and of the New-birth; but he knows but only to *talk* of them. I have been in his Family, and have observed him both at home and abroad; and I know what I say of him is the truth. His house is as empty of Religion as the white of an Egg is of savour. There is there neither Prayer, nor sign of Repentance for sin; yea, the brute in his kind serves God better than he. He is the very stain, reproach, and shame of Religion, to all that know him; it can hardly have a good word in all that end of the Town where he dwells through him. Thus say the common people that know him, *A Saint abroad, and a Devil at home.* His poor Family finds it so; he is such a churl, such a railer at, and so unreasonable with his Servants, that they neither know how to do for, or speak to him. Men that have any dealings with him, say 'tis better to deal with a *Turk* than with him; for fairer dealing they shall have at their hands. This *Talkative* (if it be possible) will go beyond them, defraud, beguile, and over-reach them. Besides he brings up his Sons to follow his steps; and if he findeth in any of them *a foolish timorousness,* (for so he calls the first appearance of a tender conscience) he calls them fools and blockheads and by no means will imploy them in much, or speak to their commendations before others. For my part I am of opinion that he has by his wicked life caused many to stumble and fall; and will be, if God prevent not, the ruine of many more.

Talkative talks, but does not

His house is empty of religion

He is a stain to religion

The proverb that goes of him

Men shun to deal with him

FAITH. Well, my Brother, I am bound to believe you; not only because you say you know him, but also because like a Christian, you make your reports of men, For I cannot think that you speak these things of ill will, but because it is even so as you say.

CHR. Had I known him no more than you, I might perhaps have thought of him as at the first you did; yea, had he received this report at their hands only that are enemies to Religion, I should have thought it had been a slander: (a lot that often falls from bad men's mouths upon good men's names and professions;) but all these things, yea and a great many more as bad, of my own knowledge I can prove him guilty of. Besides, good men are ashamed of him; they can neither call him *Brother,* nor *Friend;* the very naming of him among them, makes them blush, if they know him.

FAITH. Well, I see that *saying* and *doing* are two things, and hereafter I shall better observe this distinction.

The carcass of religion

CHR. They are two things indeed, and are as diverse as are the Soul and the Body; for as the Body without the Soul is but a dead Carcass, so *Saying,* if it be alone, is but a dead Carcass also. The Soul of Religion is the practick part: *Pure Religion and undefiled, before God and the Father, is this, To visit the fatherless and widows in their affliction, and to keep himself unspotted from the world.* This *Talkative* is not aware of; he thinks that *hearing* and *saying* will make a good Christian, and thus he deceiveth his own soul. *Hearing* is but as the sowing of the Seed; *talking* is not sufficient to prove that fruit is indeed in the heart and life; and let us assure ourselves, that at the day of Doom men shall be judged according to their fruits. It will not be said then, *Did you believe?* but Were you *Doers,* or *Talkers* only? and accordingly shall they be judged. The end of the world is compared to our Harvest, and you know men at Harvest regard nothing but fruit. Not that anything can be accepted that is not of *Faith;* but I speak this to shew you how insignificant the profession of *Talkative* will be at that day.

Faithful convinced of the badness of Talkative

FAITH. This brings to my mind that of *Moses,* by which he describeth the beast that is clean. He is such an one that parteth the Hoof and cheweth the Cud: not that parteth the Hoof only, or that cheweth the Cud only. The Hare cheweth the Cud, but yet is unclean, because he parteth not the Hoof. And this truly resembleth *Talkative;* he cheweth the Cud, he seeketh knowledge, he cheweth upon the Word; but he divideth not the Hoof, he parteth not with the way of sinners; but as the Hare, he retaineth the foot of a Dog or Bear, and therefore is unclean.

Talkative like to things that sound without life

CHR. You have spoken, for ought I know, the true Gospel sense of those Texts: And I will add another thing; *Paul* calleth some men, yea and those great Talkers too, *sounding Brass and tinkling Cymbals;* that is, as he expounds them in another place, *Things without life, giving sound.* Things without life, that is, without the true Faith and Grace of the Gospel; and consequently things that shall never be placed in the Kingdom of Heaven among those that are the Children of life; though their *sound,* by their *talk,* be as if it were the tongue or voice of an Angel.

FAITH. Well, I was not so fond of his company at first, but I am as sick of it now. What shall we do to be rid of him?

CHR. Take my advice, and do as I bid you, and you shall find that he will soon be sick of your company too, except God shall touch his heart, and turn it.

FAITH. What would you have me to do?

CHR. Why, go to him, and enter into some serious discourse about *the power of Religion;* and ask him plainly (when he has approved of it, for that he will) whether this thing be set up in his Heart, House, or Conversation.

FAITH. Then *Faithful* stepped forward again,

and said to *Talkative, Come, what chear? How is it now?*

TALK. Thank you, well. I thought we should have had a great deal of talk by this time.

FAITH. Well, if you will, we will fall to it now; and since you left it with me to state the question, let it be this; How doth the saving Grace of God discover itself, when it is in the heart of man?

Talkative's false discovery of a work of grace

TALK. I perceive then that our talk must be *about the power of things:* Well, 'tis a very good question, and I shall be willing to answer you. And take my answer in brief thus: *First,* Where the Grace of God is in the heart, it causeth there a great out-cry against sin. *Secondly*—

FAITH. Nay hold, let us consider of one at once: I think you should rather say, It shews itself by inclining the Soul to abhor its sin.

TALK. Why, what difference is there between crying out against, and abhorring of sin?

To cry out against sin

FAITH. Oh! a great deal; a man may cry out against sin, or policy; but he cannot abhor it, but by vertue of a godly antipathy against it: I have heard many cry out against sin in the Pulpit, who yet can abide it well enough in the heart, house, and conversation. *Joseph's* Mistress cried out with a loud voice, as if she had been very holy; but she would willingly, notwithstanding that, have committed uncleanness with him. Some cry out against sin, even as the Mother cries out against her Child in her lap, when she calleth it slut and naughty girl, and then falls to hugging and kissing it.

TALK. You lie at the catch, I perceive.

FAITH. No, not I; I am only for setting things right. But what is the second thing whereby you would prove a discovery of a work of Grace in the heart?

TALK. Great knowledge of *Gospel Mysteries.*

Great knowledge no sign of grace

FAITH. This sign should have been first; but first or last, it is also false; for knowledge, great knowledge may be obtained in the mysteries of the Gospel, and yet no work of Grace in the Soul. Yea, if a man have all knowledge, he may yet be nothing; and so consequently be no child of God. When Christ said, *Do you know all these things?* and the Disciples had answered, Yes; he addeth *Blessed are ye if ye do them.* He doth not lay the blessing in the knowing of them, but in the doing of them. For there is a knowledge that is not attended with doing; *He that knoweth his Master's will, and doth it not.* A man may know like an Angel, and yet be no Christian, therefore your sign of it is not true. Indeed to *know* is a thing that pleaseth Talkers and Boasters; but to *do* is that which pleaseth God. Not that the heart can be good without knowledge; for without that the heart is naught. There is therefore knowledge and knowledge. Knowledge that resteth in the bare speculation of things, and knowledge that is accompanied with the Grace of faith and love, which puts a man upon doing even the will of God from the heart; the first of these will serve the Talker; but without the other the true Christian is not content. *Give me understanding, and I shall keep thy Law; yea I shall observe it with my whole heart.*

Knowledge and knowledge

True knowledge attended with endeavours

TALK. You lie at the catch again, this is not for edification.

FAITH. Well, if you please propound another sign how this work of Grace discovereth itself where it is.

TALK. Not I, for I see we shall not agree.

FAITH. Well, if you will not, will you give me leave to do it?

TALK. You may use your liberty.

FAITH. A work of Grace in the soul discovereth itself, either to him that hath it, or to standers-by.

One good sign of grace

To him that hath it thus: It gives him conviction of sin, especially of the defilement of his nature and the sin of unbelief (for the sake of which he is sure to be damned, if he findeth not mercy at God's hand by faith in Jesus Christ). This sight and sense of things worketh in him sorrow and shame for sin; he findeth moreover revealed in him the Saviour of the world, and the absolute necessity of closing with him for life, at the which he findeth hungrings and thirstings after him, to which hungrings, *&c.* the promise is made. Now according to the strength or weakness of his Faith in his Saviour, so is his joy and peace, so is his love to holiness, so are his desires to know him more, and also to serve him in this World. But though I say it discovereth itself thus unto him, yet it is but seldom that he is able to conclude that this is a work of Grace; because his corruptions now, and his abused reason, make his mind to misjudge in this matter; therefore in him that hath this work, there is required a very sound Judgment before he can with steadiness conclude that this is a work of Grace.

To others it is thus discovered:

1. By an experimental confession of his Faith in Christ.

2. By a life answerable to that confession, to wit, a life of holiness, heart-holiness, family-holiness, (if he hath a Family) and by conversation-holiness in the World; which in the general teacheth him, inwardly to abhor his sin, and himself for that in secret, to suppress it in his Family, and to promote holiness in the World; not by talk only, as an Hypocrite or Talkative person may do, but by a practical subjection, in Faith and Love, to the power of the Word: And now Sir, as to this brief description of the work of Grace, and also the discovery of it, if you have ought to object, object; if not, then give me leave to propound to you a second question.

TALK. Nay my part is not now to object, but to hear, let me therefore have your second question.

Another good sign of grace

FAITH. It is this. Do you experience the first part of this description of it? and doth your life and conversation testify the same? or standeth your Religion in *Word* or in *Tongue,* and not in *Deed* and *Truth?* Pray, if you incline to answer me in this, say no more than you know the God above will say *Amen* to; and also nothing but what your conscience can justify you in; for, *not he that commendeth himself is approved, but whom the Lord commendeth.* Besides, to say I am thus and thus, when my Conversation and all my Neighbors tell me I lye, is great wickedness.

TALK. Then *Talkative* at first began to blush, but recovering himself, thus he replied, You come now to Experience, to Conscience, and God; and to appeal to him for justification of what is spoken: This kind of discourse I did not expect; nor am I disposed to give an answer to such questions, because I count not myself bound thereto, unless you take upon you to be a *Catechizer*, and, though you should so do, yet I may refuse to make you my Judge. But I pray will you tell me why you ask me such questions?

Talkative not pleased with Faithful's question

FAITH. Because I saw you forward to talk, and because I knew not that you had ought else but notion. Besides, to tell you all the truth, I have heard of you that you are a man whose Religion lies in talk, and that your conversation gives this your Mouth-profession the lye. They say you are a spot among Christians, and that religion fareth the worse for your ungodly Conversation, that some have already stumbled at your wicked ways, and that more are in danger of being destroyed thereby; your Religion, and an Ale-house, and Covetousness, and Uncleanness, and Swearing and Lying, and vain Company-keeping, &c. will stand together. The Proverb is true of you which is said of a Whore, to wit, That she is a shame to all Women; so you are a shame to all Professors.

The reasons why Faithful put to him that question

Faithful's plain dealing with Talkative

TALK. Since you are ready to take up reports, and to judge so rashly as you do, I cannot but conclude you are some peevish or melancholy man, not fit to be discoursed with; and so adieu.

Talkative flings away from Faithful

CHR. Then came up *Christian*, and said to his Brother, I told you how it would happen; your

A good riddance

words and his lusts could not agree; he had rather leave your company than reform his life. But he is gone, as I said; let him go, the loss is no man's but his own, he has saved us the trouble of going from him; for he continuing (as I suppose he will do) as he is, he would have been but a blot in our company: besides, the Apostle says, *From such withdraw thyself.*

FAITH. But I am glad we had this little discourse with him, it may happen that he will think of it again; however, I have dealt plainly with him, and so am clear of his blood, if he perisheth.

CHR. You did well to talk so plainly to him as you did. There is but little of this faithful dealing with men now a days, and that makes Religion to stink so in the nostrils of many, as it doth; for they are these Talkative Fools whose Religion is only in word, and are debauched and vain in their Conversation, that (being so much admitted into the fellowship of the godly) do puzzle the World, blemish Christianity, and grieve the sincere. I wish that all men would deal with such as you have done: then should they either be made more conformable to Religion, or the company of Saints would be too hot for them. Then did *Faithful* say,

How *Talkative* at first lifts up his Plumes!
How bravely doth he speak! How he presumes
To drive all before him! But so soon
As *Faithful* talks of *Heart-work,* like the Moon
That's past the full, into the wane he goes.
And so will all, but he that *Heart-work* knows.

Thus they went on talking of what they had seen by the way, and so made that way easy, which would otherwise, no doubt, have been tedious to them; for now they went through a Wilderness.

Evangelist overtakes them again

Now when they were got almost quite out of this Wilderness, *Faithful* chanced to cast his eye back, and espied one coming after them, and he knew him. Oh! said *Faithful* to his Brother, Who comes yonder? Then *Christian* looked, and said, It is my good friend *Evangelist.* Ay, and my good friend too, said *Faithful,* for 'twas he that set me the way to the Gate. Now was *Evangelist* come up unto them, and thus saluted them:

EVAN. Peace be with you, dearly beloved, and peace be to your helpers.

CHR. Welcome, welcome, my good *Evangelist,* the sight of thy countenance brings to my remembrance thy antient kindness and unwearied laboring for my eternal good.

They are glad at the sight of him

FAITH. And a thousand times welcome, said good *Faithful:* Thy company, O sweet *Evangelist,* how desirable is it to us poor Pilgrims!

EVAN. Then said *Evangelist,* How hath it fared with you my friends, since the time of our last parting? What have you met with, and how have you behaved yourselves?

Then *Christian* and *Faithful* told him of all things that had happened to them in the way; and how, and with what difficulty, they had arrived to that place.

EVAN. Right glad am I, said *Evangelist,* not that you have met with trials, but that you have been victors; and that you have (notwithstanding many weaknesses) continued in the way to this very day.

His exhortation to them

I say, right glad am I of this thing, and that for mine own sake and yours: I have sowed, and you have reaped; and the day is coming, when both he that sowed and they that reaped shall rejoice together; that is, if you hold out: for in due time ye shall reap, if you faint not. The Crown is before you, and it is an incorruptible one; so run that you may obtain it. Some there be that set out for this Crown, and after they have gone far for it, another comes in, and takes it from them; hold fast therefore that you have, let no man take your Crown. You are not yet out of the gun-shot of the Devil; you have not resisted unto blood, striving against sin; let the Kingdom be always before you, and believe stedfastly concerning things that are invisible. Let nothing that is on this side the other world get within you; and above all, look well to your own hearts, and to the lusts thereof, for they are deceitful above all things, and desperately wicked; set your faces like a flint; you have all power in Heaven and Earth on your side.

They do thank him for his exhortation

CHR. Then *Christian* thanked him for his exhortation, but told him withal, that they would have him speak farther to them for their help the rest of the way, and the rather, for that they well knew that he was a Prophet, and could tell them of things that might happen unto them, and also how they might resist and overcome them. To which request *Faithful* also consented. So *Evangelist* began as followeth:

He predicteth what troubles they shall meet with in Vanity Fair, and encourageth them to steadfastness

EVAN. My Sons, you have heard, in the words of the truth of the Gospel, that you must through many tribulations enter into the Kingdom of Heaven. And again, that in every City bonds and afflictions abide in you; and therefore you cannot expect that you should go long on your Pilgrimage without them, in some sort or other. You have found something of the truth of these testimonies upon you already, and more will immediately follow; for now, as you see, you are almost out of this Wilderness, and therefore you will soon come into a Town that you will by and by see before you; and in that Town you will be hardly beset with enemies, who will strain hard but they will kill you; and be ye sure that one or both of you must seal the testimony which you hold, with blood; but be you faithful unto death, and the King will give you a Crown of life. He that shall die there, although his death will be unnatural, and his pain perhaps great, he will yet have the better of his fellow; not only because he will be arrived at the Cœlestial City soonest, but because he will escape many miseries that the other will meet with in the rest of his Journey. But when you are come to the Town, and shall find fulfilled what I have here related, then remember your

He whose lot it will be there to suffer, will have the better of his brother friend, and quit yourselves like men, and commit the keeping of your souls to your God in well-doing, as unto a faithful Creator.

Then I saw in my Dream, that when they were got out of the Wilderness, they presently saw a Town before them, and the name of that Town is *Vanity;* and at the Town there is a Fair kept, called *Vanity Fair:* it is kept all the year long; it beareth the name of *Vanity Fair,* because the Town where 'tis kept *is lighter than Vanity;* and also because all that is there sold, or that cometh thither, is *Vanity.* As is the saying of the wise, *All that cometh is Vanity.*

This Fair is no new-erected business, but a thing of antient standing; I will shew you the original of it.

The antiquity of this fair

Almost five thousand years agone, there were Pilgrims walking to the Cœlestial City, as these two honest persons are; and *Beelzebub, Apollyon,* and *Legion,* with their Companions, perceiving by the path that the Pilgrims made, that their way to the City lay through this Town of *Vanity,* they contrived here to set up a Fair; a Fair wherein should be sold *all sorts of Vanity,* and that it should last all the year long: therefore at this Fair are all such Merchandize sold, as Houses, Lands, Trades, Places, Honours, Preferments, Titles, Countries, Kingdoms, Lusts, Pleasures, and Delights of all sorts, as Whores, Bawds, Wives, Husbands, Children, Masters, Servants, Lives, Blood, Bodies, Souls, Silver, Gold, Pearls, Precious Stones, and what not?

The merchandise of this fair

And moreover, at this Fair there is at all times to be seen Jugglings, Cheats, Games, Plays, Fools, Apes, Knaves, and Rogues, and that of every kind.

Here are to be seen too, and that for nothing, Thefts, Murders, Adulteries, false-swearers, and that of a blood-red colour.

The streets of this fair

And as in other Fairs of less moment, there are the several Rows and Streets under their proper names, where such and such Wares are vended; so here likewise you have the proper places, Rows, Streets, (*viz.* Countries and Kingdoms) where the Wares of this Fair are soonest to be found: Here is the *Britain* Row, the *French* Row, the *Italian* Row, the *Spanish* Row, the *German* Row, where several sorts of Vanities are to be sold. But as in other Fairs, some one commodity is as the chief of all the Fair, so the ware of *Rome* and her Merchandize is greatly promoted in this Fair; only our *English* nation, with some others, have taken a dislike thereat.

Christ went through this fair

Now, as I said, the way to the Cœlestial City lies just through this Town where this lusty Fair is kept; and he that will go to the City, and yet not go through this Town, must needs *go out of the world.* The Prince of Princes himself, when here, went through this Town to his own Country, and that upon a *Fair-day* too; yea, and as I think, it was *Beelzebub,* the chief Lord of this Fair, that invited him to buy of his Vanities: yea, would have made him Lord of the Fair, would he but have done him reverence as he went through the Town. Yea, because he was such a person of honour, *Beelzebub* had him from Street to Street, and shewed him all the Kingdoms of the World in a little time, that he might, (if possible) allure that Blessed One to cheapen and buy some of his Vanities; but he had no mind to the Merchandize, and therefore left the Town, without laying out so much as one Farthing upon these Vanities. This Fair therefore is an antient thing, of long standing, and a very great Fair.

Christ bought nothing in this fair

The Pilgrims enter the fair

Now these Pilgrims, as I said, must needs go through this Fair. Well, so they did; but behold, even as they entered into the Fair, all the people in the Fair were moved, and the Town itself as it were in a hubbub about them; and that for several reasons: for

The fair in a hubbub about them

First, The Pilgrims were cloathed with such kind of Raiment as was diverse from the Raiment of any that traded in that Fair. The people therefore of the Fair made a great gazing upon them: some said they were Fools, some they were Bedlams, and some they are Outlandishmen.

The first cause of the hubbub

Secondly, And as they wondered at their Apparel, so they did likewise at their Speech; for few could understand what they said: they naturally spoke the language of *Canaan,* but they that kept the Fair were the men of this World; so that, from one end of the Fair to the other, they seemed Barbarians each to the other.

Second cause of the hubbub

Thirdly, But that which did not a little amuse the Merchandizers was, that these Pilgrims set very light by all their Wares, they cared not so much as to look upon them; and if they called upon them to buy, they would put their fingers in their ears, and cry, *Turn away mine eyes from beholding Vanity,* and look upwards, signifying that their trade and traffick was in Heaven.

Third cause of the hubbub

One chanced mockingly, beholding the carriages of the men, to say unto them, What will ye buy? But they, looking gravely upon him, answered, *We buy the Truth.* At that there was an occasion taken to despise the men the more; some mocking, some taunting, some speaking reproachfully, and some calling upon others to smite them. At last things came to a hubbub and great stir in the Fair, insomuch that all order was confounded. Now was word presently brought to the Great One of the Fair, who quickly came down and deputed some of his most trusty friends to take those men into examination, about whom the Fair was almost overturned. So the men were brought to examination; and they that sat upon them, asked them whence they came, whither they went, and what they did there in such an unusual Garb? The men told them that they were Pilgrims and Strangers in the World, and that they were going to their own Country, which was the Heavenly *Jerusalem;* and that they had given no occasion to the men of the Town, nor

Fourth cause of the hubbub

They are mocked

The fair in a hubbub

They are examined

They tell who they are, and whence they came

yet to the Merchandizers, thus to abuse them, and to let them in their Journey, except it was for that, when one asked them what they would buy, they said they would *buy the Truth.* But they that were appointed to examine them did not believe them to be any other than Bedlams and Mad, or else such as came to put all things into a confusion in the Fair. Therefore they took them and beat them, and besmeared them with dirt, and then put them into the Cage, that they might be made a spectacle to all the men of the Fair.

They are not believed

They are put in the cage

Behold Vanity Fair, the Pilgrims there
Are chained and stand beside:
Even so it was our Lord passed here,
And on Mount Calvary died.

There therefore they lay for some time, and were made the objects of any man's sport, or malice, or revenge, the Great One of the Fair laughing still at all that befell them. But the men being patient, and not rendring railing for railing, but contrariwise blessing, and giving good words for bad, and kindness for injuries done, some men in the Fair that were more observing, and less prejudiced than the rest, began to check and blame the baser sort for their continual abuses done by them to the men; they therefore in angry manner let fly at them again, counting them as bad as the men in the Cage, and telling them that they seemed confederates, and should be made partakers of their misfortunes. The other replied, that for ought they could see, the men were quiet, and sober, and intended nobody any harm; and that there were many that traded in their Fair that were more worthy to be put into the Cage yea, and Pillory too, than were the men that they had abused. Thus, after divers words had passed on both sides, (the men behaving themselves all the while very wisely and soberly before them) they fell to some blows among themselves, and did harm to one another. Then were

Their behaviour in the cage

The men of the fair do fall out among themselves about these two men these two poor men brought before their examiners again, and there charged as being guilty of the late hubbub that had been in the Fair. So they beat them pitifully and hanged irons upon them, and led them in chains up and down the Fair, for an example and a terror to others, lest any should speak in their behalf, or join themselves unto them. But *Christian* and *Faithful* behaved themselves yet more wisely, and received the ignominy and shame that was cast upon them, with so much meekness and patience, that it won to their side (though but few in comparison of the rest) several of the men in the Fair. This put the other party yet into a greater rage, insomuch that they concluded the death of these two men. Wherefore they threatened, that the Cage, nor irons should serve their turn, but that they should die, for the abuse they had done, and for deluding the men of the Fair.

They are made the authors of this disturbance

They are led up and down the fair in chains, for a terror to others

Some of the men of the fair won to them

Their adversaries resolve to kill them

Then were they re-manded to the Cage again, until further order should be taken with them. So they put them in, and made their feet fast in the Stocks.

Here also they called again to mind what they had heard from their faithful friend *Evangelist,* and were the more confirmed in their way and sufferings, by what he told them would happen to them. They also now comforted each other, that whose lot it was to suffer, even he should have the best on't; therefore each man secretly wished that he might have that preferment: but committing themselves to the All-wise dispose of Him that ruleth all things, with much content they abode in the condition in which they were, until they should be otherwise disposed of.

Then a convenient time being appointed, they brought them forth to their Tryal, in order to their condemnation. When the time was come, they were brought before their enemies, and arraigned. The Judge's name was Lord *Hategood.* Their Indictment was one and the same in substance, though

They are again put into the cage, and after brought to trial

somewhat varying in form, the contents whereof was this:

Their indictment

That they were enemies to and disturbers of their Trade; that they had made Commotions and Divisions in the Town, and had won a party to their own most dangerous Opinions in contempt of the Law of their Prince.

Now *Faithful* play the Man, speak for thy God:
Fear not the wicked's malice, nor their rod:
Speak boldly man, the Truth is on thy side;
Die for it, and to Life in triumph ride.

Faithful's answer for himself

Then *Faithful* began to answer, that he had only set himself against that which had set itself against Him that is higher than the highest. And said he, as for Disturbance, I make none, being myself a man of Peace; the parties that were won to us, were won by beholding our Truth and Innocence, and they are only turned from the worse to the better. And as to the King you talk of, since he is *Beelzebub,* the enemy of Our Lord, I defy him and all his Angels.

Then Proclamation was made, that they that had ought to say for their Lord the King against the Prisoner at the Bar, should forthwith appear and give in their evidence. So there came in three witnesses, to wit, *Envy, Superstition,* and *Pickthank.* They were then asked if they knew the Prisoner at the Bar; and what they had to say for their Lord the King against him.

Envy begins

Then stood forth *Envy,* and said to this effect: My lord, I have known this man a long time, and will attest upon my Oath before this honourable Bench, that he is—

JUDGE. Hold! Give him his Oath.

So they sware him. Then he said, My Lord, this man, notwithstanding his plausible name, is one of the vilest men in our Country. He neither regardeth Prince nor People, Law nor Custom; but doth all that he can to possess all men with certain of his disloyal notions, which he in the general calls Principles of Faith and Holiness. And in particular, I heard him once myself affirm *That Christianity and the Customs of our Town of* Vanity *were diametrically opposite, and could not be reconciled.* By which saying, my Lord, he doth at once not only condemn all our laudable doings, but us in the doing of them.

JUDGE. Then did the Judge say to him, Hast thou any more to say?

ENVY. My Lord, I could say much more, only I would not be tedious to the Court. Yet if need be, when the other Gentlemen have given in their Evidence, rather than anything shall be wanting that will dispatch him, I will enlarge my Testimony against him. So he was bid stand by.

Then they called *Superstition,* and bid him look upon the Prisoner. They also asked, what he could say for their Lord the King against him? Then they sware him; so he began:

Superstition follows

SUPER. My Lord, I have no great acquaintance with this man, nor do I desire to have further knowledge of him; however, this I know, that he is a very pestilent fellow, from some discourse that the other day I had with him in this Town; for then talking with him, I heard him say, That our Religion was naught, and such by which a man could by no means please God. Which sayings of his, my Lord, your Lordship very well knows, what necessarily thence will follow, to wit, That we still do worship in vain, are yet in our sins, and finally shall be damned; and this is that which I have to say.

Then was *Pickthank* sworn, and bid say what he knew, in behalf of their Lord the King, against the Prisoner at the Bar.

Pickthank's testimony

PICK. My Lord, and you Gentlemen all, This fellow I have known of a long time, and have heard him speak things that ought not to be spoke; for he hath railed on our noble Prince *Beelzebub,* and hath spoken contemptibly of his honourable

Sins are all lords, and great ones

Friends, whose names are the Lord *Old Man,* the Lord *Carnal Delight,* the Lord *Luxurious,* the Lord *Desire of Vain Glory,* my old Lord *Lechery,* Sir *Having Greedy,* with all the rest of our Nobility; and he hath said moreover, That if all men were of his mind, if possible, there is not one of these Noble men should have any longer a being in this Town; besides, he hath not been afraid to rail on you, my Lord, who are now appointed to be his Judge, calling you an ungodly villain, with many other suchlike vilifying terms, with which he hath bespattered most of the Gentry of our Town.

When this *Pickthank* had told his tale, the Judge directed his speech to the Prisoner at the Bar, saying, Thou Runagate, Heretick, and Traitor, hast thou heard what these honest Gentlemen have witnessed against thee?

FAITH. May I speak a few words in my own defence?

JUDGE. Sirrah, sirrah, thou deservedst to live no longer, but to be slain immediately upon the place; yet that all men may see our gentleness towards thee, let us see what thou hast to say.

Faithful's defence of himself

FAITH. 1. I say then, in answer to what Mr. *Envy* hath spoken, I never said ought but this, *That what Rule, or Laws, or Custom, or People, were flat against the Word of God, are diametrically opposite to Christianity.* If I have said amiss in this, convince me of my error, and I am ready here before you to make my recantation.

2. As to the second, to wit, Mr. *Superstition,* and his charge against me, I said only this, *That in the worship of God there is required a Divine Faith; but there can be no Divine Faith without a Divine Revelation of the will of God: therefore whatever is thrust into the Worship of God that is not agreeable to Divine Revelation, cannot be done but by a human faith, which faith will not be profit to Eternal Life.*

3. As to what Mr. *Pickthank* hath said, I say,

(avoiding terms, as that I am said to rail, and the like) that the Prince of this Town, with all the rabblement his attendants, by this Gentleman named, are more fit for a being in Hell, than in this Town and Country: *and so, the Lord have mercy upon me.*

The Judge's speech to the jury

Then the Judge called to the Jury (who all this while stood by, to hear and observe) Gentlemen of the Jury, you see this man about whom so great an uproar hath been made in this Town: you have also heard what these worthy Gentlemen have witnessed against him: also you have heard his reply and confession: It lieth now in your breasts to hang him, or save his life; but yet I think meet to instruct you into our Law.

There was an Act made in the days of *Pharaoh* the Great, Servant to our Prince, that lest those of a contrary Religion should multiply and grow too strong for him, their Males should be thrown into the river. There was also an Act made in the days of *Nebuchadnezzar* the Great, another of his Servants, that whoever would not fall down and worship his Golden Image, should be thrown into a Fiery Furnace. There was also an Act made in the days of *Darius,* that whoso, for some time, called upon any God but him, should be cast into the Lions' Den. Now the substance of these Laws this Rebel has broken, not only in thought (which is not to be borne) but also in word and deed; which must therefore needs be intolerable.

For that of *Pharaoh,* his Law was made upon a supposition, to prevent mischief, no Crime being yet apparent; but here is a Crime apparent. For the second and third, you see he disputeth against our Religion; and for the Treason he hath confessed, he deserveth to die the death.

The jury, and their names

Then went the Jury out, whose names were, Mr *Blind-man,* Mr *No-good,* Mr *Malice,* Mr *Love-lust,* Mr *Live-loose,* Mr *Heady,* Mr *High-mind,* Mr *Enmity,* Mr *Lyar,* Mr *Cruelty,* Mr *Hate-light,* and

Mr *Implacable;* who every one gave in his private Verdict against him among themselves, and afterwards unanimously concluded to bring him in guilty before the Judge. And first among themselves, Mr *Blind-man* the Foreman, said, *I see clearly that this man is an Heretick.* Then said Mr *No-good, Away with such a fellow from the earth. Ay,* said Mr *Malice, for I hate the very looks of him.* Then said Mr *Love-lust, I could never endure him. Nor I,* said Mr *Live-loose, for he would always be condemning my way. Hang him, hang him,* said Mr *Heady. A sorry Scrub,* said Mr *High-mind. My heart riseth against him,* said Mr *Enmity. He is a Rogue,* said Mr *Lyar. Hanging is too good for him,* said Mr *Cruelty. Let us dispatch him out of the way,* said Mr *Hate-light.* Then said Mr *Implacable, Might I have all the world given me, I could not be reconciled to him; therefore let us forthwith bring him in guilty of death.* And so they did; therefore he was presently condemned to be had from the place where he was, to the place from whence he came, and there to be put to the most cruel death that could be invented.

Every one's private verdict

They conclude to bring him in guilty of death

The cruel death of Faithful

They therefore brought him out, to do with him according to their Law; and first they Scourged him, then they Buffeted him, then they Lanced his flesh with Knives; after that they Stoned him with stones, then pricked him with their Swords; and last of all they burned him to ashes at the Stake. Thus came *Faithful* to his end.

A chariot and horses wait to take away Faithful

Now I saw that there stood behind the multitude a Chariot and a couple of Horses, waiting for *Faithful,* who (so soon as his adversaries had dispatched him) was taken up into it, and straitway was carried up through the Clouds, with sound of Trumpet, the nearest way to the Cœlestial Gate.

Brave *Faithful,* bravely done in word and deed;
Judge, Witnesses, and Jury have, instead
Of overcoming thee, but shewn their rage:
When they are Dead, thou'lt Live from age to age.

But as for *Christian*, he had some respite, and was remanded back to prison; so he there remained for a space: But he that over-rules all things, having the power of their rage in his own hand, so wrought it about, that *Christian* for that time escaped them, and went his way. And as he went he sang, saying,

Christian is still alive

The Song that Christian made of Faithful after his death

Well *Faithful*, thou hast faithfully profest
Unto thy Lord; with whom thou shalt be blest,
When *faithless* ones, with all their vain delights,
Are crying out under their hellish plights:
Sing, *Faithful*, sing, and let thy name survive;
For though they kill'd thee, thou art yet alive.

Now I saw in my Dream, that *Christian* went not forth alone, for there was one whose name was *Hopeful*, (being made so by the beholding of *Christian* and *Faithful* in their words and behaviour, in their sufferings at the Fair) who joined himself unto him, and entring into a brotherly covenant, told him that he would be his Companion. Thus one died to make Testimony to the Truth, and another rises out of his ashes to be a Companion with *Christian* in his Pilgrimage. This *Hopeful* also told *Christian*, that there were many more of the men in the Fair that would take their time and follow after.

Christian has another companion

There are more of the men of the Fair will follow

So I saw that quickly after they were got out of the Fair, they overtook one that was going before them, whose name was *By-ends*: so they said to him, What Country-man, Sir? and how far go you this way? He told them that he came from the Town of *Fair-speech*, and he was going to the Cœlestial City, (but told them not his name.)

They overtake By-ends

From *Fair-speech*, said *Christian*. Is there any good that lives there?

BY-ENDS. Yes, said *By-ends*, I hope.

CHR. Pray Sir, what may I call you?

BY-ENDS. I am a Stranger to you, and you to me: if you be going this way, I shall be glad of your company; if not, I must be content.

By-ends loath to tell his name

CHR. This Town of *Fair-speech*, said *Christian*,

I have heard of it, and, as I remember, they say it's a wealthy place.

BY-ENDS. Yes, I will assure you that it is; and I have very many rich Kindred there.

CHR. Pray, who are your Kindred there? if a man may be so bold.

BY-ENDS. Almost the whole Town; and in particular, my Lord *Turn-about*, my Lord *Time-server*, my Lord *Fair-speech*, (from whose ancestors that Town first took its name) also Mr *Smooth-man*, Mr *Facing-both-ways*, Mr *Anything;* and the Parson of our Parish, Mr *Two-tongues*, was my Mother's own Brother by Father's side; and to tell you the truth, I am become a Gentleman of good Quality, yet my Great Grandfather was but a waterman, looking one way and rowing another; and I got most of my estate by the same occupation.

CHR. Are you a married man?

The wife and kindred of By-ends

BY-ENDS. Yes, and my Wife is a very vertuous woman, the Daughter of a vertuous woman; she was my Lady *Feigning's* Daughter, therefore she came of a very honourable Family, and is arrived to such a pitch of breeding, that she knows how to carry it to all, even to Prince and Peasant. 'Tis true we somewhat differ in Religion from those of the stricter sort, yet but in two small points: First, we never strive against Wind and Tide: Secondly, we are always most zealous when Religion goes in his Silver Slippers; we love much to walk with him in the Street, if the Sun shines, and the people applaud him.

Where By-ends differs from others in religion

Then *Christian* stepped a little aside to his fellow *Hopeful*, saying, It runs in my mind that this is one *By-ends* of *Fair-speech*, and if it be he, we have as very a Knave in our company as dwelleth in all these parts. Then said *Hopeful*, Ask him; methinks he should not be ashamed of his name. *So Christian* came up with him again, and said, Sir, you talk as if you knew something more than all the world doth; and if I take not my mark amiss, I deem I have half a guess of you: Is not your name Mr *By-ends* of *Fair-speech?*

BY-ENDS. This is not my name, but indeed it is a nick-name that is given me by some that cannot abide me; and I must be content to bear it as a reproach, as other good men have borne theirs before me.

CHR. But did you never give an occasion to men to call you by this name?

BY-ENDS. Never, never! The worst that ever I did to give them an occasion to give me this name, was, that I had always the luck to jump in my Judgment with the present way of the times whatever it was, and my chance was to get thereby; but if things are thus cast upon me, let me count them a blessing, but let not the malicious load me therefore with reproach.

How By-ends got his name

CHR. I thought indeed that you were the man that I heard of, and to tell you what I think, I fear this name belongs to you more properly than you are willing we should think it doth.

BY-ENDS. Well, if you will thus imagine, I cannot help it; you shall find me a fair company-keeper, if you will still admit me your associate.

He desires to keep company with Christian

CHR. If you will go with us, you must go against Wind and Tide, the which, I perceive, is against your opinion; you must also own Religion in his Rags, as well as when in his Silver Slippers, and stand by him too, when bound in Irons, as well as when he walketh the Streets with applause.

BY-ENDS. You must not impose, nor lord it over my Faith; leave me to my liberty, and let me go with you.

CHR. Not a step further, unless you will do in what I propound, as we.

Then said *By-ends,* I shall never desert my old Principles, since they are harmless and profitable. If I may not go with you, I must do as I did before you overtook me, even go by myself, until some overtake me that will be glad of my company.

By-ends and Christian part

Now I saw in my Dream that *Christian* and *Hopeful* forsook him, and kept their distance before him; but one of them looking back, saw three men following Mr *By-ends,* and behold, as they came up with him, he made them a very low congee, and they also gave him a compliment. The men's names were Mr *Hold-the-world,* Mr *Money-love,* and Mr *Save-all;* men that Mr *By-ends* had formerly been acquainted with; for in their minority they were School-fellows, and were taught by one Mr *Gripe-man,* a School-master in *Love-gain,* which is a Market-town in the County of *Coveting,* in the North. This School-master taught them the Art of Getting, either by violence, cousenage, flattery, lying, or by putting on a guise of Religion; and these four Gentlemen had attained much of the Art of their Master, so that they could each of them have kept such a School themselves.

He has new companions

Well when they had, as I said, thus saluted each other, Mr *Money-love* said to Mr *By-ends,* Who are they upon the Road before us? For *Christian* and *Hopeful* were yet within view.

By-ends' character of the pilgrims

BY-ENDS. They are a couple of far country-men, that *after their mode* are going on Pilgrimage.

MONEY-LOVE. Alas! Why did they not stay, that we might have had their good company? for they, and we, and you Sir, I hope are all going on a Pilgrimage.

BY-ENDS. We are so indeed; but the men before us are so rigid, and love so much their own notions, and do also so lightly esteem the opinions of others, that let a man be never so godly, yet if he jumps not with them in all things, they thrust him quite out of their company.

SAVE-ALL. That's bad; but we read of some that are *righteous overmuch;* and such men's rigidness prevails with them to judge and condemn all but themselves. But I pray *what,* and *how many,* were the things wherein you differed?

BY-ENDS. Why they after their head-strong manner, conclude that it is duty to rush on their Journey all weathers, and I am for waiting for Wind and Tide. They are for hazarding all for God at a clap, and I am for taking all advantages to secure my Life and Estate. They are for holding their notions, though all other men are against them; but I am for Religion in what, and so far as the times and my safety will bear it. They are for Religion when in Rags and Contempt; but I am for him when he walks in his Golden Slippers in the Sun-shine, and with applause.

HOLD-THE-WORLD. Ay, and hold you there still, good Mr *By-ends;* for for my part I can count him but a Fool, that having the liberty to keep what he has, shall be so unwise as to lose it. Let us be wise *as Serpents;* 'tis best to make hay when the Sun shines; you see how the Bee lieth still all winter, and bestirs her only when she can have Profit with Pleasure. God sends sometimes Rain, and sometimes Sun-shine; if they be such fools to go through the first, yet let us be content to take fair weather along with us. For my part I like that Religion best that will stand with the security of God's good blessings unto us; for who can imagine that is ruled by his Reason, since God has bestowed upon us the good things of this Life, but that he would have us keep them for his sake? *Abraham* and *Solomon* grew rich in Religion. And *Job* says, that a good man *shall lay up Gold as Dust.* But he must not be such as the men before us, if they be as you have described them.

SAVE-ALL. I think that we are all agreed in this matter, and therefore there needs no more words about it.

MONEY-LOVE. No, there needs no more words about this matter indeed; for he that believes neither Scripture nor Reason (and you see we have both on our side) neither knows his own liberty, nor seeks his own safety.

BY-ENDS. My Brethren, we are, as you see, going all on Pilgrimage; and for our better diversion from things that are bad, give me leave to propound unto you this question:

Suppose a man, a Minister, or a Tradesman, *&c.* should have an advantage lie before him to get the good blessings of this life, yet so as that he can by no means come by them, except in appearance at least, he becomes extraordinary zealous in some points of Religion that he meddled not with before; may he not use this means to attain his end, and yet be a right honest man?

MONEY-LOVE. I see the bottom of your question, and, with these Gentlemen's good leave, I will endeavour to shape you an answer. And first, to speak to your question as it concerns a *Minister* himself: Suppose a Minister, a worthy man, possess'd but of a very small benefice, and has in his eye a greater, more fat and plump by far; he has also now an opportunity of getting of it, yet so as by being more studious, by preaching more frequently and zealously, and because the temper of the people requires it, by altering of some of his principles; for my part I see no reason but a man may do this, (provided he has a Call) ay, and more a great deal besides, and yet be an honest man. For why?

1. His desire of greater benefice is lawful (this cannot be contradicted since 'tis set before him by Providence); so then he may get it if he can, making no question for Conscience sake.

2. Besides, his desire after that benefice makes him more studious, a more zealous Preacher, *&c.* and so makes him a better man; yea makes him better improve his parts, which is according to the Mind of God.

3. Now as for his complying with the temper of his people, by dissenting, to serve them, some of his Principles, this argueth, 1. That he is of a self-denying temper; 2. Of a sweet and winning deport-

ment; 3. And so more fit for the Ministerial function.

4. I conclude then, that a Minister that changes a *small* for a *great,* should not for so doing be judged as covetous; but rather, since he has improved in his parts and industry thereby, be counted as one that pursues his Call, and the opportunity put into his hand to do Good.

And now to the second part of the question, which concerns the *Tradesman* you mentioned. Suppose such an one to have but a poor imploy in the world, but by becoming Religious, he may mend his Market, perhaps get a rich Wife, or more and far better Customers to his shop; for my part I see no reason but this may be lawfully done. For why?

1. To become *Religious* is a Virtue, by what means soever a man becomes so.

2. Nor is it unlawful to get a rich Wife, or more Custom to my Shop.

3. Besides, the man that gets these by becoming religious, gets that which is good of them that are good, by becoming good himself; so then here is a good Wife, and good Customers, and good Gain, and all these by becoming religious, which is good; therefore to become religious to get all these, is a good and profitable design.

This answer thus made by this Mr *Money-love* to Mr *By-ends'* question was highly applauded by them all; wherefore they concluded upon the whole that it was most wholesome and advantageous. And because, as they thought, no man was able to contradict it, and because *Christian* and *Hopeful* were yet within call, they jointly agreed to assault them with the question as soon as they overtook them, and the rather because they had opposed Mr *By-ends* before. So they called after them, and they stopt, and stood still till they came up to them; but they concluded as they went that not Mr *By-ends,* but old Mr *Hold-the-world,* should propound the question to them, because, as they supposed, their answer to him would be without the remainder of that heat that was kindled betwixt Mr *By-ends* and them, at their parting a little before.

So they came up to each other, and after a short salutation, Mr *Hold-the-world* propounded the question to *Christian* and his fellow, and bid them to answer it if they could.

CHR. Then said *Christian,* Even a babe in Religion may answer ten thousand such questions. For if it be unlawful to follow Christ for loaves, as it is *John* 6. how much more abominable is it to make of him and Religion a Stalking-horse, to get and enjoy the world. Nor do we find any other than Heathens, Hypocrites, Devils, and Witches, that are of this opinion.

1. *Heathens;* for when *Hamor* and *Shechem* had a mind to the Daughter and Cattle of *Jacob,* and saw that there was no ways for them to come at them, but by becoming circumcised; they said to their companions, If every male of us be circumcised, as they are circumcised, shall not their Cattle, and their substance, and every beast of theirs, be ours? Their Daughter and their Cattle were that which they sought to obtain, and their Religion the Stalking-horse they made use of to come at them. Read the whole story, *Gen.* 34. 20, 21, 22, 23.

2. The Hypocritical *Pharisees* were also of this Religion; Long Prayers were their Pretence, but to get widows' houses was their Intent; and greater damnation was from God their Judgment, *Luke* 20. 46, 47.

3. *Judas* the Devil was also of this Religion; he was religious for the Bag, that he might be possessed of what was therein; but he was lost, cast away, and the very son of Perdition.

4. *Simon* the *Witch* was of this Religion too; for he would have had the Holy Ghost, that he might have got Money therewith, and his sentence from *Peter's* mouth was according, *Acts* 8, 19, 20, 21, 22.

5. Neither will it out of my mind, but that that man that takes up Religion for the World, will throw away Religion for the World; for so surely as *Judas* designed the World in becoming religious, so surely did he also sell Religion and his Master for the same. To answer the question therefore affirmatively, as I perceive you have done, and to accept of as authentick such answer, is both Heathenish, Hypocritical, and Devilish, and your Reward will be according to your Works. Then they stood staring one upon another, but had not wherewith to answer *Christian*. *Hopeful* also approved of the soundness of *Christian's* answer; so there was a great Silence among them. Mr *By-ends* and his company also staggered and kept behind, that *Christian* and *Hopeful* might outgo them. Then said *Christian* to his fellow, If these men cannot stand before the sentence of men, what will they do with the sentence of God? And if they are mute when dealt with by vessels of Clay, what will they do when they shall be rebuked by the flames of a devouring Fire?

The ease that pilgrims have is but little in this life

Then *Christian* and *Hopeful* out-went them again, and went till they came to a delicate Plain called *Ease*, where they went with much content; but that Plain was but narrow, so they were quickly got over it. Now at the further side of that Plain was a little Hill called *Lucre*, and in that Hill a *Silver-Mine*, which some of them that had formerly gone that way, because of the rarity of it, had turned aside to see; but going too near the brink of the pit, the ground being deceitful under them, broke, and they were slain; some also had been maimed there, and could not to their dying day be their own men again.

Lucre Hill a dangerous hill

Demas at the Hill Lucre. He calls to Christian and Hopeful to come to him

Then I saw in my Dream, that a little off the road, over against the *Silver-Mine*, stood *Demas* (gentlemanlike) to call to Passengers to come and see; who said to *Christian* and his fellow, Ho, turn aside hither, and I will shew you a thing.

CHR. What thing so deserving as to turn us out of the way?

DEMAS. Here is a *Silver-Mine,* and some digging in it for Treasure. If you will come, with a little pains you may richly provide for yourselves.

Hopeful tempted to go, but Christian holds him back

HOPE. Then said *Hopeful,* Let us go see.

CHR. Not I, said *Christian;* I have heard of this place before now, and how many have there been slain; and besides that Treasure is a snare to those that seek it, for it hindereth them in their Pilgrimage. Then *Christian* called to *Demas,* saying, Is not the place dangerous? Hath it not hindred many in their Pilgrimage?

DEMAS. Not very dangerous, except to those that are careless: but withal, he blushed as he spake.

CHR. Then said *Christian* to *Hopeful,* Let us not stir a step, but still keep on our way.

HOPE. I will warrant you, when *By-ends* comes up, if he hath the same invitation as we, he will turn in thither to see.

CHR. No doubt thereof, for his Principles lead him that way, and a hundred to one but he dies there.

DEMAS. Then *Demas* called again, saying, But will you not come over and see?

Christian roundeth up Demas

CHR. Then *Christian* roundly answered, saying, *Demas,* thou art an Enemy to the right ways of the Lord of this way, and hast been already condemned for thine own turning aside, by one of his Majesties Judges; and why seekest thou to bring us into the like condemnation? Besides, if we at all turn aside, our Lord the King will certainly hear thereof, and will there put us to shame, where we would stand with boldness before him.

Demas cried again, that he also was one of their fraternity; and that if they would tarry a little, he also himself would walk with them.

CHR. Then said *Christian,* What is thy name? Is it not the same by the which I have called thee?

DEMAS. Yes, my name is *Demas,* I am the Son of *Abraham.*

CHR. I know you, *Gehazi* was *your* Great Grandfather, and *Judas* your Father, and you have trod in their steps. It is but a devilish prank that thou usest; thy Father was hanged for a Traitor, and thou deservest no better reward. Assure thyself, that when we come to the King, we will do him word of this thy behaviour. Thus they went their way.

By this time *By-ends* and his Companions were come again within sight, and they at the first beck went over to *Demas*. Now whether they fell into the Pit by looking over the brink thereof, or whether they went down to dig, or whether they were smothered in the bottom by the damps that commonly arise, of these things I am not certain; but this I observed, that they never were seen again in the way. Then sang *Christian,*

By-ends goes over to Demas

> *By-ends* and Silver *Demas* both Agree;
> One calls, the other runs, that he may be
> A Sharer in his Lucre; so these do
> Take up in this World, and no further go.

Now I saw, that just on the other side of this Plain, the Pilgrims came to a place where stood an old *Monument,* hard by the High-way-side, at the sight of which they were both concerned, because of the strangeness of the form thereof; for it seemed to them as if it had been a *Woman* transformed into the shape of a Pillar; here therefore they stood looking and looking upon it, but could not for a time tell what they should make thereof. At last *Hopeful* espied written above upon the head thereof, a writing in an unusual hand; but he being no Scholar, called to *Christian* (for he was learned) to see if he could pick out the meaning; so he came, and after a little laying of letters together, he found the same to be this, *Remember Lot's Wife.* So he read it to his fellow; after which they both concluded that that was the Pillar of Salt into which *Lot's* Wife was turned, for her looking back with a *covetous heart,* when she was going from

They see a strange monument

Sodom for safety. Which sudden and amazing sight gave them occasion of this discourse.

CHR. Ah my Brother, this is a seasonable sight; it came opportunely to us after the invitation which *Demas* gave us to come over to view the Hill *Lucre;* and had we gone over as he desired us, and as thou wast inclining to do, my Brother, we had, for ought I know, been made ourselves like this Woman, a spectacle for those that shall come after to behold.

HOPE. I am sorry that I was so foolish, and am made to wonder that I am not now as *Lot's* Wife; for wherein was the difference 'twixt her sin and mine? she only looked back, and I had a desire to go see: let Grace be adored, and let me be ashamed that ever such a thing should be in mine heart.

CHR. Let us take notice of what we see here, for our help for time to come: This woman escaped one Judgment, for she fell not by the destruction of *Sodom;* yet she was destroyed by another, as we see she is turned into a Pillar of Salt.

HOPE. True, and she may be to us both *Caution* and *Example; caution,* that we should shun her sin, or a sign of what Judgment will overtake such as shall not be prevented by this caution: so *Korah, Dathan,* and *Abiram,* with the two hundred and fifty men that perished in their sin, did also become a sign or *example* to others to beware. But above all, I muse at one thing, to wit, how *Demas* and his fellows can stand so confidently yonder to look for that treasure, which this Woman, but for looking behind her after (for we read not that she stept one foot out of the way) was turned into a pillar of salt; especially since the Judgment which overtook her did make her an example, within sight of where they are: for they cannot chuse but see her, did they but lift up their eyes.

CHR. It is a thing to be wondered at, and it argueth that their hearts are grown desperate in the case; and I cannot tell who to compare them to so fitly, as to them that pick pockets in the presence of the Judge, or that will cut purses under the Gallows. It is said of the men of *Sodom, That they were sinners exceedingly,* because they were sinners *before the Lord;* that is, in his eye-sight, and notwithstanding the kindnesses that he had shewed them; for the land of *Sodom* was now, like the Garden of *Eden* heretofore. This therefore provoked him the more to jealousy, and made their plague as hot as the fire of the Lord out of Heaven could make it. And it is most rationally to be concluded, that such, even such as these are, that shall sin in the sight, yea, and that too in despite of such examples that are set continually before them, to caution them to the contrary, must be partakers of severest Judgments.

HOPE. Doubtless thou hast said the truth; but what a mercy is it, that neither thou, but especially I, am not made myself this example: this ministreth occasion to us to thank God, to fear before him, and always to remember *Lot's* Wife.

A river

I saw then that they went on their way to a pleasant River, which *David* the King called the *River of God,* but *John,* the *River of the Water of Life.* Now their way lay just upon the bank of the River; here therefore *Christian* and his Companion walked with great delight; they drank also of the water of the River, which was pleasant and enlivening to their weary spirits: besides, on the banks of this River on either side were *green Trees,* that bore all manner of Fruit; and the Leaves of the Trees were good for Medicine; with the Fruit of these Trees they were also much delighted; and the Leaves they ate to prevent Surfeits, and other Diseases that are incident to those that heat their blood by Travels. On either side of the River was also a Meadow, curiously beautified with Lilies; and it was green all the year long. In this Meadow they lay down and slept, for here they might *lie down safely.* When they awoke, they gathered again of the Fruit of the Trees, and drank again of the water of the

Trees by the river. The fruit and leaves of the trees

A meadow in which they lie down to sleep

River, and then lay down again to sleep. Thus they did several days and nights. Then they sang,

Behold ye how these Cristal streams do glide,
(To comfort Pilgrims) by the High-way side;
The Meadows green, beside their fragrant smell,
Yield dainties for them: And he that can tell
What pleasant fruit; yea Leaves, these Trees do yield,
Will soon sell all, that he may buy this field.

So when they were disposed to go on (for they were not as yet at their Journey's end) they eat and drank, and departed.

By-path Meadow

Now I beheld in my Dream, that they had not journeyed far, but the River and the way for a time parted; at which they were not a little sorry, yet they durst not go out of the way. Now the way from the River was rough, and their feet tender by reason of their Travels; *so the soul of the Pilgrims was much discouraged because of the way.* Wherefore still as they went on, they wished for better way. Now a little before them, there was on the left hand of the road a *Meadow,* and a Stile to go over into it, and that Meadow is called *By-path-Meadow.* Then said *Christian* to his fellow, If this Meadow lieth along by our way-side, let's go over into it. Then he went to the Stile to see, and behold a Path lay along by the way on the other side of the fence. 'Tis according to my wish, said *Christian,* here is the easiest going; come good *Hopeful,* and let us go over.

One temptation does make way for another

HOPE. But how if this Path should lead us out of the way?

Strong Christians may lead weak ones out of the way

CHR. That's not like, said the other; look, doth it not go along by the way-side? So *Hopeful,* being persuaded by his fellow, went after him over the Stile. When they were gone over, and were got into the Path, they found it very easy for their feet: and withal, they looking before them, espied a man walking as they did, (and his name was *Vain-confidence*) so they called after him, and asked him whither that way led? He said, To the Cœlestial

Gate. Look, said *Christian,* did I not tell you so? by this you may see we are right. So they followed, and he went before them. But behold the night came on, and it grew very dark, so that they that were behind lost the sight of him that went before.

See what it is too suddenly to fall in with strangers

He therefore that went before (*Vain-confidence* by name) not seeing the way before him, fell into a deep Pit, which was on purpose there made by the Prince of those grounds, to catch *vain-glorious* fools withal, and was dashed in pieces with his fall.

A pit to catch the vainglorious in

Now *Christian* and his fellow heard him fall. So they called to know the matter, but there was none to answer, only they heard a groaning. Then said *Hopeful,* Where are we now? Then was his fellow silent, as mistrusting that he had led him out of the way; and now it began to rain, and thunder, and lighten in a very dreadful manner, and the water rose amain.

Reasoning between Christian and Hopeful

Then *Hopeful* groaned in himself, saying, *Oh that I had kept on my way!*

CHR. Who could have thought that this Path should have led us out of the way?

HOPE. I was afraid on't at the very first, and therefore gave you that gentle caution. I would have spoken plainer, but that you are older than I.

CHR. Good Brother be not offended; I am sorry I have brought thee out of the way, and that I have put thee into such imminent danger; pray my Brother forgive me, I did not do it of an evil intent.

Christian's repentance for leading of his brother out of the way

HOPE. Be comforted my brother, for I forgive thee; and believe too that this shall be for our good.

CHR. I am glad I have with me a merciful Brother; but we must not stand thus, let's try to go back again.

HOPE. But good Brother let me go before.

CHR. No, if you please let me go first, that if there be any danger, I may be first therein, because by my means we are both gone out of the way.

HOPE. No, said *Hopeful,* you shall not go first; for your mind being troubled may lead you out of

They are in danger of drowning as they go back

the way again. Then for their encouragement, they heard the voice of one saying *Let thine heart be towards the High-way, even the way that thou wentest, turn again.* But by this time the waters were greatly risen; by reason of which the way of going back was very dangerous. (Then I thought that it is easier going out of the way when we are in, than going in when we are out.) Yet they adventured to go back; but it was so dark, and the flood was so high, that in their going back they had like to have been drowned nine or ten times.

They sleep in the grounds of Giant Despair

Neither could they, with all the skill they had, get again to the Stile that night. Wherefore at last, lighting under a little shelter, they sat down there till the day brake; but being weary, they fell asleep. Now there was not far from the place where they lay, a Castle called *Doubting* Castle, the owner whereof was Giant *Despair,* and it was in his grounds they were now sleeping: wherefore he, getting up in the morning early, and walking up and down in his fields, caught *Christian* and *Hopeful* asleep in his grounds. Then with a *grim* and *surly* voice he bid them awake, and asked them whence they were? and what they did in his grounds? They told him they were Pilgrims, and that they had lost their way. Then said the Giant, You have this night trespassed on me, by trampling in and lying on my grounds, and therefore you must go along with me. So they were forced to go, because he was stronger than they. They also had but little to say, for they knew themselves in a fault. The Giant therefore drove them before him, and put them into his Castle, into a very dark Dungeon, nasty and stinking to the spirits of these two men. Here then they lay from *Wednesday* morning till *Saturday* night, without one bit of bread, or drop of drink, or light, or any to ask how they did; they were therefore here in evil case, and were far from friends and acquaintance. Now in this place *Christian* had double sorrow, because 'twas through

He finds them in his grounds, and carries them to Doubting Castle

The grievousness of their imprisonment

his unadvised haste that they were brought into this distress.

The Pilgrims now, to gratify the Flesh,
Will seek its Ease; but oh! how they afresh
Do thereby plunge themselves new Griefs into!
Who seek to please the flesh themselves undo.

On Thursday, Giant Despair beats his prisoners

Now Giant *Despair* had a Wife, and her name was *Diffidence*. So when he was gone to bed, he told his Wife what he had done, to wit, that he had taken a couple of Prisoners and cast them into his Dungeon, for trespassing on his grounds. Then he asked her also what he had best do further to them. So she asked him what they were, whence they came, and whither they were bound; and he told her. Then she counselled him that when he arose in the morning he should beat them without any mercy. So when he arose, he getteth him a grievous Crab-tree Cudgel, and goes down into the Dungeon to them, and there first falls to rating of them, as if they were dogs, although they gave him never a word of distaste. Then he falls upon them, and beats them fearfully, in such sort, that they were not able to help themselves, or to turn them upon the floor. This done, he withdraws and leaves them, there to condole their misery, and to mourn under their distress: so all that day they spent the time in nothing but sighs and bitter lamentations. The next night she talking with her Husband about them further, and understanding that they were yet alive, did advise him to counsel them to make away themselves. So when morning was come, he goes to them in a surly manner as before, and perceiving them to be very sore with the stripes that he had given them the day before, he told them, that since they were never like to come out of that place, their only way would be forthwith to make an end of themselves, either with Knife, Halter, or Poison; For why, said he, should you chuse life, seeing it is attended with so much bitterness? But they desired

On Friday, Giant Despair counsels them to kill themselves

The Giant sometimes has fits

him to let them go. With that he looked ugly upon them, and rushing to them had doubtless made an end of them himself, but that he fell into one of his Fits, (for he sometimes in Sun-shine weather fell into Fits) and lost for a time the use of his hand; wherefore he withdrew, and left them as before, to consider what to do. Then did the Prisoners consult between themselves, whether 'twas best to take his counsel or no; and thus they began to discourse:

Christian crushed

CHR. Brother, said *Christian,* what shall we do? The life that we now live is miserable: for my part I know not whether is best, to live thus, or to die out of hand. *My soul chuseth strangling rather than life,* and the Grave is more easy for me than this Dungeon. Shall we be ruled by the Giant?

Hopeful comforts him

HOPE. Indeed our present condition is dreadful, and death would be far more welcome to me than *thus* for ever to abide; but yet let us consider, the Lord of the Country to which we are going hath said, Thou shalt do no murder, no not to another man's person; much more then are we forbidden to take his counsel to kill ourselves. Besides, he that kills another can but commit murder upon his body; but for one to kill himself is to kill body and soul at once. And moreover, my Brother, thou talkest of ease in the Grave; but hast thou forgotten the Hell, whither for certain the murderers go? For no murderer hath eternal life, *&c.* And let us consider again, that all the Law is not in the hand of Giant *Despair.* Others, so far as I can understand, have been taken by him as well as we, and yet have escaped out of his hand. Who knows but that God that made the world may cause that Giant *Despair* may die? or that at some time or other he may forget to lock us in? or but he may in short time have another of his Fits before us, and may lose the use of his limbs? and if ever that should come to pass again, for my part I am resolved to pluck up the heart of a man, and to try my utmost to get from under his hand. I was a fool that I did not try to do it before; but however, my Brother, let's be patient, and endure a while; the time may come that may give us a happy release; but let us not be our own murderers. With these words *Hopeful* at present did moderate the mind of his Brother; so they continued together (in the dark) that day, in their sad and doleful condition.

Well, towards evening the Giant goes down into the Dungeon again, to see if his prisoners had taken his counsel; but when he came there he found them alive, and truly, alive was all; for now, what for want of Bread and Water, and by reason of the Wounds they received when he beat them, they could do little but breathe: But, I say, he found them alive; at which he fell into a grievous rage, and told them that seeing they disobeyed his counsel, it should be worse with them than if they had never been born.

Christian still dejected

At this they trembled greatly, and I think that *Christian* fell into a Swoon; but coming a little to himself again, they renewed their discourse about the Giant's counsel, and whether yet they had best to take it or no. Now *Christian* again seemed to be for doing it, but *Hopeful* made his second reply as followeth:

Hopeful comforts him again, by calling former things to remembrance

HOPE. My Brother, said he, rememberest thou not how valiant thou hast been heretofore? *Apollyon* could not crush thee, nor could all that thou didst hear, or see, or feel in the Valley of the *Shadow of Death*. What hardship, terror, and amazement hast thou already gone through, and art thou now nothing but fear? Thou seest that I am in the Dungeon with thee, a far weaker man by nature than thou art; also this Giant has wounded me as well as thee, and hath also cut off the Bread and Water from my mouth; and with thee I mourn without the light. But let's exercise a little more patience, remember how thou playedst the man at *Vanity Fair,* and wast neither afraid of the Chain, nor Cage, nor yet of bloody Death: wherefore let us (at least to avoid the shame, that becomes not a Christian to be found in) bear up with patience as well as we can.

Now night being come again, and the Giant and his Wife being in bed, she asked him concerning the Prisoners, and if they had taken his counsel: To which he replied, They are sturdy Rogues, they chuse rather to bear all hardship, than to make away themselves. Then said she, Take them into the Castle-yard to-morrow, and shew them the Bones and Skulls of those that thou hast already dispatch'd, and make them believe, e'er a week comes to an end, thou also wilt tear them in pieces, as thou hast done their fellows before them.

On Saturday, the Giant threatened that shortly he would pull them in pieces

So when the morning was come, the Giant goes to them again, and takes them into the Castle-yard and shews them as his Wife had bidden him. These, said he, were Pilgrims as you are, once, and they trespassed in my grounds, as you have done; and when I thought fit, I tore them in pieces, and so within ten days I will do you. Go get you down to your Den again; and with that he beat them all the way thither. They lay therefore all day on *Saturday* in a lamentable case, as before. Now when night was come, and when Mrs Diffidence and her Husband the Giant were got to bed, they began to renew their discourse of their Prisoners; and withal the old Giant wondered, that he could neither by his blows nor counsel bring them to an end. And with that his Wife replied, I fear, said she, that they live in hope that some will come to relieve them, or that they have pick-locks about them, by the means of which they hope to escape. And sayest thou so, my dear? said the Giant, I will therefore search them in the morning.

Well on *Saturday* about midnight they began to *pray,* and continued in Prayer till almost break of day.

Now a little before it was day, good *Christian,* as

one half amazed, brake out in passionate speech: *What a fool,* quoth he, *am I, thus to lie in a stinking Dungeon, when I may as well walk at liberty.* I have a Key in my bosom called Promise, that will, I am persuaded, open any Lock in *Doubting* Castle. Then said *Hopeful,* That's good news; good Brother pluck it out of thy bosom and try.

A key in Christian's bosom, called Promise, opens any lock in Doubting Castle

Then *Christian* pulled it out of his bosom, and began to try at the Dungeon door, whose bolt (as he turned the Key) gave back, and the door flew open with ease, and *Christian* and *Hopeful* both came out. Then he went to the outward door that leads into the Castle-yard, and with his Key opened that door also. After he went to the iron Gate, for that must be opened too, but that Lock went damnable hard, yet the Key did open it. Then they thrust open the Gate to make their escape with speed; but that Gate as it opened made such a creaking, that it waked Giant *Despair,* who hastily rising to pursue his Prisoners, felt his limbs to fail, for his Fits took him again, so that he could by no means go after them. Then they went on, and came to the King's High-way again, and so were safe, because they were out of his jurisdiction.

Now when they were gone over the Stile, they began to contrive with themselves what they should do at that Stile, to prevent those that should come after from falling into the hands of Giant *Despair.* So they consented to erect there a Pillar, and to engrave upon the side thereof this sentence, *Over this Stile is the way to* Doubting *Castle, which is kept by Giant* Despair, *who despiseth the King of the Cœlestial Country, and seeks to destroy his holy Pilgrims.* Many therefore that followed after read what was written, and escaped the danger. This done, they sang as follows:

A pillar erected by Christian and his fellow

Out of the way we went, and then we found
What 'twas to tread upon forbidden ground;
And let them that come after have a care,
Lest heedlessness makes them, as we, to fare.

Lest they for trespassing his prisoners are,
Whose Castle's *Doubting*, and whose name's *Despair*.

The Delectable Mountains

They went then till they came to the *Delectable Mountains,* which Mountains belong to the Lord of that Hill of which we have spoken before; so they went up to the Mountains, to behold the Gardens and Orchards, the Vineyards and Fountains of water; where also they drank, and washed themselves, and did freely eat of the Vineyards. Now there were on the tops of these Mountains *Shepherds* feeding their flocks, and they stood by the High-way side. The Pilgrims therefore went to them, and leaning upon their staves (as is common with weary Pilgrims, when they stand to talk with any by the way) they asked, *Whose Delectable Mountains are these? And whose be the sheep that feed upon them?*

They are refreshed in the mountains

Talk with the Shepherds

Mountains Delectable they now ascend,
Where Shepherds be, which to them do commend
Alluring things, and things that Cautious are,
Pilgrims are steady kept by Faith and Fear.

SHEP. These mountains are *Immanuel's Land,* and they are within sight of his City; and the sheep also are his, and he laid down his life for them.

CHR. Is this the way to the Cœlestial City?

SHEP. You are just in your way.

CHR. How far is it thither?

SHEP. Too far for any but those that shall get thither indeed.

CHR. Is the way safe or dangerous?

SHEP. Safe for those for whom it is to be safe, *but transgressors shall fall therein.*

CHR. Is there in this place any relief for Pilgrims that are weary and faint in the way?

SHEP. The Lord of these Mountains hath given us a charge *not to be forgotten to entertain strangers;* therefore the good of the place is before you.

I saw also in my Dream, that when the Shepherds

perceived that they were way-faring men, they also put questions to them (to which they made answer as in other places) as, Whence came you? and, How got you into the way? and, By what means have you so persevered therein? For but few of them that begin to come hither do shew their face on these Mountains. But when the Shepherds heard their answers, being pleased therewith, they looked very lovingly upon them, and said, *Welcome to the Delectable Mountains.*

The Shepherds welcome them

The Shepherds, I say, whose names were *Knowledge, Experience, Watchful,* and *Sincere,* took them by the hand, and had them to their Tents, and made them partake of that which was ready at present. They said moreover, We would that ye should stay here a while, to be acquainted with us; and yet more to solace yourselves with the good of these Delectable Mountains. They then told them, that they were content to stay; and so they went to their rest that night, because it was very late.

The names of the Shepherds

Then I saw in my Dream, that in the morning the Shepherds called up *Christian* and *Hopeful* to walk with them upon the Mountains; so they went forth with them, and walked a while, having a pleasant prospect on every side. Then said the Shepherds one to another, Shall we shew these Pilgrims some wonders? So when they had concluded to do it, they had them first to the top of a Hill called *Error,* which was very steep on the furthest side, and bid them look down to the bottom. So *Christian* and *Hopeful* looked down, and saw at the bottom several men dashed all to pieces by a fall, that they had from the top. Then said *Christian,* What meaneth this? The Shepherds answered, Have you not heard of them that were made to err, by hearkening to *Hymeneus* and *Philetus,* as concerning the Faith of the Resurrection of the Body? They answered, Yes. Then said the Shepherds, Those that you see lie dashed in pieces at the bottom of this Mountain are they; and they

They are shown wonders

The Mountain of Error

have continued to this day unburied (as you see) for an example to others to take heed how they clamber too high, or how they come too near the brink of this Mountain.

Mount Caution

Then I saw that they had them to the top of another Mountain, and the name of that is *Caution,* and bid them look afar off; which when they did, they perceived, as they thought, several men walking up and down among the Tombs that were there; and they perceived that the men were blind, because they stumbled sometimes upon the Tombs, and because they could not get out from among them. Then said *Christian, What means this?*

The Shepherds then answered, Did you not see a little below these Mountains a Stile, that led into a Meadow, on the left hand of this way? They answered, Yes. Then said the Shepherds, From that Stile there goes a path that leads directly to *Doubting* Castle, which is kept by Giant *Despair;* and these men (pointing to them among the Tombs) came once on Pilgrimage, as you do now, even till they came to that same Stile; and because the right way was rough in that place, they chose to go out of it into that Meadow, and there were taken by Giant *Despair,* and cast into *Doubting* Castle; where, after they had been awhile kept in the Dungeon, he at last did put out their eyes, and led them among those Tombs, where he has left them to wander to this very day, that the saying of the Wise Man might be fulfilled, *He that wandereth out of the way of understanding, shall remain in the congregation of the dead.* Then *Christian* and *Hopeful* looked upon one another, with tears gushing out, but yet said nothing to the Shepherds.

A by-way to hell

Then I saw in my Dream, that the Shepherds had them to another place, in a bottom, where was a door in the side of a Hill, and they opened the door, and bid them look in. They looked in therefore, and saw that within it was very dark and smoky; they also thought that they heard there a rumbling noise as of Fire, and a cry of some tormented, and that they smelt the scent of Brimstone. Then said *Christian, What means this?* The Shepherds told them, This is a by-way to Hell, a way that Hypocrites go in at; namely, such as sell their Birth-right, with *Esau;* such as sell their Master, as *Judas;* such as blaspheme the Gospel, with *Alexander;* and that lie and dissemble, with *Ananias* and *Sapphira* his Wife. Then said *Hopeful* to the Shepherds, I perceive that these had on them, even every-one, a shew of Pilgrimage, as we have now; had they not?

SHEP. Yes, and held it a long time too.

HOPE. How far might they go on in Pilgrimage in their day, since they notwithstanding were thus miserably cast away?

SHEP. Some further, and some not so far as these Mountains.

Then said the Pilgrims one to another, *We had need to cry to the Strong for strength.*

SHEP. Ay, and you will have need to use it when you have it too.

The Shepherds' perspective glass

By this time the Pilgrims had a desire to go forwards, and the Shepherds a desire they should; so they walked together towards the end of the Mountains. Then said the Shepherds one to another, Let us here shew to the Pilgrims the Gates of the Cœlestial City, if they have skill to look through our Perspective-Glass. The Pilgrims then lovingly accepted the motion; so they had them to the top of a high Hill, called *Clear,* and gave them their Glass to look.

The Hill Clear

The fruits of servile fear

Then they assayed to look, but the remembrance of that last thing that the Shepherds had shewed them, made their hands shake, by means of which impediment they could not look steadily through the Glass; yet they thought they saw something like the Gate, and also some of the Glory of the place.

Then they went away and sang this song,

Thus by the Shepherds Secrets are reveal'd:
Which from all other men are kept conceal'd
Come to the Shepherds then if you would see
Things deep, things hid, and that mysterious be.

A twofold caution

When they were about to depart, one of the Shepherds gave them a *Note of the way.* Another of them bid them *beware of the Flatterer.* The third bid them *take heed that they sleep not on the Inchanted Ground.* And the fourth bid them *Godspeed.* So I awoke from my Dream.

And I slept, and Dreamed again, and saw the same two Pilgrims going down the Mountains along the High-way towards the City. Now a little below these Mountains, on the left hand lieth the Country of *Conceit;* from which Country there comes into the way in which the Pilgrims walked, a little crooked Lane. Here therefore they met with a very brisk Lad, that came out of that Country; and his name was *Ignorance.* So *Christian* asked him *From what parts he came, and whither he was going?*

The country of Conceit, out of which came Ignorance

Christian and Ignorance have some talk

IGNOR. Sir, I was born in the Country that lieth off there a little on the left hand, and I am going to the Cœlestial City.

CHR. But how do you think to get in at the Gate, for you may find some difficulty there?

IGNOR. As other good people do, said he.

CHR. But what have you to shew at that Gate, that may cause that the Gate should be opened to you?

The ground of Ignorance's hope

IGNOR. I know my Lord's will, and I have been a good liver; I pay every man his own; I Pray, Fast, pay Tithes, and give Alms, and have left my Country for whither I am going.

CHR. But thou camest not in at the Wicket-Gate that is at the head of this way; thou camest in hither through that same crooked Lane, and therefore I fear, however thou mayest think of thyself, when the reckoning day shall come, thou wilt have laid to thy charge that thou art a Thief and a Robber, instead of getting admittance into the City.

IGNOR. Gentlemen, ye be utter strangers to me, I know you not; be content to follow the Religion of your Country, and I will follow the Religion of mine. I hope all will be well. And as for the Gate that you talk of, all the world knows that that is a great way off of our Country. I cannot think that any man in all our parts doth so much as know the way to it, nor need they matter whether they do or no, since we have, as you see, a fine pleasant Green Lane, that comes down from our Country the next way into the way.

He saith to every one that he is a fool

When *Christian* saw that the man was wise in his own conceit, he said to *Hopeful* whisperingly, *There is more hopes of a fool than of him.* And said moreover, *When he that is a fool walketh by the way, his wisdom faileth him, and he saith to every one that he is a fool.* What, shall we talk further with him, or outgo him at present, and so leave him to think of what he hath heard already, and then stop again for him afterwards, and see if by degrees we can do any good of him? Then said *Hopeful,*

How to carry it to a fool

Let *Ignorance* a little while now muse
On what is said, and let him not refuse
Good counsel to imbrace, lest he remain
Still ignorant of what's the chiefest gain.
God saith, Those that no understanding have,
(Although he made them) them he will not save.

HOPE. He further added, It is not good, I think, to say all to him at once; let us pass him by, if you will, and talk to him anon, *even as he is able to bear it.*

So they both went on, and *Ignorance* he came after. Now when they had passed him a little way, they entered into a very dark Lane, where they met a man whom seven Devils had bound with seven strong cords, and were carrying of him back to the Door that they saw on the side of the Hill. Now good *Christian* began to tremble, and so did *Hopeful* his Companion; yet as the Devils led

The destruction of one Turnaway

away the man, *Christian* looked to see if he knew him, and he thought it might be one *Turn-away* that dwelt in the Town of *Apostacy.* But he did not perfectly see his face, for he did hang his head like a Thief that is found. But being gone past, *Hopeful* looked after him, and espied on his back a paper with this inscription, *Wanton Professor and damnable Apostate.* Then said *Christian* to his fellow, Now I call to remembrance that which was told me of a thing that happened to a good man hereabout. The name of the man was *Little-faith,* but a good man, and he dwelt in the Town of *Sincere.* The thing was this; At the entering in of this passage, there comes down from *Broad-way Gate,* a Lane called *Dead Man's Lane;* so called because of the Murders that are commonly done there; and this *Little-faith* going on Pilgrimage as we do now, chanced to sit down there and slept. Now there happened at that time, to come down the *Lane* from *Broad-way Gate,* three sturdy Rogues, and their names were *Faint-heart, Mistrust,* and *Guilt,* (three Brothers) and they espying *Little-faith* where he was, came galloping up with speed. Now the good man was just awaked from his sleep, and was getting up to go on his Journey. So they came up all to him, and with threatning language bid him stand. At this *Little-faith* looked as white as a Clout, and had neither power to fight nor fly. Then said *Faint-heart,* Deliver thy Purse. But he making no haste to do it (for he was loth to lose his Money) *Mistrust* ran up to him, and thrusting his hand into his Pocket, pull'd out thence a bag of silver. Then he cried out, Thieves, Thieves. With that *Guilt* with a great Club that was in his hand, struck *Little-faith* on the head, and with that blow fell'd him flat to the ground, where he lay bleeding as one that would bleed to death. All this while the Thieves stood by. But at last, they hearing that some were upon the road, and fearing lest it should be one *Great-grace* that dwells in the City of *Good-*

Christian telleth his companion a story of Little-faith

Broad-way Gate

Dead Man's Lane

Little-faith robbed by Faint-heart, Mistrust, and Guilt

They got away his silver, and knocked him down

confidence, they betook themselves to their heels, and left this good man to shift for himself. Now after a while *Little-faith* came to himself, and getting up made shift to scrabble on his way. This was the story.

HOPE. But did they take from him all that ever he had?

CHR. No; the place where his Jewels were they never ransacked, so those he kept still; but as I was told, the good man was much afflicted for his loss, for the Thieves got most of his spending Money. That which they got not (as I said) were Jewels, also he had a little odd Money left, but scarce enough to bring him to his Journey's end; nay, if I was not misinformed, he was forced to beg as he went, to keep himself alive, for his Jewels he might not sell. But beg, and do what he could, he went (as we say) *with many a hungry belly* the most part of the rest of the way.

Little-faith lost not his best things

Little-faith forced to beg to his journey's end

HOPE. But is it not a wonder that they got from him his Certificate, by which he was to receive his admittance at the Cœlestial Gate?

CHR. 'Tis a wonder but they got not that, though they missed it not through any good cunning of his; for he being dismayed with their coming upon him, had neither power nor skill to hide anything; so 'twas more by good Providence than by his endeavour, that they miss'd of that good thing.

He kept not his best things by his own cunning (2 Tim. i. 14)

HOPE. But it must needs be a comfort to him that they got not this Jewel from him.

CHR. It might have been great comfort to him, had he used it as he should; but they that told me the story said that he made but little use of it all the rest of the way, and that because of the dismay that he had in their taking away his Money; indeed he forgot it a great part of the rest of his Journey; and besides, when at any time it came into his mind, and he began to be comforted therewith, then would fresh thoughts of his loss come again upon him, and those thoughts would swallow up all.

He is pitied by both

HOPE. Alas poor man! This could not but be a great grief to him.

CHR. Grief! ay, a grief indeed. Would it not have been so to any of us, had we been used as he, to be robbed, and wounded too, and that in a strange place, as he was? 'Tis a wonder he did not die with grief, poor heart! I was told that he scattered almost all the rest of the way with nothing but doleful and bitter complaints; telling also to all that over-took him, or that he over-took in the way as he went, where he was robbed, and how; who they were that did it, and what he lost; how he was wounded, and that he hardly escaped with his life.

HOPE. But 'tis a wonder that his necessity did not put him upon *selling* or *pawning* some of his Jewels, that he might have wherewith to relieve himself in his Journey.

Christian snubbeth his fellow for unadvised speaking

CHR. Thou talkest like one upon whose head is the Shell to this very day; for what should he pawn them, or to whom should he sell them? In all that Country where he was robbed, his Jewels were not accounted of; nor did he want that relief which could from thence be administered to him. Besides, had his Jewels been missing at the Gate of the Cœlestial City, he had (and that he knew well enough) been excluded from an Inheritance there; and that would have been worse to him than the appearance and villany of ten thousand Thieves.

HOPE. Why art thou so tart my Brother? *Esau* sold his Birth-right, and that for a mess of Pottage, and that Birth-right was his greatest Jewel; and if he, why might not *Little-faith* do so too?

A discourse about Esau and Little-faith

CHR. *Esau* did sell his Birth-right indeed, and so do many besides, and by so doing exclude themselves from the chief blessing, as also that caitiff did; but you must put a difference betwixt *Esau* and *Little-faith,* and also betwixt their Estates. *Esau's* Birth-right was typical, but *Little-faith's* Jewels were not so: *Esau's* belly was his god, but *Little-faith's* belly was not so: *Esau's* want lay in

Esau was ruled by his lusts

his fleshly appetite, *Little-faith's* did not so. Besides, *Esau* could see no further than to the fulfilling of his lusts: *For I am at the point to die,* said he, *and what good will this Birth-right do me?* But *Little-faith,* though it was his lot to have but a *little faith,* was by his *little faith* kept from such extravagancies, and made to see and prize his Jewels more than to sell them, as *Esau* did his Birth-right. You read not anywhere that *Esau* had *faith,* no not so much as a *little;* therefore no marvel if where the flesh only bears sway (as it will in that man where no faith is to resist) if he sells his Birth-right, and his Soul and all, and that to the Devil of Hell; for it is with such, as it is with the Ass, *who in her occasions cannot be turned away.* When their minds are set upon their lusts, they will have them whatever they cost. But *Little-faith* was of another temper, his mind was on things Divine; his livelihood was upon things that were Spiritual, and from above; therefore to what end should he that is of such a temper sell his Jewels (had there been any that would have bought them) to fill his mind with empty things? Will a man give a penny to fill his belly with Hay? or can you persuade the *Turtle-dove* to live upon Carrion like the *Crow?* Though *faithless* ones can, for carnal Lusts, pawn or mortgage, or sell what they have, and themselves outright to boot; yet they that have *faith, saving faith,* though but a little of it, cannot do so. Here therefore my Brother is thy mistake.

Esau never had faith

Little-faith could not live upon Esau's pottage

A comparison between the turtle-dove and the crow

HOPE. I acknowledge it; but yet your severe reflection had almost made me angry.

CHR. Why, I did but compare thee to some of the Birds that are of the brisker sort, who will run to and fro in trodden paths, with the Shell upon their heads; but pass by that, and consider the matter under debate, and all shall be well betwixt thee and me.

HOPE. But *Christian,* these three fellows, I am persuaded in my heart, are but a company of Cow-

Hopeful swaggers

ards; would they have run else, think you, as they did, at the noise of one that was coming on the road? Why did not *Little-faith* pluck up a greater heart? He might, methinks, have stood one brush with them, and have yielded when there had been no remedy.

No great heart for God, where there is but little faith

We have more courage when out, than when in the conflict

CHR. That they are Cowards, many have said, but few have found it so in the time of Trial. As for a great heart, *Little-faith* had none; and I perceive by thee, my Brother, hadst thou been the man concerned, thou art but for a brush, and then to yield. And verily since this is the height of thy stomach, now they are at a distance from us, should they appear to thee as they did to him, they might put thee to second thoughts.

Christian tells his own experience in this case

But consider again, they are but journeymen Thieves; they serve under the King of the bottomless Pit, who, if need be, will come in to their aid himself, and his voice is *as the roaring of a Lion.* I myself have been engaged as this *Little-faith* was, and I found it a terrible thing. These three Villains set upon me, and I beginning like a Christian to resist, they gave but a call, and in came their Master: I would, as the saying is, have given my life for a penny; but that, as God would have it, I was cloathed with Armor of proof. Ay, and yet though I was so harnessed, I found it hard work to quit myself like a man: no man can tell what in that Combat attends us, but he that hath been in the Battle himself.

HOPE. Well, but they ran, you see, when they did but suppose that one *Great-grace* was in the way.

The King's champion

CHR. True, they have often fled, both they and their Master, when *Great-grace* hath but appeared; and no marvel, for he is the *King's Champion.* But I tro you will put some difference between *Little-faith* and the *King's Champion.* All the King's Subjects are not his Champions, nor can they when tried do such feats of War as he. Is it meet to think that a little child should handle *Goliah* as *David* did? Or that there should be the strength of an *Ox* in a *Wren?* Some are strong, some are weak; some have great faith, some have little: this man was one of the weak, and therefore he went to the wall.

HOPE. I would it had been *Great-grace* for their sakes.

CHR. If it had been he, he might have had his hands full; for I must tell you, that though *Great-grace* is excellent good at his Weapons, and has, and can, so long as he keeps them at Sword's point, do well enough with them; yet if they get within him, even *Faint-heart, Mistrust,* or the other, it shall go hard but they will throw up his heels. And when a man is down, you know, what can he do?

Whoso looks well upon *Great-grace's* face, shall see those scars and cuts there, that shall easily give demonstration of what I say. Yea, once I heard he should say, (and that when he was in the Combat) *We despaired even of life.* How did these sturdy Rogues and their fellows make *David* groan, mourn, and roar? Yet, *Heman* and *Hezekiah* too, though Champions in their day, were forced to bestir them when by these assaulted; and yet notwithstanding they had their Coats soundly brushed by them. *Peter* upon a time would go try what he could do; but though some do say of him that he is the Prince of the Apostles, they handled him so, that they made him at last afraid of a sorry Girl.

Leviathan's sturdiness

Besides their King is at their whistle. He is never out of hearing; and if at any time they be put to the worst, he if possible comes in to help them; and of him it is said, *The Sword of him that layeth at him cannot hold, the Spear, the Dart, nor the Habergeon: he esteemeth Iron as Straw, and Brass as rotten Wood. The Arrow cannot make him fly; Sling-stones are turned with him into Stubble, Darts are counted as Stubble: he laugheth at the shaking of a Spear.* What can a man do in this case? 'Tis true, if a man could at every turn have *Job's* Horse, and had skill and courage to

The excellent mettle that is in Job's horse

ride him, he might do notable things; *for his Neck is cloathed with Thunder, he will not be afraid as the Grasshopper, the glory of his Nostrils is terrible, he paweth in the Valley, rejoiceth in his strength, and goeth out to meet the armed men. He mocketh at fear, and is not affrighted, neither turneth back from the Sword. The Quiver rattleth against him, the glittering Spear, and the Shield. He swalloweth the ground with fierceness and rage, neither believeth he that it is the sound of the Trumpet. He saith among the Trumpets, Ha, ha; and he smelleth the Battle afar off, the thundering of the Captains, and the Shoutings.*

But for such footmen as thee and I are, let us never desire to meet with an enemy, nor vaunt as if we could do better, when we hear of others that they have been foiled, nor be tickled at the thoughts of our own manhood; for such commonly come by the worst when tried. Witness *Peter,* of whom I made mention before. He would swagger, ay he would; he would, as his vain mind prompted him to say, do better, and stand more for his Master than all men; but who so foiled and run down by these Villains as he?

When therefore we hear that such Robberies are done on the King's High-way, two things become us to do: First, To go out harnessed and to be sure to take a Shield with us; for it was for want of that, that he that laid so lustily at *Leviathan* could not make him yield; for indeed if that be wanting he fears us not at all. Therefore he that had skill hath said, *Above all take the Shield of Faith, wherewith ye shall be able to quench all the fiery darts of the wicked.*

It is good to have a convoy

'Tis good also that we desire of the King a Convoy, yea that he will go with us himself. This made *David* rejoice when in the Valley of the *Shadow of Death:* and *Moses* was rather for dying where he stood, than to go one step without his God. O my Brother, if he will but go along with us, what need we be afraid of ten thousands that shall set themselves against us? But without him, *the proud helpers fall under the slain.*

I for my part have been in the fray before now, and though (through the goodness of him that is best) I am, as you see, alive; yet I cannot boast of my manhood. Glad shall I be, if I meet with no more such brunts, though I fear we are not got beyond all danger. However, since the Lion and the Bear have not as yet devoured me, I hope God will also deliver us from the next uncircumcised *Philistine.* Then sang *Christian,*

Poor *Little-faith!* Hast been among the Thieves?
Wast robb'd? Remember this: Whoso believes
And gets more Faith, shall then a victor be
Over ten thousand, else scarce over three.

So they went on, and *Ignorance* followed. They went then till they came at a place where they saw a way put itself into their way, and seemed withal to lie as straight as the way which they should go: and here they knew not which of the two to take, for both seemed straight before them; therefore here they stood still to consider. And as they were thinking about the way, behold a man black of flesh, but covered with a very light Robe, came to them, and asked them why they stood there? They answered they were going to the Cœlestial City, but knew not which of these ways to take. Follow me, said the man, it is thither that I am going. So they followed him in the way that but now came into the road, which by degrees turned, and turned them so from the City that they desired to go to, that in little time their faces were turned away from it: yet they followed him. But by-and-by, before they were aware, he led them both within the compass of a Net, in which they were both so intangled, that they knew not what to do; and with that *the white Robe fell off the black man's back:* then they saw where they were. Wherefore there they lay

A way, and a way

The flatterer finds them

Christian and his fellow deluded

They are taken in a net

crying some time, for they could not get themselves out.

They bewail their condition

CHR. Then said *Christian* to his fellow, Now do I see myself in an error. Did not the Shepherds bid us beware of the flatterers? As is the saying of the Wise man, so we have found it this day, *A man that flattereth his Neighbour, spreadeth a Net for his feet.*

A Shining One comes to them with a whip in his hand

HOPE. They also gave us a Note of directions about the way, for our more sure finding thereof; but therein we have also forgotten to read, and have not kept ourselves from the paths of the destroyer. Here *David* was wiser than we; for saith he, *Concerning the works of men, by the word of thy lips I have kept me from the paths of the destroyer.* Thus they lay bewailing themselves in the Net. At last they espied a Shining One coming towards them with a Whip of small cord in his hand. When he was come to the place where they were, he asked them whence they came? and what they did there? They told him that they were poor Pilgrims going to *Sion,* but were led out of their way by a black man, cloathed in white, who bid us, said they, follow him, for he was going thither too. Then said he with the Whip, It is *Flatterer,* a false Apostle, that hath transformed himself into an Angel of Light. So he rent the Net, and let the men out. Then said he to them, Follow me, that I may set you in your way again: so he led them back to the way which they had left to follow the *Flatterer.* Then he asked them, saying, Where did you lie the last night?

They are examined, and convicted of forgetfulness

They said, With the Shepherds upon the Delectable Mountains. He asked them then, If they had not of those Shepherds *a Note of direction for the way?* They answered, Yes. But did you, said he, when you were at a stand pluck out and read your Note? They answered, No. He asked them, Why? They said they forgot. He asked moreover, If the Shepherds did not bid them beware of the *Flatterer?*

Deceivers fine spoken

They answered, Yes; but we did not imagine, said they, *that this fine-spoken man had been he.*

Then I saw in my Dream, that he commanded them to *lie down;* which when they did, he chastised them sore, to teach them the good way wherein they should walk; and as he chastised them he said, *As many as I love, I rebuke and chasten; be zealous therefore, and repent.* This done, he bid them go on their way, and take good heed to the other directions of the Shepherds. So they thanked him for all his kindness, and went softly along the right way, singing,

They are whipped, and sent on their way

Come hither, you that walk along the way,
See how the Pilgrims fare that go astray;
They catched are in an intangling Net,
'Cause they good Counsel lightly did forget;
'Tis true they rescu'd were, but yet you see
They're scourg'd to boot: Let this your caution be.

Now after a while, they perceived afar off one coming softly and alone all along the High-way to meet them. Then said *Christian* to his fellow, Yonder is a man with his back toward *Sion,* and he is coming to meet us.

HOPE. I see him, let us take heed to ourselves now, lest he should prove a *Flatterer* also. So he drew nearer and nearer, and at last came up unto them. His name was *Atheist,* and he asked them whither they were going.

The Atheist meets them

CHR. We are going to the Mount *Sion.*

Then *Atheist* fell into a very great Laughter.

He laughs at them

CHR. What is the meaning of your Laughter?

ATHEIST. I laugh to see what ignorant persons you are, to take upon you so tedious a Journey, and you are like to have nothing but your travel for your pains.

CHR. Why man? Do you think we shall not be received?

They reason together

ATHEIST. Received! There is no such place as you dream of in all this World.

CHR. But there is in the World to come.

ATHEIST. When I was at home in mine own Country, I heard as you now affirm, and from that hearing went out to see, and have been seeking this City this twenty years; but find no more of it than I did the first day I set out.

CHR. We have both heard and believe that there is such a place to be found.

The Atheist takes up his content in this world

ATHEIST. Had not I when at home believed, I had not come thus far to seek; but finding none, (and yet I should, had there been such a place to be found, for I have gone to seek it further than you) I am going back again, and will seek to refresh myself with the things that I then cast away, for hopes of that which I now see is not.

Christian proveth his brother

CHR. Then said *Christian* to *Hopeful* his fellow, Is it true which this man hath said?

Hopeful's gracious answer

A remembrance of former chastisements is a help against present temptations

HOPE. Take heed, he is one of the Flatterers; remember what it hath cost us once already for our hearkening to such kind of fellows. What! no Mount *Sion?* Did we not see from the Delectable Mountains the Gate of the City? Also, are we not now to walk by Faith. Let us go on, said *Hopeful,* lest the man with the Whip overtake us again. You should have taught me that lesson, which I will round you in the ears withal: *Cease, my Son, to hear the instruction that causeth to err from the words of knowledge.* I say my Brother, cease to hear him, and let us believe to the saving of the Soul.

A fruit of an honest heart

CHR. My Brother, I did not put the question to thee for that I doubted of the Truth of our belief myself, but to prove thee, and to fetch from thee a fruit of the honesty of thy heart. As for this man, I know that he is blinded by the god of this World. Let thee and I go on, knowing that we have belief of the Truth, and no lie is of the Truth.

HOPE. Now do I rejoice in hope of the glory of God. So they turned away from the man; and he laughing at them went his way.

They are come to the Enchanted Ground

I saw then in my Dream, that they went till they come into a certain Country, whose air naturally tended to make one drowsy, if he came a stranger into it. And here *Hopeful* began to be very dull and heavy of sleep; wherefore he said unto *Christian,* I do now begin to grow so drowsy that I can scarcely hold up mine eyes, let us lie down here and take one nap.

Hopeful begins to be drowsy

CHR. By no means, said the other, lest sleeping we never awake more.

Christian keeps him awake

HOPE. Why my Brother? Sleep is sweet to the labouring man; we may be refreshed if we take a nap.

CHR. Do you not remember that one of the Shepherds bid us beware of the Inchanted Ground? He meant by that, that we should beware of sleeping; wherefore let us not sleep as do others, but let us watch and be sober.

HOPE. I acknowledge myself in a fault, and had I been here alone I had by sleeping run the danger of death. I see it is true that the Wise man saith, *Two are better than one.* Hitherto hath thy company been my mercy, *and thou shalt have a good reward for thy labour.*

He is thankful

Now then, said *Christian,* to prevent drowsiness in this place, let us fall into good discourse.

To prevent drowsiness they fall to good discourse

HOPE. With all my heart, said the other.

CHR. Where shall we begin?

HOPE. Where God began with us. But do you begin, if you please.

Good discourse prevents drowsiness

CHR. I will sing you first this song:

When Saints do sleepy grow, let them come hither,
And hear how these two Pilgrims talk together:
Yea, let them learn of them in any wise,
Thus to keep ope their drowsy, slumbring eyes.
Saints' fellowship, if it be managed well,
Keeps them awake, and that in spite of Hell.

The dreamer's note

CHR. Then *Christian* began and said, I will ask you a question: How came you to think at first of doing as you do now?

They begin at the beginning of their conversion

HOPE. Do you mean, how came I at first to look after the good of my soul?

CHR. Yes, that is my meaning.

HOPE. I continued a great while in the delight

of those things which were seen and sold at our Fair; things which I believe now would have (had I continued in them still) drowned me in perdition and destruction.

CHR. What things were they?

Hopeful's life before conversion

HOPE. All the Treasures and Riches of the World. Also I delighted much in Rioting, Revelling, Drinking, Swearing, Lying, Uncleanness, Sabbath-breaking, and what not, that tended to destroy the Soul. But I found at last, by hearing and considering of things that are Divine, which indeed I heard of you, as also of beloved *Faithful,* that was put to death for his faith and good living in *Vanity Fair, That the end of these things is death.* And that for these things' sake the wrath of God cometh upon the children of disobedience.

CHR. And did you presently fall under the power of this conviction?

Hopeful at first shuts his eyes against the light

HOPE. No, I was not willing presently to know the evil of sin, nor the damnation that follows upon the commission of it; but endeavoured, when my mind at first began to be shaken with the Word, to shut mine eyes against the light thereof.

CHR. But what was the cause of your carrying of it thus to the first workings of God's blessed Spirit upon you?

Reasons of his resisting of the light

HOPE. The causes were, 1. I was ignorant that this was the work of God upon me. I never thought that by awakenings for sin God at first begins the conversion of a sinner. 2. Sin was yet very sweet to my flesh, and I was loth to leave it. 3. I could not tell how to part with mine old Companions, their presence and actions were so desirable unto me. 4. The hours in which convictions were upon me, were such troublesome and such heart-affrighting hours, that I could not bear, no not so much as the remembrance of them upon my heart.

CHR. Then as it seems, sometimes you got rid of your trouble.

HOPE. Yes verily, but it would come into my mind

again, and then I should be as bad, nay worse, than I was before.

CHR. Why, what was it that brought your sins to mind again?

When he had lost his sense of sin, what brought this again

HOPE. Many things; as

1. If I did but meet a good man in the Streets; or,

2. If I have heard any read in the Bible; or,

3. If mine Head did begin to ake; or,

4. If I were told that some of my Neighbors were sick; or,

5. If I heard the Bell toll for some that were dead; or,

6. If I thought of Dying myself; or,

7. If I heard that sudden Death happened to others;

8. But especially, when I thought of myself, that I must quickly come to Judgment.

CHR. And could you at any time with ease get off the guilt of sin, when by any of these ways it came upon you?

HOPE. No, not latterly, for then they got faster hold of my conscience; and then, if I did but think of going back to sin, (though my mind was turned against it) it would be double torment to me.

CHR. And how did you do then?

HOPE. I thought I must endeavour to mend my life; for else, thought I, I am sure to be damned.

When he could no longer shake off his guilt by sinful courses, then he endeavours to mend

CHR. And did you endeavour to mend?

HOPE. Yes, and fled from not only my sins, but sinful Company too; and betook me to religious duties, as Prayer, Reading, Weeping for Sin, speaking Truth to my Neighbors, &c. These things did I, with many others, too much here to relate.

CHR. And did you think yourself well then?

HOPE. Yes, for a while; but at the last my trouble came tumbling upon me again, and that over the neck of all my reformations.

Then he thought himself well

CHR. How came that about, since you were now reformed?

HOPE. There were several things brought it upon

Reformation at last could not help, and why

me, especially such sayings as these: *All our righteousnesses are as filthy rags. By the works of the Law no man shall be justified. When you have done all things, say, We are unprofitable:* with many more such like. From whence I began to reason with myself thus: If *all* my righteousnesses are filthy rags, if by the deeds of the Law, *no* man can be justified; and if, when we have done *all,* we are yet unprofitable, then 'tis but a folly to think of Heaven by the Law. I further thought thus: If a man runs 100l. into the Shop-keeper's debt, and after that shall pay for all that he shall fetch; yet his old debt stands still in the Book uncrossed, for the which the Shop-keeper may sue him, and cast him into Prison till he shall pay the debt.

His being a debtor by the law troubled him

CHR. Well, and how did you apply this to yourself?

HOPE. Why, I thought thus with myself: I have by my sins run a great way into God's Book, and that my now reforming will not pay off that score; therefore I should think still under all my present amendments, But how shall I be freed from that damnation that I have brought myself in danger of by my former transgressions?

CHR. A very good application: but pray go on.

HOPE. Another thing that hath troubled me, even since my late amendments, is, that if I look narrowly into the best of what I do now, I still see sin, new sin, mixing itself with the best of that I do; so that now I am forced to conclude, that notwithstanding my former fond conceits of myself and duties, I have committed sin enough in one duty to send me to Hell, though my former life had been faultless.

His espying bad things in his best duties troubled him

CHR. And what did you do then?

HOPE. Do! I could not tell what to do, till I brake my mind to *Faithful,* for he and I were well acquainted. And he told me, that unless I could obtain the righteousness of a man that never had sinned, neither mine own, nor all the righteousness of the world could save me.

This made him break his mind to Faithful, who told him the way to be saved

CHR. And did you think he spake true?

HOPE. Had he told me so when I was pleased and satisfied with mine own amendments, I had called him Fool for his pains: but now, since I see mine own infirmity, and the sin that cleaves to my best performance, I have been forced to be of his opinion.

CHR. But did you think, when at first he suggested it to you, that there was such a man to be found, of whom it might justly be said, That he never committed sin?

HOPE. I must confess the words at first sounded strangely; but after a little more talk and company with him, I had full conviction about it.

At which he started at present

CHR. And did you ask him what man this was, and how you must be justified by him?

HOPE. Yes, and he told me it was the Lord *Jesus*, that dwelleth on the right hand of the Most High. And thus, said he, you must be justified by him, even by trusting to what he hath done by himself in the days of his flesh, and suffered when he did hang on the Tree. I asked him further, How that man's righteousness could be of that efficacy to justify another before God? And he told me he was the mighty God, and did what he did, and died the death also, not for himself, but for me; to whom his doings, and the worthiness of them should be imputed, if I believed on him.

A more particular discovery of the way to be saved

CHR. And what did you do then?

HOPE. I made my objections against my believing, for that I thought he was not willing to save me.

He doubts of acceptation

CHR. And what said *Faithful* to you then?

HOPE. He bid me go to him and see: then I said it was presumption: but he said, No, for I was invited to come. Then he gave me a Book of *Jesus* his inditing, to encourage me the more freely to come; and he said concerning that Book, that every jot and tittle thereof stood firmer than Heaven and Earth. Then I asked him, What I must do when I came? and he told me, I must entreat upon my knees, with all my heart and soul, the Father to

He is better instructed

reveal him to me. Then I asked him further, How I must make my supplication to him? And he said, Go, and thou shalt find him upon a mercy-seat, where he sits all the year long, to give pardon and forgiveness to them that come. I told him that I knew not what to say when I came. And he bid me say to this effect: *God be merciful to me a sinner, and make me to know and believe in Jesus Christ; for I see that if his righteousness had not been, or I have not faith in that righteousness, I am utterly cast away: Lord, I have heard that thou art a merciful God, and hast ordained that thy Son Jesus Christ should be the Saviour of the world; and moreover, that thou art willing to bestow him upon such a poor sinner as I am,* (*and I am a sinner indeed*) *Lord, take therefore this opportunity, and magnify thy grace in the Salvation of my soul, through thy Son Jesus Christ.* Amen.

He is bid to pray

He prays

CHR. And did you do as you were bidden?

HOPE. Yes, over and over and over.

CHR. And did the Father reveal his Son to you?

HOPE. Not at the first, nor second, nor third, nor fourth, nor fifth, no nor at the sixth time neither.

CHR. What did you do then?

HOPE. What! why I could not tell what to do.

CHR. Had you not thought of leaving off praying?

He thought to leave off praying

HOPE. Yes, an hundred times twice told.

CHR. And what was the reason you did not?

HOPE. I believed that that was true which had been told me, to wit, that without the righteousness of this Christ all the world could not save me; and therefore thought I with myself, If I leave off, I die, and can but die at the Throne of Grace. And withal, this came into my mind, *If it tarry, wait for it, because it will surely come, it will not tarry.* So I continued praying until the Father shewed me his Son.

He durst not leave off praying, and why

CHR. And how was he revealed unto you?

HOPE. I did not see him with my bodily eyes, but

with the eyes of mine understanding; and thus it was: One day I was very sad, I think sadder than at any one time in my life, and this sadness was through a fresh sight of the greatness and vileness of my sins: and as I was then looking for nothing but Hell, and the everlasting damnation of my Soul, suddenly, as I thought, I saw the Lord Jesus look down from Heaven upon me, and saying, *Believe on the Lord Jesus Christ, and thou shalt be saved.*

Christ is revealed to him, and how

But I replied, Lord, I am a great, a very great sinner. And he answered *My grace is sufficient for thee.* Then I said, But Lord, what is believing? And then I saw from that saying, *He that cometh to me shall never hunger, and he that believeth on me shall never thirst,* that believing and coming was all one; and that he that came, that, is, ran out in his heart and affections after salvation by Christ, he indeed believed in Christ. Then the water stood in mine eyes, and I asked further, But Lord, may such a great sinner as I am be indeed accepted of thee, and be saved by thee? And I heard him say, *And him that cometh to me I will in no wise cast out.* Then I said, But how, Lord, must I consider of thee in my coming to thee, that my faith may be placed aright upon thee? Then he said, *Christ Jesus came into the World to save sinners. He is the end of the Law for righteousness to every one that believes. He died for our sins, and rose again for our justification. He loved us and washed us from our sins in his own blood. He is Mediator between God and us. He ever liveth to make intercession for us.* From all which I gathered, that I must look for Righteousness in his Person, and for Satisfaction for my Sins by his Blood; that what he did in obedience to his Father's Law, and in submitting to the penalty thereof, was not for himself, but for him that will accept it for his Salvation, and be thankful. And now was my heart full of joy, mine eyes full of tears, and mine affections running over with love to the Name, People, and Ways of Jesus Christ.

CHR. This was a revelation of Christ to your soul indeed; but tell me particulaly what effect this had upon your spirit.

HOPE. It made me see that all the World, notwithstanding all the righteousness thereof, is in a state of condemnation. It made me see that God the Father, though he be just, can justly justify the coming sinner. It made me greatly ashamed of the vileness of my former life, and confounded me with the sense of mine own ignorance; for there never came thought into my heart before now, that shewed me so the beauty of Jesus Christ. It made me love a holy life, and long to do something for the Honour and Glory of the Name of the Lord Jesus; yea, I thought that had I now a thousand gallons of blood in my body, I could spill it all for the sake of the Lord Jesus.

I saw then in my Dream that *Hopeful* looked back and saw *Ignorance,* whom they had left behind, coming after. Look, said he to *Christian,* how far yonder youngster loitereth behind.

CHR. Ay, ay, I see him; he careth not for our company.

HOPE. But I tro it would not have hurt him, had he kept pace with us hitherto.

CHR. That's true, but I warrant you he thinketh otherwise.

Young Ignorance comes up again; their talk

HOPE. That I think he doth, but however let us tarry for him. So they did.

Then *Christian* said to him, Come away man, why do you stay so behind?

IGNOR. I take my pleasure in walking alone, even more a great deal than in Company, unless I like it the better.

Then said *Christian* to *Hopeful* (but softly) Did I not tell you he cared not for our company? But however, said he, come up, and let us talk away the time in this solitary place. Then directing his speech to *Ignorance,* he said, Come, how do you? How stands it between God and your Soul now?

IGNOR. I hope well; for I am always full of good motions, that come into my mind to comfort me as I walk.

Ignorance's hope, and the ground of it

CHR. What good motions? pray tell us.

IGNOR. Why, I think of God and Heaven.

CHR. So do the Devils and damned Souls.

IGNOR. But I think of them and desire them.

CHR. So do many that are never like to come there. *The Soul of the Sluggard desires, and hath nothing.*

IGNOR. But I think of them, and leave all for them.

CHR. That I doubt, for leaving all is an hard matter, yea a harder matter than many are aware of. But why, or by what, art thou persuaded that thou hast left all for God and Heaven?

IGNOR. My heart tells me so.

CHR. The wise man says, *He that trusts his own heart is a fool.*

IGNOR. This is spoken of an evil heart, but mine is a good one.

CHR. But how dost thou prove that?

IGNOR. It comforts me in hopes of Heaven.

CHR. That may be through its deceitfulness, for a man's heart may minister comfort to him in the hopes of that thing for which he yet has no ground to hope.

IGNOR. But my heart and life agree together, and therefore my hope is well grounded.

CHR. Who told thee that thy heart and life agree together?

IGNOR. My heart tells me so.

CHR. Ask my fellow if I be a Thief! Thy heart tells thee so! Except the Word of God beareth witness in this matter, other testimony is of no value.

IGNOR. But is it not a good heart that has good thoughts? and is not that a good life that is according to God's Commandments?

CHR. Yes, that is a good heart that hath good thoughts, and that is a good life that is according to God's Commandments; but it is one thing indeed to have these, and another thing only to think so.

IGNOR. Pray, what count you good thoughts, and a life according to God's Commandments?

CHR. There are good thoughts of divers kinds, some respecting ourselves, some God, some Christ, some other things.

What are good thoughts

IGNOR. What be good thoughts respecting ourselves?

CHR. Such as agree with the Word of God.

IGNOR. When do our thoughts of ourselves agree with the Word of God?

CHR. When we pass the same Judgment upon ourselves which the Word passes. To explain myself, the Word of God saith of persons in a natural condition, *There is none righteous, there is none that doth good.* It saith also, *That every imagination of the heart of man is only evil, and that continually.* And again, *The imagination of man's heart is evil from his youth.* Now then, when we think thus of ourselves, having sense thereof, then are our thoughts good ones, because according to the Word of God.

IGNOR. I will never believe that my heart is thus bad.

CHR. Therefore thou never hadst one good thought concerning thyself in thy life. But let me go on: As the Word passeth a Judgment upon our *Heart,* so it passeth a Judgment upon our *Ways;* and when our thoughts of our *Hearts* and *Ways* agree with the Judgment which the Word giveth of both, then are both good, because agreeing thereto.

IGNOR. Make out your meaning.

CHR. Why, the Word of God saith that man's ways are crooked ways, not good, but perverse. It saith they are naturally out of the good way, that they have not known it. Now when a man thus thinketh of his ways, I say, when he doth sensibly, and with heart-humiliation thus think, then hath he good thoughts of his own ways, because his thoughts now agree with the Judgment of the Word of God.

IGNOR. What are good thoughts concerning God?

CHR. Even as I have said concerning ourselves, when our thoughts of God do agree with what the Word saith of him; and that is, when we think of his Being and Attributes as the Word hath taught, of which I cannot now discourse at large: but to speak of him with reference to us, then we have right thoughts of God, when we think that he knows us better than we know ourselves, and can see sin in us when and where we can see none in ourselves; when we think he knows our inmost thoughts, and that our heart with all its depths is always open unto his eyes; also when we think that all our Righteousness stinks in his nostrils, and that therefore he cannot abide to see us stand before him in any confidence, even in all our best performances.

IGNOR. Do you think that I am such a fool as to think God can see no further than I? or that I would come to God in the best of my performances?

CHR. Why, how dost thou think in this matter?

IGNOR. Why, to be short, I think I must believe in Christ for Justification.

CHR. How! think thou must believe in Christ, when thou seest not thy need of him! Thou neither seest thy original or actual infirmities; but hast such an opinion of thyself, and of what thou doest, as plainly renders thee to be one that did never see a necessity of Christ's personal righteousness to justify thee before God. How then dost thou say I believe in Christ?

IGNOR. I believe well enough for all that.

CHR. How dost thou believe?

The faith of Ignorance

IGNOR. I believe that Christ died for sinners, and that I shall be justified before God from the curse, through his gracious acceptance of my obedience to his Law. Or thus, Christ makes my Duties that are religious, acceptable to his Father by virtue of his Merits; and so shall I be justified.

CHR. Let me give an answer to this Confession of thy Faith.

1. Thou believest with a fantastical Faith, for this Faith is nowhere described in the Word.

2. Thou believest with a false Faith, because it taketh Justification from the personal righteousness of Christ, and applies it to thy own.

3. This Faith maketh not Christ a Justifier of thy person, but of thy actions; and of thy person for thy actions' sake, which is false.

4. Therefore this Faith is deceitful, even such as will leave thee under wrath in the day of God Almighty; for true Justifying Faith puts the soul (as sensible of its lost condition by the Law) upon flying for refuge unto Christ's righteousness, (which righteousness of his is not an act of grace, by which he maketh for Justification *thy* obedience accepted by God; but *his* personal obedience to the Law, in doing and suffering for us what that required at our hands.) This righteousness, I say, true Faith accepteth; under the skirt of which the soul being shrouded, and by it presented as spotless before God, it is accepted, and acquit from condemnation.

IGNOR. What! would you have us trust to what Christ in his own person has done without us? This conceit would loosen the reins of our lust, and tolerate us to live as we list. For what matter how we live, if we may be Justified by Christ's personal righteousness from all, when we believe it?

CHR. *Ignorance* is thy name, and as thy name is, so art thou; even this thy answer demonstrateth what I say. *Ignorant* thou art of what Justifying Righteousness is, and as ignorant how to secure thy Soul through the Faith of it from the heavy wrath of God. Yea, thou also art ignorant of the true effects of saving Faith in this Righteousness of

Christ, which is to bow and win over the heart to God in Christ, to love his Name, his Word, Ways, and People, and not as thou ignorantly imaginest.

HOPE. Ask him if ever he had Christ revealed to him from Heaven.

IGNOR. What! you are a man for revelations! I believe that what both you, and all the rest of you, say about that matter, is but the fruit of distracted brains.

Ignorance jangles with them

HOPE. Why man! Christ is so hid in God from the natural apprehensions of all flesh, that he cannot by any man be savingly known, unless God the Father reveals him to them.

IGNOR. That is your Faith, but not mine; yet mine I doubt not is as good as yours, though I have not in my head so many whimsies as you.

He speaks reproachfully of what he knows not

CHR. Give me leave to put in a word: You ought not so slightly to speak of this matter: for this I will boldly affirm (even as my good Companion hath done) that no man can know Jesus Christ but by the revelation of the Father; yea, and Faith too, by which the soul layeth hold upon Christ, (if it be right) must be wrought by the exceeding greatness of his mighty power; the working of which Faith, I perceive, poor *Ignorance,* thou art ignorant of.

Be awakened then, see thine own wretchedness, and fly to the Lord Jesus; and by his righteousness, which is the righteousness of God, (for he himself is God) thou shalt be delivered from condemnation.

IGNOR. You go so fast I cannot keep pace with you, do you go on before, I must stay a while behind.

The talk broke up

Then they said,

Well *Ignorance*, wilt thou yet foolish be,
To slight good Counsel, ten times given thee?
And if thou yet refuse it, thou shalt know
E're long the evil of thy doing so:
Remember, man, in time; stoop, do not fear,
Good Counsel taken well, saves; therefore hear:
But if thou yet shall slight it, thou wilt be
The loser, *Ignorance*, I'll warrant thee.

Then *Christian* addressed thus himself to his fellow.

CHR. Well, come my good *Hopeful,* I perceive that thou and I must walk by ourselves again.

So I saw in my Dream that they went on apace before, and *Ignorance* he came hobbling after. Then said *Christian* to his Companion, It pities me much for this poor man, it will certainly go ill with him at last.

HOPE. Alas, there are abundance in our Town in his condition, whole families, yea, whole Streets, and that of Pilgrims too; and if there be so many in our parts, how many think you, must there be in the place where he was born?

CHR. Indeed the Word saith, *He hath blinded their eyes, lest they should see,* &c. But now we are by ourselves, what do you think of such men? Have they at no time, think you, convictions of sin, and so consequently fears that their state is dangerous?

HOPE. Nay, do you answer that question yourself, for you are the elder man.

The good use of fear

CHR. Then I say, sometimes (as I think) they may, but they being naturally ignorant, understand not that such convictions tend to their good; and therefore they do desperately seek to stifle them, and presumptuously continue to flatter themselves in the way of their own hearts.

HOPE. I do believe, as you say, that fear tends much to men's good, and to make them right at their beginning to go on Pilgrimage.

CHR. Without all doubt it doth, if it be right; for so says the Word, *The fear of the Lord is the beginning of Wisdom.*

Right fear

HOPE. How will you describe right fear?

CHR. True or right fear is discovered by three things:

1. By its rise; it is caused by saving convictions for sin.

2. It driveth the soul to lay fast hold of Christ for salvation.

3. It begetteth and continueth in the soul a great reverence of God, his Word, and Ways, keeping it tender, and making it afraid to turn from them, to the right hand or to the left, to anything that may dishonour God, break its peace, grieve the Spirit, or cause the Enemy to speak reproachfully.

HOPE. Well said; I believe you have said the truth. Are we now almost got past the Inchanted Ground?

CHR. Why, art thou weary of this discourse?

HOPE. No, verily, but that I would know where we are.

CHR. We have not now above two miles further to go thereon. But let us return to our matter. Now the Ignorant know not that such convictions as tend to put them in fear are for their good, and therefore they seek to stifle them.

Why ignorant persons stifle convictions

In general

HOPE. How do they seek to stifle them?

CHR. 1. They think that those fears are wrought by the Devil, (though indeed they are wrought of God) and thinking so, they resist them as things that directly tend to their overthrow. 2. They also think that these fears tend to the spoiling of their Faith, when alas for them, poor men that they are, they have none at all! and therefore they harden their hearts against them. 3. They presume they ought not to fear, and therefore in despite of them wax presumptuously confident. 4. They see that these fears tend to take away from them their pitiful old self-holiness, and therefore they resist them with all their might.

In particular

HOPE. I know something of this myself; for before I knew myself it was so with me.

CHR. Well, we will leave at this time our Neighbor *Ignorance* by himself, and fall upon another profitable question.

HOPE. With all my heart, but you shall still begin.

CHR. Well then, did you not know about ten years

Talk about one Temporary

ago, one *Temporary* in your parts, who was a forward man in Religion then?

Where he dwelt

HOPE. Know him! yes, he dwelt in *Graceless,* a town about two miles off of *Honesty,* and he dwelt next door to one *Turn-back.*

He was towardly once

CHR. Right, he dwelt under the same roof with him. Well, that man was much awakened once; I believe that then he had some sight of his sins, and of the wages that were due thereto.

HOPE. I am of your mind, for (my house not being above three miles from him) he would ofttimes come to me, and that with many tears. Truly I pitied the man, and was not altogether without hope of him; but one may see it is not every one that cries, *Lord, Lord.*

CHR. He told me once, That he was resolved to go on Pilgrimage, as we do now; but all of a sudden he grew acquainted with one *Saveself,* and then he became a stranger to me.

HOPE. Now since we are talking about him, let us a little enquire into the reason of the sudden backsliding of him and such others.

CHR. It may be very profitable, but do you begin.

HOPE. Well then, there are in my judgment four reasons for it.

Reasons why towardly ones go back

1. Though the consciences of such men are awakened, yet their minds are not changed; therefore when the power of guilt weareth away, that which provoked them to be religious ceaseth. Wherefore they naturally turn to their own course again, even as we see the Dog that is sick of what he has eaten, so long as his sickness prevails, he vomits and casts up all; not that he doth this of a free mind, (if we may say a Dog has a mind) but because it troubleth his Stomach; but now when his sickness is over, and so his Stomach eased, his desire being not at all alienate from his vomit, he turns him about and licks up all; and so it is true which is written, *The Dog is turned to his own vomit again.* This I say, being hot for Heaven by vertue only of

the sense and fear of the torments of Hell, as their sense of Hell and the fears of damnation chills and cools, so their desires for Heaven and Salvation cool also. So then it comes to pass, that when their guilt and fear is gone, their desires for Heaven and Happiness die, and they return to their course again.

2. Another reason is, they have slavish fears that do over-master them; I speak now of the fears that they have of men, *For the fear of men bringeth a snare.* So then, though they seem to be hot for Heaven, so long as the flames of Hell are about their ears, yet when that terror is a little over, they betake themselves to second thoughts; namely, that 'tis good to be wise, and not to run (for they know not what) the hazard of losing all; or at least, of bringing themselves into unavoidable and unnecessary troubles, and so they fall in with the world again.

3. The shame that attends Religion lies also as a block in their way; they are proud and haughty, and Religion in their eye is low and contemptible; therefore when they have lost their sense of Hell and wrath to come, they return again to their former course.

4. Guilt, and to meditate terror, are grievous to them; they like not to see their misery before they come into it. Though perhaps the sight of it first, if they loved that sight, might make them fly whither the righteous fly and are safe. But because they do, as I hinted before, even shun the thoughts of guilt and terror, therefore when once they are rid of their awakenings about the terrors and wrath of God, they harden their hearts gladly, and chuse such ways as will harden them more and more.

CHR. You are pretty near the business, for the bottom of all is, for want of a change in their mind and will. And therefore they are but like the Felon that standeth before the Judge, he quakes and trembles, and seems to repent most heartily, but the bottom of all is the fear of the Halter, not that he hath any detestation of the offence; as is evident, because, let but this man have his liberty, and he will be a Thief, and so a Rogue still; whereas, if his mind was changed, he would be otherwise.

HOPE. Now I have shewed you the reasons of their going back, do you show me the manner thereof.

CHR. So I will willingly.

How the apostate goes back

1. They draw off their thoughts, all that they may, from the remembrance of God, Death and Judgment to come.

2. Then they cast off by degrees private Duties, as Closet-prayer, Curbing their Lusts, Watching, Sorrow for Sin, and the like.

3. Then they shun the company of lively and warm Christians.

4. After that they grow cold to public Duty, as Hearing, Reading, Godly Conference, and the like.

5. Then they begin to pick holes, as we say, in the Coats of some of the Godly; and that devilishly, that they may have a seeming colour to throw Religion (for the sake of some infirmity they have spied in them) behind their backs.

6. Then they begin to adhere to, and associate themselves with carnal, loose and wanton men.

7. Then they give way to carnal and wanton discourses in secret; and glad are they if they can see such things in any that are counted honest, that they may the more boldly do it through their example.

8. After this, they begin to play with little sins openly.

9. And then, being hardened, they shew themselves as they are. Thus being launched again into the gulf of misery, unless a Miracle of Grace prevent it, they everlastingly perish in their own deceivings.

Angels

Now I saw in my Dream, that by this time the Pilgrims were got over the Inchanted Ground, and entering into the Country of *Beulah,* whose air was very sweet and pleasant, the way lying directly through it, they solaced themselves tnere for a season. Yea, here they heard continually the singing of Birds, and saw every day the Flowers appear in the earth, and heard the voice of the Turtle in the land. In this Country the Sun shineth night and day; wherefore this was beyond the Valley of the *Shadow of Death,* and also out of the reach of Giant *Despair,* neither could they from this place so much as see *Doubting* Castle. Here they were within sight of the City they were going to, also here met them some of the inhabitants thereof; for in this land the Shining Ones commonly walked, because it was upon the borders of Heaven. In this land also the contract between the Bride and the Bridegroom was renewed; yea here, *as the Bridegroom rejoiceth over the Bride, so did their God rejoice over them.* Here they had no want of Corn and Wine; for in this place they met with abundance of what they had sought for in all their Pilgrimage. Here they heard voices from out of the City, loud voices, saying, *Say ye to the daughter of* Zion *Behold thy salvation cometh, behold his reward is with him.* Here all the inhabitants of the Country called them, *The holy People, The redeemed of the Lord, Sought out,* &c.

Now as they walked in this land, they had more rejoicing than in parts more remote from the Kingdom to which they were bound; and drawing near to the City, they had yet a more perfect view thereof. It was builded of Pearls and Precious Stones, also the Street thereof was paved with Gold; so that by reason of the natural glory of the City, and the reflections of the Sun-beams upon it, *Christian* with desire fell sick, *Hopeful* also had a fit or two of the same disease. Wherefore here they lay by it a while, crying out because of their pangs, *If you see my Beloved, tell him that I am sick of love.*

But being a little strengthened, and better able to bear their sickness, they walked on their way, and came yet nearer and nearer, where were Orchards,

Vineyards, and Gardens, and their gates opened into the High-way. Now as they came up to these places, behold the Gardener stood in the way, to whom the Pilgrims said, Whose goodly Vineyards and Gardens are these? He answered, They are the King's and are planted here for his own delights, and also for the solace of Pilgrims. So the Gardener had them into the Vineyards, and bid them refresh themselves with Dainties. He also shewed them there the King's walks, and the Arbors where he delighted to be; and here they tarried and slept.

Now I beheld in my Dream, that they talked more in their sleep at this time than ever they did in all their Journey; and being in a muse thereabout, the Gardener said even to me, Wherefore musest thou at the matter? It is the nature of the fruit of the Grapes of these Vinyards to go down so sweetly as to cause the lips of them that are asleep to speak.

So I saw that when they awoke, they addressed themselves to go up to the City. But, as I said, the reflection of the Sun upon the City (for the City was pure Gold) was so extremely glorious, that they could not as yet with open face behold it, but through an *Instrument* made for that purpose. So I saw that as they went on, there met them two men, in Raiment that shone like Gold, also their faces shone as the light.

These men asked the Pilgrims whence they came? and they told them. They also asked them where they had lodged, what difficulties and dangers, what comforts and pleasures they had met in the way? and they told them. Then said the men that met them, You have but two difficulties more to meet with, and then you are in the City.

Christian then and his Companion asked the men to go along with them, so they told them they would. But, said they, you must obtain it by your own Faith. So I saw in my Dream that they went on together till they came in sight of the Gate.

Now I further saw that betwixt them and the Gate was a River, but there was no Bridge to go over, the River was very deep: at the sight therefore of this River the Pilgrims were much stunned; but the men that went with them said, You must go through, or you cannot come at the Gate.

Death

The Pilgrims then began to enquire if there was no other way to the Gate; to which they answered, Yes, but there hath not any, save two, to wit, *Enoch* and *Elijah,* been permitted to tread that path, since the foundation of the World, nor shall, until the last Trumpet shall sound. The Pilgrims then, especially *Christian,* began to dispond in his mind, and looked this way and that, but no way could be found by them by which they might escape the River. Then they asked the men if the Waters were all of a depth? They said, No; yet they could not help them in that case, for said they, *you shall find it deeper or shallower, as you believe in the King of the place.*

Death is not welcome to nature, though by it we pass out of this world in to glory

Angels help us not comfortably through death

They then addressed themselves to the Water; and entring, *Christian* began to sink, and crying out to his good friend *Hopeful,* he said, I sink in deep Waters; the Billows go over my head, all his Waves go over me, *Selah.*

Then said the other, Be of good cheer my Brother, I feel the bottom, and it is good. Then said *Christian,* Ah my friend, the sorrows of death have compassed me about, I shall not see the land that flows with milk and honey. And with that a great darkness and horror fell upon *Christian,* so that he could not see before him. Also here he in great measure lost his senses, so that he could neither remember, nor orderly talk of any of those sweet refreshments that he had met with in the way of his Pilgrimage. But all the words that he spake still tended to discover that he had horror of mind, and heart-fears that he should die in that River, and never obtain entrance in at the Gate. Here also, as they that stood by perceived, he was much in the trouble-

Christian's conflict at the hour of death

some thoughts of the sins that he had committed, both since and before he began to be a Pilgrim. 'Twas also observed that he was troubled with apparitions of Hobgoblins and evil Spirits, for ever and anon he would intimate so much by words. *Hopeful* therefore here had much ado to keep his Brother's head above water; yea sometimes he would be quite gone down, and then ere a while he would rise up again half dead. *Hopeful* also would endeavour to comfort him, saying, Brother, I see the Gate, and men standing by to receive us. But *Christian* would answer, 'Tis you, 'tis you they wait for, you have been *hopeful* ever since I knew you. And so have you, said he to *Christian.* Ah Brother, said he, surely if I was right, he would now arise to help me; but for my sins he hath brought me into the snare, and hath left me. Then said *Hopeful,* My Brother, you have quite forgot the Text, where it is said of the wicked, *There is no band in their death, but their strength is firm, they are not troubled as other men, neither are they plagued like other men.* These troubles and distresses that you go through in these Waters are no sign that God hath forsaken you, but are sent to try you, whether you will call to mind that which heretofore you have received of his goodness, and live upon him in your distresses.

Christian delivered from his fears in death

Then I saw in my Dream, that *Christian* was as in a muse a while. To whom also *Hopeful* added this word, *Be of good cheer, Jesus Christ maketh thee whole;* and with that *Christian* brake out with a loud voice, Oh I see him again, and he tells me, *When thou passest through the Waters, I will be with thee; and through the Rivers, they shall not overflow thee.* Then they both took courage, and the Enemy was after that as still as a stone, until they were gone over. *Christian* therefore presently found ground to stand upon, and so it followed that the rest of the River was but shallow. Thus they got over. Now upon the bank of the River on the other side, they saw the two shining men again, who there waited for them; wherefore being come out of the River, they saluted them saying, *We are ministring Spirits, sent forth to minister for those that shall be heirs of salvation.* Thus they went along towards the Gate.

The angels do wait for them, so soon as they are passed out of this world

Now, now, look how the holy Pilgrims ride,
Clouds are their Chariots, Angels are their Guide:
Who would not here for him all hazards run,
That thus provides for his when this World's done?

Now you must note that the City stood upon a mighty Hill, but the Pilgrims went up that Hill with ease because they had these two men to lead them up by the arms; also they had left their *mortal Garments* behind them in the River, for though they went in with them, they came out without them. They therefore went up here with much agility and speed, though the foundation upon which the City was framed was higher than the Clouds. They therefore went up through the Regions of the Air, sweetly talking as they went, being comforted, because they safely got over the River, and had such glorious Companions to attend them.

They have put off mortality

The talk that they had with the Shining Ones was about the glory of the place, who told them that the beauty and glory of it was inexpressible. There, said they, is the Mount *Sion,* the heavenly *Jerusalem,* the innumerable company of Angels, and the Spirits of just men made perfect. You are going now, said they, to the Paradise of God, wherein you shall see the Tree of Life, and eat of the never-fading fruits thereof; and when you come there, you shall have white Robes given you, and your walk and talk shall be every day with the King, even all the days of Eternity. There you shall not see again such things as you saw when you were in the lower Region upon the earth, to wit, sorrow, sickness, affliction, and death, *for the former things are passed away.* You are now going to *Abraham,* to *Isaac,* and *Jacob,* and to the Prophets, men that God hath taken away from the evil to come, and that are now resting upon their beds, each one walking in his righteousness. The men then asked, What must we do in the holy place? To whom it was answered, You must there receive the comfort of all your toil, and have joy for all your sorrow; you must reap what you have sown, even the fruit of all your Prayers and Tears, and sufferings for the King by the way. In that place you must wear Crowns of Gold, and enjoy the perpetual sight and vision of the Holy one, *for there you shall see him as he is.* There also you shall serve him continually with praise, with shouting, and thanksgiving, whom you desired to serve in the World, though with much difficulty, because of the infirmity of your flesh. There your eyes shall be delighted with seeing, and your ears with hearing the pleasant voice of the Mighty One. There you shall enjoy your friends again, that are gone thither before you; and there you shall with joy receive even every one that follows into the holy place after you. There also shall you be cloathed with Glory and Majesty, and put into an equipage fit to ride out with the King of Glory. When he shall come with sound of Trumpet in the Clouds, as upon the wings of the Wind, you shall come with him; and when he shall sit upon the Throne of Judgment, you shall sit by him; yea, and when he shall pass sentence upon all the workers of iniquity, let them be Angels or Men, you also shall have a voice in that Judgment, because they were his and your Enemies. Also when he shall again return to the City, you shall go too, with sound of Trumpet, and be ever with him.

Now while they were thus drawing towards the Gate, behold a company of the Heavenly Host came out to meet them; to whom it was said by the other two Shining Ones, These are the men that have loved our Lord when they were in the World, and that have left all for his Holy Name, and he hath sent us to fetch them, and we have brought them thus far on their desired Journey, that they may go in and look their Redeemer in the face with joy. Then the Heavenly Host gave a great shout, saying, *Blessed are they that are called to the Marriage Supper of the Lamb.* There came out also at this time to meet them, several of the King's Trumpeters, cloathed in white and shining Raiment, who with melodious noises and loud, made even the Heavens to echo with their sound. These Trumpeters saluted *Christian* and his fellow with ten thousand welcomes from the World, and this they did with shouting and sound of Trumpet.

This done, they compassed them round on every side; some went before, some behind, and some on the right hand, some on the left, (as 'twere to guard them through the upper Regions) continually sounding as they went with melodious noise, in notes on high: so that the very sight was to them that could behold it, as if Heaven itself was come down to meet them. Thus therefore they walked on together; and as they walked, ever and anon these Trumpeters, even with joyful sound, would, by mixing their musick with looks and gestures, still signify to *Christian* and his Brother, how welcome they were into their company, and with what gladness they came to meet them; and now were these two men as 'twere in Heaven before they came at it, being swallowed up with the sight of Angels, and with hearing of their melodious notes. Here also they had the City itself in view, and they thought they heard all the Bells therein ring to welcome them thereto. But above all, the warm and joyful thoughts that they had about their own dwelling there, with such company, and that for ever and ever. Oh, by what tongue or pen can their glorious joy be expressed! And thus they came up to the Gate.

Now when they were come up to the Gate, there

was written over it in Letters of Gold, *Blessed are they that do his Commandments, that they may have right to the Tree of Life, and may enter in through the Gates into the City.*

Then I saw in my Dream, that the Shining Men bid them call at the Gate; the which when they did, some from above looked over the Gate, to wit, *Enoch, Moses,* and *Elijah, &c.*, to whom it was said, These Pilgrims are come from the City of *Destruction* for the love that they bear to the King of this place; and then the Pilgrims gave in unto them each man his Certificate, which they had received in the beginning; those therefore were carried in to the King, who when he had read them, said, Where are the men? To whom it was answered, They are standing without the Gate. The King then commanded to open the Gate, *That the righteous nation,* saith he, *that keepeth Truth may enter in.*

Now I saw in my Dream that these two men went in at the Gate: and lo, as they entered, they were transfigured, and they had Raiment put on that shone like Gold. There was also that met them with Harps and Crowns, and gave them to them, the Harps to praise withal, and the Crowns in token of honour. Then I heard in my Dream that all the Bells in the City rang again for joy, and that it was said unto them, *Enter ye into the joy of your Lord.* I also heard the men themselves, that they sang with a loud voice, saying, *Blessing, Honour, Glory, and Power, be to him that sitteth upon the Throne, and to the Lamb for ever and ever.*

Now just as the Gates were opened to let in the men, I looked in after them, and behold, the City shone like the Sun: the Streets also were paved with Gold, and in them walked many men, with Crowns on their heads, Palms in their hands, and golden Harps to sing praises withal.

There were also of them that had wings, and they answered one another without intermission, saying, *Holy, Holy, Holy, is the Lord.* And after that they shut up the Gates. Which when I had seen, I wished myself among them.

Now while I was gazing upon all these things, I turned my head to look back, and saw *Ignorance* come up to the River-side; but he soon got over, and that without half that difficulty which the other two men met with. For it happened that there was then in that place one *Vain-hope* a Ferry-man, that with his Boat helped him over; so he, as the other I saw, did ascend the Hill to come up to the Gate, only he came alone; neither did any man meet him with the least encouragement. When he was come up to the Gate, he looked up to the writing that was above, and then began to knock, supposing that entrance should have been quickly administered to him; but he was asked by the men that looked over the top of the Gate, Whence came you? and what would you have? He answered, I have eat and drank in the presence of the King, and he has taught in our Streets. Then they asked him for his Certificate, that they might go in and shew it to the King. So he fumbled in his bosom for one, and found none. Then said they, Have you none? But the man answered never a word. So they told the King, but he would not come down to see him, but commanded the two Shining Ones that conducted *Christian* and *Hopeful* to the City, to go out and take *Ignorance,* and bind him hand and foot, and have him away. Then they took him up, and carried him through the air to the door that I saw in the side of the Hill, and put him in there. Then I saw that there was a way to Hell even from the Gates of Heaven, as well as from the City of *Destruction.* So I awoke, and behold it was a Dream.

Ignorance comes up to the river

Vain-hope does ferry him over

THE CONCLUSION

Now Reader, *I have told my Dream to thee;*
See if thou can'st interpret it to me,
Or to thyself, or Neighbor; but take heed
Of mis-interpreting; for that, instead
Of doing good, will but thyself abuse:
By mis-*interpreting, evil insues.*

Take heed also, that thou be not extreme,
In playing with the out-side of my Dream:
Nor let my figure or similitude
Put thee into a laughter or a feud;
Leave this for Boys and Fools; but as for thee,
Do thou the substance of my matter see.

Put by the Curtains, look within my Vail;
Turn up my Metaphors, and do not fail
There, if thou seekest them, such things to find
As will be helpful to an honest mind.

What of my dross *thou findest there, be bold*
To throw away, but yet preserve the Gold;
What if my Gold be wrapped up in Ore?
None throws away the Apple for the Core.
But if thou shalt cast away all as vain,
I know not but 'twill make me Dream again.

THE
PILGRIM'S PROGRESS

FROM THIS WORLD

TO THAT WHICH IS TO COME

THE SECOND PART

DELIVERED UNDER THE SIMILITUDE OF A DREAM

Wherein is set forth
the manner of the setting out of Christian's
Wife and Children, their Dangerous Journey, and
Safe Arrival at the Desired Country

BY JOHN BUNYAN

I have used Similitudes. HOS. 12. 10.

THE AUTHOR'S WAY OF SENDING FORTH HIS

SECOND PART OF THE PILGRIM

Go now my little Book, to every place
Where my first Pilgrim *has but shewn his Face:*
Call at their door; If any say, Who's there?
Then answer thou, Christiana is here.
If they bid thee Come in, *then enter thou,*
With all thy Boys; and then, as thou know'st how,
Tell who they are, also from whence they came;
Perhaps they'll know them by their looks, or name.
But if they should not, ask them yet again
If formerly they did not entertain
One Christian *a* Pilgrim? *If they say*
They did, and was delighted in his Way;
Then let them know that those related were
Unto him, yea, his Wife and Children are.
Tell them that they have left their House and Home,
Are turned Pilgrims, *seek a World to come;*
That they have met with Hardships in the way:
That they do meet with Troubles night and day;
That they have trod on Serpents, fought with Devils,
Have also overcame a many evils.
Yea, tell them also of the next, who have
Of love to Pilgrimage *been stout and brave*
Defenders of that Way, and how they still
Refuse this World, to do their Father's will.
Go tell them also of those dainty things,
That Pilgrimage *unto the* Pilgrim *brings.*
Let them acquainted be too, how they are

Beloved of their King, under his care;
What goodly Mansions for them he provides,
Tho' they meet with rough Winds and swelling Tides.
How brave a Calm they will enjoy at last,
Who to their Lord, and by his ways hold fast.
Perhaps with heart and hand they will embrace
Thee, as they did my Firstling, and will grace
Thee, and thy fellows, with such cheer and fare,
As shew will they of Pilgrims *lovers are.*

I Objection

But how if they will not believe of me
That I am truly thine, 'cause some there be
That counterfeit the Pilgrim and his name,
Seek by disguise to seem the very same,
And by that means have wrought themselves into
The hands and houses of I know not who?

Answer

'Tis true, some have of late, to counterfeit
My Pilgrim, *to their own my Title set;*
Yea others half my Name and Title too
Have stitched to their Book, to make them do;
But yet they by their Features do declare
Themselves not mine to be, whose ere they are.
If such thou meetst with, then thine only way
Before them all is to say out thy say,
In thine own native language, which no man
Now useth, nor with ease dissemble can.
If after all they still of you shall doubt,
Thinking that you like Gipsies *go about*
In naughty wise the Country to defile,
Or that you seek good people to beguile
With things unwarrantable; send for me,
And I will testifie you Pilgrims *be;*
Yea, I will testifie that only you
My Pilgrims *are; and that alone will do.*

2 OBJECTION

But yet perhaps I may inquire for him,
Of those that wish him damned life and limb.
What shall I do, when I at such a door
For *Pilgrims* ask, and they shall rage the more?

ANSWER

Fright not thyself my Book, for such Bugbears
Are nothing else but ground for groundless fears:
My Pilgrim's *Book has travell'd sea and land,*
Yet could I never come to understand
That it was slighted, or turn'd out of door
By any Kingdom, were they rich or poor.
In France *and* Flanders, *where men kill each other,*
My Pilgrim *is esteem'd a Friend, a Brother.*
In Holland *too 'tis said, as I am told,*
My Pilgrim *is with some worth more than Gold.*
Highlanders *and* Wild Irish *can agree*
My Pilgrim *should familiar with them be.*
'Tis in New England *under such advance,*
Receives there so much loving countenance,
As to be trimm'd, new cloth'd, and deck't with Gems,
That it may shew its features and its limbs,
Yet more, so comely doth my Pilgrim *walk,*
That of him thousands daily sing and talk.
If you draw nearer home, it will appear
My Pilgrim *knows no ground of shame or fear;*
City and Country will him entertain
With ***Welcome*** Pilgrim; *yea, they can't refrain*
From smiling, if my Pilgrim *be* ***but*** *by,*
Or shews his head in any Company,
Brave Galants do my Pilgrim *hug and love,*
Esteem it much, yea, value it above
Things of a greater bulk: yea, with delight,
Say my Lark's leg *is better than a* Kite.
Young Ladies, and young Gentle-women too,
Do no small kindness to my Pilgrim *shew;*
Their Cabinets, their Bosoms, and their Hearts
My Pilgrim *has, 'cause he to them imparts*

His pretty riddles in such wholesome strains,
As yield them profit double to their pains
Of reading. Yea, I think I may be bold
To say some prize him far above their Gold.
The very Children that do walk the street,
If they do but my holy Pilgrim *meet,*
Salute him will, will wish him well, and say,
He is the only Stripling *of the Day.*
They that have never seen him, yet admire
What they have heard of him, and much desire
To have his company, and hear him tell
Those Pilgrim stories *which he knows so well.*
Yea, some who did not love him at the first,
But call'd him Fool *and* Noddy, *say they must*
Now they have seen *and* heard *him, him commend;*
And to those whom they love they do him send.
Wherefore my Second Part, *thou need'st not be*
Afraid to shew thy Head; none can hurt thee,
That wish but well to him that went before,
'Cause thou com'st after with a second store
Of things as good, as rich, as profitable,
For Young, for Old, for Stagg'ring, and for Stable.

3 Objection

But some there be that say he laughs too loud;
And some do say his Head is in a Cloud.
Some say his Words and Stories are so dark,
They know not how by them to find his mark.

Answer

One may (I think) say, Both his laughs and cries
May well be guess'd at by his watery eyes.
Some things are of that nature as to make
One's Fancie chuckle, while his Heart doth ake,
When Jacob *saw his* Rachel *with the sheep,*
He did at the same time both kiss and weep.
Whereas some say, A Cloud is in his Head,
That doth but shew how Wisdom's covered
With its own mantles, and to stir the mind

To a search after what it fain would find:
Things that seem to be hid in words obscure,
Do but the Godly mind the more allure;
To study what those sayings should contain
That speak to us in such a Cloudy strain.
I also know a dark Similitude
Will on the Fancie more itself intrude,
And will stick faster in the Heart and Head,
Than things from Similies not borrowed.
Wherefore my Book, let no discouragement
Hinder thy travels. Behold, thou art sent
To Friends, not foes: to Friends that will give place
To thee, thy Pilgrims *and thy words embrace.*
Besides, what my first Pilgrim *left conceal'd,*
Thou my brave Second Pilgrim *hast reveal'd;*
What Christian *left lock't up, and went his way,*
Sweet Christiana *opens with her Key.*

4 Objection

But some love not the method of your first,
Romance they count it, throw't away as dust.
If I should meet with such, what should I say?
Must I slight them as they slight me, or nay?

Answer

My Christiana, *if with such thou meet,*
By all means in all loving wise them greet;
Render them not reviling for revile;
But if they frown, I prithee on them smile;
Perhaps 'tis Nature, or some ill report,
Has made them thus *despise, or* thus *retort.*
Some love no Cheese, some love no Fish, and some
Love not their Friends, nor their own House or Home;
Some start at Pig, slight Chicken, love not Fowl,
More than they love a Cuckow or an Owl;
Leave such, my Christiana, *to their choice,*
And seek those who to find thee will rejoice;
By no means strive, but in all humble wise
Present thee to them in thy Pilgrim's *guise.*

Go then my little Book, and shew to all
That entertain, and bid thee welcome shall,
What thou shalt keep close, shut up from the rest,
And wish what thou shalt shew them may be blest
To them for good, may make them chuse to be
Pilgrims *better by far than thee or me.*
Go then, I say, tell all men who thou art,
Say, I am Christiana, *and my part*
Is now, with my four Sons, to tell you what
It is for men to take a Pilgrim's *lot:*
Go also tell them who and what they be,
That now do go on Pilgrimage *with thee;*
Say, Here's my Neighbor Mercy, *she is one*
That has long time with me a Pilgrim *gone.*
Come see her in her Virgin Face, and learn
'Twixt Idle ones and Pilgrims *to discern.*
Yea, let young Damsels learn of her to prize
The World which is to come, in any wise.
When little tripping Maidens follow God,
And leave old doting Sinners to his Rod;
'Tis like those days wherein the young ones cried
Hosanah, *to whom old ones did deride.*
Next tell them of old Honest, *who you found*
With his white hairs treading the Pilgrim's *ground.*
Yea, tell them how plain-hearted this man was,
How after his good Lord he bare his Cross;
Perhaps with some grey Head this may prevail
With Christ to fall in Love, and Sin bewail.
Tell them also how Master Fearing *went*
On Pilgrimage, *and how the time he spent*
In Solitariness, with Fears and Cries,
And how at last he won the joyful Prize.
He was *a good man, though much down in Spirit,*
He is *a good man, and doth Life inherit.*
Tell them of Master Feeble-mind also,
Who not before, but still behind would go;
Shew them also how he had like been slain,
And how one Great-heart *did his life regain.*
This man was true of Heart, tho' weak in Grace,
One might true Godliness read in his Face.

Then tell them of Master Ready-to-halt,
A man with Crutches, but much without fault;
Tell them how Master Feeble-mind *and he*
Did love, and in opinions much agree.
And let all know, tho' weakness was their chance,
Yet sometimes one could sing, *the other* dance.
Forget not Master Valiant-for-the-truth,
That Man of courage, though a very Youth.
Tell every one his Spirit was so stout,
No man could ever make him face about,
And how Great-heart *and he could not forbear,*
But put-down Doubting Castle, slay Despair.
Overlook not Master Despondancie,
Nor Much-afraid, *his daughter, tho' they lie*
Under such Mantles as may make them look
(With some) as if their God had them forsook.
They softly went, but sure, and at the end
Found that the Lord of Pilgrims *was their Friend.*
When thou hast told the world of all these things,
Then turn about, my Book, and touch these strings,
Which if but touched, will such Musick make,
They'll make a Cripple dance, a Giant quake.
These Riddles that lie couch't within thy breast,
Freely propound, expound; and for the rest
Of thy mysterious lines, let them remain
For those whose nimble Fancies shall them gain.

Now may this little Book a blessing be
To those who love this little Book and me,
And may its Buyer have no cause to say,
His Money is but lost or thrown away;
Yea, may this Second Pilgrim *yield that fruit,*
As may with each good Pilgrim's *Fancie suit;*
And may it persuade some that go astray,
To turn their Feet and Heart to the right way:

Is the Hearty Prayer
of the Author
JOHN BUNYAN.

THE PILGRIM'S PROGRESS

IN THE SIMILITUDE OF A DREAM,

THE SECOND PART

COURTEOUS Companions, some time since, to tell you my Dream that I had of *Christian* the Pilgrim, and of his dangerous Journey toward the Cœlestial Country, was pleasant to me, and profitable to you. I told you then also what I saw concerning his *Wife* and *Children*, and how unwilling they were to go with him on Pilgrimage, insomuch that he was forced to go on his Progress without them; for he durst not run the danger of that destruction which he feared would come by staying with them in the City of *Destruction*. Wherefore as I then shewed you, he left them and departed.

Now it hath so happened, through the multiplicity of Business, that I have been much hindred and kept back from my wonted Travels into those parts whence he went, and so could not till now obtain an opportunity to make further enquiry after whom he left behind, that I might give you an account of them. But having had some concerns that way of late, I went down again thitherward. Now having taken up my Lodgings in a Wood about a mile off the place, as I slept I dreamed again.

And as I was in my Dream, behold an aged Gentleman came by where I lay; and because he was to go some part of the way that I was travelling, methought I got up and went with him. So as we walked, and as Travellers usually do, I was as if we fell into discourse, and our talk happened to be about *Christian* and his Travels; for thus I began with the old man.

Sir, said I, what Town is that there below, that lieth on the left hand of our way?

Then said Mr *Sagacity,* (for that was his name) It is the City of *Destruction,* a populous place, but possessed with a very ill-conditioned and idle sort of People.

I thought that was the City, quoth I, I went once myself through that Town, and therefore know that this report you give of it is true.

SAG. Too true, I wish I could speak truth in speaking better of them that dwell therein.

Well, Sir, quoth I, then I perceive you to be a well-meaning man; and so one that takes pleasure to hear and tell of that which is good: pray did you never hear what happened to a man some time ago in this Town (whose name was *Christian*) that went of Pilgrimage up towards the higher Regions?

Christians are well spoken of when gone; though called fools while they are here

SAG. Hear of him! Ay, and I also heard of the Molestations, Troubles, Wars, Captivities, Cries, Groans, Frights, and Fears that he met with and had in his Journey. Besides, I must tell you, all our Country rings of him; there are but few houses that have heard of him and his doings but have sought after and got the Records of his Pilgrimage; yea, I think I may say that his hazardous Journey has got a many well-wishers to his ways; for though when he was here, he was *Fool* in every man's mouth, yet now he is gone, he is highly commended of all. For 'tis said he lives bravely where he is; yea, many of them that are resolved never to run his hazards, yet have their mouths water at his gains.

They may, quoth I, well think, if they think anything that is true, that he liveth well where he is; for he now lives at and in the Fountain of Life, and has what he has without labour and sorrow, for there is no grief mixed therewith.

SAG. Talk! the people talk strangely about him. Some say that he now walks in White, that he has a Chain of Gold about his neck, that he has a Crown of Gold, beset with Pearls, upon his head. Others say that the Shining Ones that sometimes shewed themselves to him in his Journey, are become his Companions, and that he is as familiar with them in the place where he is, as here one Neighbor is with another. Besides, 'tis confidently affirmed concerning him, that the King of the place where he is has bestowed upon him already a very rich and pleasant dwelling at Court; and that he every day eateth and drinketh, and walketh, and talketh with him; and receiveth of the smiles and favours of him that is Judge of all there. Moreover, it is expected of some, that his Prince, the Lord of that Country, will shortly come into these parts, and will know the reason, if they can give any, why his Neighbors set so little by him, and had him so much in derision when they perceived that he would be a Pilgrim. For they say, that now he is so in the affections of his Prince, and that his Sovereign is so much concerned with the indignities that were cast upon *Christian* when he became a Pilgrim, that he will look upon all as if done unto himself; and no marvel, for 'twas for the love that he had to his Prince that he ventured as he did.

Christian's King will take Christian's part

I dare say, quoth I, I am glad on't; I am glad for the poor man's sake, for that he now has rest from his labour, and for that he now reapeth the benefit of his Tears with Joy; and for that he has got beyond the Gun-shot of his Enemies, and is out of the reach of them that hate him. I also am glad for that a rumour of these things is noised abroad in this Country; who can tell but that it may work some good effect on some that are left behind? But pray Sir, while it is fresh in my mind, do you hear anything of his Wife and Children? Poor hearts, I wonder in my mind what they do!

SAG. Who! *Christiana* and her sons? They are

Good tidings of Christian's wife and children

like to do as well as did *Christian* himself; for though they all play'd the fool at the first, and would by no means be persuaded by either the tears or entreaties of *Christian,* yet second thoughts have wrought wonderfully with them; so they have packt up, and are also gone after him.

Better and better, quoth I. But what! Wife and Children and all?

SAG. It is true; I can give you an account of the matter, for I was upon the spot at the instant, and was throughly acquainted with the whole affair.

Then, said I, a man it seems may report it for a Truth?

SAG. You need not fear to affirm it, I mean that they are all gone on Pilgrimage, both the good Woman and her four Boys. And being we are, as I perceive, going some considerable way together, I will give you an account of the whole of the matter.

First Part, p. 162

This *Christiana* (for that was her name from the day that she with her Children betook themselves to a Pilgrim's life) after her Husband was gone *over the River,* and she could hear of him no more, her thoughts began to work in her mind. First, for that she had lost her Husband, and for that the loving bond of that relation was utterly broken betwixt them. For you know, said he to me, Nature can do no less but entertain the living with many a heavy cogitation in the remembrance of the loss of loving Relations. This therefore of her Husband did cost her many a tear. But this was not all, for *Christiana* did also begin to consider with herself, whether her unbecoming behaviour towards her Husband was not one cause that she saw him no more, and that in such sort he was taken away from her. And upon this came into her mind by *swarms,* all her unkind, unnatural, and ungodly carriages to her dear Friend; which also clogged her Conscience, and did load her with guilt. She was moreover much broken with calling to remembrance the restless groans, brinish tears, and self-bemoanings

Mark this, you that are churls to your godly relations

of her Husband, and how she did harden her heart against all his entreaties and loving persuasions (of her and her Sons) to go with him; yea, there was not anything that *Christian* either said to her, or did before her all the while that his Burden did hang on his back, but it returned upon her like a flash of lightning, and rent the caul of her Heart in sunder. Specially that bitter outcry of his, *What shall I do to be saved?* did ring in her ears most dolefully.

First Part p. 14

Then said she to her Children, Sons, we are all undone. I have sinned away your Father, and he is gone: he would have had us with him; but I would not go myself, I also have hindred you of Life. With that the Boys fell all into tears, and cried out to go after their Father. Oh! said *Christiana,* that it had been but our lot to go with him, then had it fared well with us, beyond what 'tis like to do now; for tho' I formerly foolishly imagin'd concerning the troubles of your Father, that they proceeded of a foolish Fancy that he had, or for that he was overrun with melancholy Humours; yet now 'twill not out of my mind but that they sprang from another cause, to wit, for that the Light of Light was given him, by the help of which, as I perceive, he has escaped the snares of Death. Then they all wept again, and cried out, O Wo worth the day.

Christiana's dream

The next night *Christiana* had a Dream; and behold she saw as if a broad Parchment was opened before her, in which were recorded the sum of her ways; and the times, as she thought, look'd very black upon her. Then she cried out aloud in her sleep, *Lord have Mercy upon me a Sinner;* and the little Children heard her.

Mark this, this is the quintessence of hell

After this she thought she saw two very ill-favoured ones standing by her Bedside, and saying, *What shall we do with this Woman? for she cries out for Mercy waking and sleeping; if she be suffered to go on as she begins, we shall lose her as we have lost her Husband.* Wherefore we must by one way or other, seek to take her off from the thoughts of what shall be hereafter, else all the World cannot help it but she will become a Pilgrim.

Help against discouragement

Now she awoke in a great sweat, also a trembling was upon her, but after a while she fell to sleeping again. And then she thought she saw *Christian* her Husband in a place of Bliss among many *Immortals,* with an *Harp* in his Hand, standing and playing upon it before one that sat on a Throne with a Rainbow about his Head. She saw also as if he bowed his Head with his Face to the pav'd-work that was under the Prince's feet, saying, *I heartily thank my Lord and King for bringing of me into this Place.* Then shouted a company of them that stood round about, and harped with their Harps; but no man living could tell what they said, but *Christian* and his Companions.

Convictions seconded with fresh tidings of God's readiness to pardon

Next morning when she was up, had prayed to God, and talked with her Children a while, one knocked hard at the door, to whom she spake out, saying, *If thou comest in God's name, come in.* So he said *Amen,* and opened the Door, and saluted her with *Peace be to this house.* The which when he had done, he said, *Christiana,* knowest thou wherefore I am come? Then she blushed and trembled, also her Heart began to wax warm with desires to know whence he came, and what was his errand to her. So he said unto her, My name is *Secret,* I dwell with those that are high. It is talked of where I dwell, as if thou hadst a desire to go thither; also there is a report that thou art aware of the evil thou hast formerly done to thy Husband, in hardening of thy Heart against his way, and in keeping of these thy Babes in their Ignorance. *Christiana,* the Merciful One has sent me to tell thee that he is a God ready to forgive, and that he taketh delight to multiply to pardon offences. He would also have thee know that he inviteth thee to come into his presence, to his Table, and that he will feed thee with the Fat of his house, and with the Heritage of *Jacob* thy Father.

There is *Christian* thy Husband *that was,* with Legions more his Companions, ever beholding that Face that doth minister Life to beholders; and they will all be glad when they shall hear the sound of thy feet step over thy Father's threshold.

Christiana at this was greatly abashed in herself, and bowing her head to the ground, this *Visitor* proceeded and said, *Christiana,* here is also a Letter for thee, which I have brought from thy Husband's King. So she took it and opened it, but it smelt after the manner of the best Perfume, also it was written in letters of Gold. The contents of the Letter was, *That the King would have her do as did* Christian *her Husband; for that was the way to come to his City, and to dwell in his Presence with Joy for ever.* At this the good Woman was quite overcome; so she cried out to her *Visitor, Sir, will you carry me and my Children with you, that we also may go and worship this King?*

Christiana quite overcome

Then said the *Visitor, Christiana, the bitter is before the sweet:* thou must through troubles, as did he that went before thee, enter this Cœlestial City. Wherefore I advise thee to do as did *Christian* thy Husband: Go to the Wicket-gate yonder, over the Plain, for that stands in the head of the way up which thou must go, and I wish thee all good speed. Also I advise that thou put this Letter in thy bosom; that thou read therein to thyself and to thy Children, until you have got it by rote of heart, for it is one of the Songs that thou must sing while thou art in this House of thy Pilgrimage; also this thou must deliver in at the further Gate.

Further instruction to Christiana

Now I saw in my Dream, that this old Gentleman, as he told me this story, did himself seem to be greatly affected therewith. He moreover proceeded and said, So *Christiana* called her Sons together, and began thus to address herself unto them: My Sons, I have as you may perceive, been of late under

Christiana prays well for her journey

much exercise in my Soul about the Death of your Father; not for that I doubt at all of his Happiness, for I am satisfied now that he is well. I have also been much affected with the thoughts of mine own state and yours, which I verily believe is by nature miserable. My carriages also to your Father in his distress, is a great load to my Conscience; for I hardened both my own heart and yours against him, and refused to go with him on Pilgrimage.

The thoughts of these things would now kill me outright, but that for a Dream which I had last night, and but for the encouragement that this stranger has given me this morning. Come my Children, let us pack up and be gone to the Gate that leads to the Cœlestial Country, that we may see your Father, and be with him and his Companions in peace, according to the Laws of that Land.

Then did her Children burst out into tears for joy that the heart of their Mother was so inclined. So their *Visitor* bid them farewell, and they began to prepare to set out for their Journey.

Christiana's new language stuns her old neighbors

But while they were thus about to be gone, two of the women that were *Christiana's* Neighbors, came up to her house and knocked at her door. To whom she said as before, *If you come in God's name, come in.* At this the women were stunned, for this kind of language they used not to hear, or to perceive to drop from the lips of *Christiana.* Yet they came in: but behold they found the good woman a preparing to be gone from her house.

So they began and said, *Neighbor, pray what is your meaning by this?*

First Part, p. 47

Christiana answered and said to the eldest of them, whose name was Mrs. *Timorous,* I am preparing for a Journey. (This *Timorous* was daughter to him that met *Christian* upon the Hill *Difficulty,* and would a had him gone back for fear of the Lions.)

TIM. For what Journey I pray you?

CHRIS. *Even to go after my good Husband.* And with that she fell a weeping.

TIM. I hope not so, good Neighbor, pray for your poor Children's sakes, do not so unwomanly cast away yourself.

Timorous comes to visit Christiana, with Mercy, one of her neighbors

CHRIS. Nay, my Children shall go with me, not one of them is willing to stay behind.

TIM. I wonder in my very heart, what or who has brought you into this mind.

CHRIS. Oh, Neighbor, knew you but as much as I do, I doubt not but that you would go with me.

TIM. Prithee what new knowledge hast thou got, that so worketh off thy mind from thy Friends, and that tempteth thee to go nobody knows where?

Death

CHRIS. Then *Christiana* replied, I have been sorely afflicted since my Husband's departure from me, but specially since he went over the River. But that which troubleth me most, is my churlish carriages to him when he was under his distress. Besides, I am *now* as he was *then;* nothing will serve me but going on Pilgrimage. I was a dreaming last night that I saw him. O that my Soul was with him. He dwelleth in the presence of the King of the Country, he sits and eats with him at his table, he is become a Companion of *Immortals,* and has a House now given him to dwell in, to which the best Palaces on Earth if compared, seem to me to be but as a Dunghill. The Prince of the place has also sent for me, with promise of entertainment if I shall come to him; his messenger was here even now, and has brought me a Letter, which invites me to come. And with that she pluck'd out her Letter, and read it, and said to them, What now will you say to this?

First Part, pp. 15-20

TIM. Oh the madness that has possessed thee and thy Husband, to run yourselves upon such difficulties! You have heard, I am sure, what your Husband did meet with, even in a manner at the first step that he took on his way, as our Neighbor *Obstinate* can yet testify, for he went along with him; yea and *Pliable* too, until they like wise men, were afraid to go any further. We also heard over and above, how he met with the Lions, *Apollyon*, the Shadow of Death, and many other things. Nor is the danger that he met with at *Vanity Fair* to be forgotten by thee; for if he, tho' a Man, was so hard put to it, what canst thou, being but a poor Woman, do? Consider also that these four sweet Babes are thy Children, thy Flesh and thy Bones. Wherefore though thou shouldest be so rash as to cast away thyself, yet for the sake of the Fruit of thy Body keep thou at home.

The reasonings of the flesh

A pertinent reply to fleshly reasonings

But *Christiana* said unto her, tempt me not, my Neighbor. I have now a price put into mine hand to get gain, and I should be a Fool of the greatest size if I should have no heart to strike in with the opportunity. And for that you tell me of all these Troubles that I am like to meet with in the way, they are so far off from being to me a discouragement, that they shew I am in the right. *The bitter must come before the sweet,* and that also will make the sweet the sweeter. Wherefore since you came not to my house *in God's name,* as I said, I pray you to be gone, and not to disquiet me farther.

Mercy's bowels yearn over Christiana

Then *Timorous* also revil'd her, and said to her fellow, Come Neighbor *Mercy,* let us leave her in her own hands, since she scorns our Counsel and Company. But *Mercy* was at a stand, and could not so readily comply with her Neighbor, and that for a twofold reason. First, her bowels yearned over *Christiana:* so she said within herself, If my Neighbor will needs be gone, I will go a little way with her and help her. Secondly, her bowels yearned over her own Soul, (for what *Christiana* had said had taken some hold upon her mind.) Wherefore she said within herself again, I will yet have more talk with this *Christiana,* and if I find Truth and Life in what she shall say, myself with my heart shall also go with her. Wherefore *Mercy* began thus to reply to her Neighbor *Timorous.*

Mercy. Neighbor, I did indeed come with you to see *Christiana* this morning; and since she is, as you see, a taking of her last farewell of her Country, I think to walk this Sun-shine morning a little way with her to help her on the way. But she told her not of her second reason, but kept that to herself.

Timorous forsakes her, but Mercy cleaves to her

Tim. Well, I see you have a mind to go a fooling too, but take heed in time, and be wise: while we are out of danger, we are out; but when we are in, we are in. So Mrs *Timorous* returned to her house, and *Christiana* betook herself to her Journey. But when *Timorous* was got home to her house, she sends for some of her Neighbors, to wit, Mrs *Bat's-eyes,* Mrs *Inconsiderate,* Mrs *Light-mind,* and Mrs *Know-nothing.* So when they came to her house, she falls to telling of the story of *Christiana* and of her intented Journey. And thus she began her tale.

Timorous acquaints her friends what the good Christiana intends to do

Tim. Neighbors, having had little to do this morning, I went to give *Christiana* a visit; and when I came at the door, I knocked, as you know 'tis our custom. And she answered, *If you come in God's name, come in.* So in I went, thinking all was well. But when I came in, I found her preparing herself to depart the Town, she and also her Children. So I asked her what was her meaning by that? And she told me in short, that she was now of a mind to go on Pilgrimage, as did her Husband. She told me also a Dream that she had, and how the King of the Country where her Husband was had sent her an inviting Letter to come thither.

Then said Mrs *Know-nothing,* And what do you think she will go?

Mrs Know-nothing

Tim. Ay, go she will, whatever come on't; and methinks I know it by this, for that which was my great argument to persuade her to stay at home (to wit, the Troubles she was like to meet with in the way) is one great argument with her to put her forward on her Journey. For she told me in so many words, *The bitter goes before the sweet.* Yea, and for as much as it so doth, it makes the sweet the sweeter.

Mrs Bat's-eyes

Mrs *Bat's-eyes.* Oh this blind and foolish woman, said she, will she not take warning by her Husband's afflictions? For my part I see if he was here again, he would rest him content in a whole skin, and never run so many hazards for nothing.

Mrs Inconsiderate

Mrs *Inconsiderate* also replied, saying, Away with such Fantastical Fools from the Town! A good riddance for my part I say of her. Should she stay where she dwells, and retain this her mind, who could live quietly by her? for she will either be dumpish or unneighborly, or talk of such matters as no wise body can abide; wherefore for my part I shall never be sorry for her departure; let her go, and let better come in her room: 'twas never a good World since these whimsical Fools dwelt in it.

Mrs Light-mind

Madame Wanton, she that had like to have been too hard for Faithful in time past

First Part, p. 73

Then Mrs *Light-mind* added as followeth: Come put this kind of talk away. I was yesterday at Madam *Wanton's,* where we were as merry as the maids. For who do you think should be there, but I and Mrs *Love-the-flesh,* and three or four more, with Mr *Lechery,* Mrs *Filth,* and some others. So there we had musick and dancing, and what else was meet to fill up the pleasure. And I dare say my Lady herself is an admirably well-bred Gentle-woman, and Mr *Lechery* is as pretty a fellow.

Discourse betwixt Mercy and good Christiana

By this time *Christiana* was got on her way, and *Mercy* went along with her. So as they went, her Children being there also, *Christiana* began to discourse. And *Mercy,* said *Christiana,* I take this as an unexpected favour, that thou shouldst set foot out of doors with me, to accompany me a little in my way.

Mercy inclines to go

MERCY. Then said young *Mercy* (for she was but young) If I thought it would be to purpose to go with you, I would never go near the Town any more.

CHRIS. Well *Mercy,* said *Christiana,* cast in thy lot with me: I well know what will be the end of our Pilgrimage; my Husband is where he would not but be for all the Gold in the *Spanish* Mines. Nor shalt thou be rejected, though thou goest but upon *my Invitation.* The King who hath sent for me and my Children is one that delighteth in *Mercy.* Besides, if thou wilt, I will hire thee, and thou shalt go along with me as my servant; yet we will have all things in common betwixt thee and me, only go along with me.

Christiana would have her neighbour with her

MERCY. But how shall I be ascertained that I also shall be entertained? Had I this hope but from one that can tell, I would make no stick at all, but would go, being helped by him that can help, tho' the way was never so tedious.

Mercy doubts of acceptance

CHRIS. Well loving *Mercy,* I will tell thee what thou shalt do. Go with me to the *Wicket-gate,* and there I will further enquire for thee; and if there thou shalt not meet with encouragement, I will be content that thou shalt return to thy place. I also will pay thee for thy kindness which thou shewest to me and my Children, in thy accompanying us in our way as thou doest.

Christiana allures her to the gate, which is Christ, and promiseth there to inquire for her

MERCY. Then I will go thither, and will take what shall follow, and the Lord grant that my lot may there fall even as the King of Heaven shall have his heart upon me.

Mercy prays

Christiana then was glad at her heart, not only that she had a Companion, but also for that she had prevailed with this poor Maid to fall in love with her own Salvation. So they went on together, and *Mercy* began to weep. Then said *Christiana,* Wherefore weepeth my Sister so?

Christiana glad of Mercy's company

MERCY. Alas! said she, who can but lament, that shall but rightly consider what a state and condition my poor Relations are in that yet remain in our sinful Town: and that which makes my grief the more heavy is, because they have no Instructor, nor any to tell them what is to come.

Mercy grieves for her carnal relations

Christian's prayers were answered for his relations after he was dead

CHRIS. Bowels becometh Pilgrims; and thou dost for thy Friends as my good *Christian* did for me when he left me; he mourned for that I would not heed nor regard him, but his Lord and ours did gather up his Tears, and put them into his Bottle; and now both I and thou and these my sweet Babes, are reaping the fruit and benefit of them. I hope, *Mercy,* these Tears of thine will not be lost; for the truth hath said, *That they that sow in Tears shall reap in Joy, in singing. And he that goeth forth and weepeth, bearing precious seed, shall doubtless come again with rejoicing, bringing his Sheaves with him.*

Then said *Mercy,*

Let the Most Blessed be my guide,
If 't be his blessed will,
Unto his Gate, unto his Fold,
Up to his Holy Hill.

And let him never suffer me
To swerve or turn aside
From his free grace and holy ways,
Whate'er shall me betide.

And let him gather them of mine,
That I have left behind;
Lord make them pray they may be thine,
With all their heart and mind.

First Part, p. 19

Now my old Friend proceeded and said: But when *Christiana* came up to the Slough of *Dispond,* she began to be at a stand; for said she, This is the place in which my dear Husband had like to have been smothered with mud. She perceived also, that notwithstanding the command of the King to make this place for Pilgrims good, yet it was rather worse than formerly. So I asked if that was true. Yes, said the Old Gentleman, too true, for that many there be that pretend to be the King's Labourers, and that say they are for mending the King's Highway, that bring *dirt* and *dung* instead of *stones,* and so mar instead of mending. Here *Christiana* therefore with her Boys, did make a stand; but said

Their own carnal conclusions, instead of the Word of life

Mercy, Come let us venture, only let us be wary. Then they looked well to the *steps,* and made a shift to get staggeringly over. Mercy the boldest at the Slough of Dispond

Yet *Christiana* had like to a been in, and that not once nor twice. Now they had no sooner got over, but they thought they heard words that said unto them, *Blessed is she that believeth, for there shall be a performance of the things that have been told her from the Lord.*

Then they went on again; and said *Mercy* to *Christiana,* Had I as good ground to hope for a loving reception at the *Wicket-gate* as you, I think no Slough of *Dispond* would discourage me.

Well, said the other, you know your sore, and I know mine; and good friend, we shall all have enough evil before we come at our Journey's end.

For can it be imagined, that the people that design to attain such excellent Glories *as we do,* and that are so envied that Happiness *as we are;* but that we shall meet with what Fears and Scares, with what Troubles and Afflictions, they can possibly assault us with that hate us?

And now Mr. *Sagacity* left me to dream out my Dream by myself. Wherefore me-thought I saw *Christiana* and *Mercy* and the Boys go all of them up to the Gate; to which when they were come, they betook themselves to a short debate about *how* they must manage their calling at the Gate, and what should be said to him that did open to them. So it was concluded, since *Christiana* was the eldest, that she should knock for entrance, and that she should speak to him that did open for the rest. So *Christiana* began to knock, and as her poor Husband did, she *knocked* and *knocked* again. But instead of any that answered, they all thought that they heard as if a Dog came barking upon them; a Dog, and a great one too, and this made the Women and Children afraid: nor durst they for a while to knock any more, for fear the Mastiff should fly upon them. Now therefore they were greatly tumbled up and

Prayer should be made with considera- tion and fear, as well as in faith and hope

First Part, p. 29

The dog, the devil, an enemy to prayer

Christiana and her companions perplexed about prayer

down in their minds, and knew not what to do. Knock they durst not, for fear of the Dog; go back they durst not, for fear that the Keeper of that Gate should espy them as they so went, and should be offended with them. At last they thought of knocking again, and knocked more vehemently than they did at the first. Then said the Keeper of the Gate, Who is there? So the Dog left off to bark, and he opened unto them.

Then *Christiana* made low obeisance and said, Let not our Lord be offended with his Handmaidens, for that we have knocked at this princely Gate. Then said the Keeper, Whence come ye, and what is that you would have?

Christiana answered, We are come from whence *Christian* did come, and upon the same Errand as he; to wit, to be if it shall please you, graciously admitted by this Gate into the way that leads to the Cœlestial City. And I answer, my Lord, in the next place, that I am *Christiana,* once the Wife of *Christian* that now is gotten above.

With that the Keeper of the Gate did marvel, saying, *What is she become now a Pilgrim, that but a while ago abhorred that life?* Then she bowed her head, and said, Yes, and so are these my sweet Babes also.

How Christiana is entertained at the gate

Then he took her by the hand, and let her in, and said also, *Suffer the little Children to come unto me;* and with that he shut up the Gate. This done, he called to a Trumpeter that was above over the Gate, to entertain *Christiana* with shouting and sound of Trumpet for joy. So he obeyed and sounded, and filled the air with his melodious notes.

Now all this while poor *Mercy* did stand without, trembling and crying for fear that she was rejected. But when *Christiana* had gotten admittance for herself and her Boys, then she began to make intercession for *Mercy*.

CHRIS. And she said, My Lord, I have a Companion of mine that stands yet without, that is come hither upon the same account as myself; one that is much dejected in her mind, for that she comes, as she thinks, without sending for, whereas I was sent to by my Husband's King to come.

Christiana's prayer for her friend Mercy

Now *Mercy* began to be very impatient, for each minute was as long to her as an hour, wherefore she prevented *Christiana* from a fuller interceding for her, by knocking at the Gate herself. And she knocked *then* so loud, that she made *Christiana* to start. Then said the Keeper of the Gate, Who is there? and said *Christiana*, It is my Friend.

The delays make the hungering soul the ferventer

So he opened the Gate, and looked out; but *Mercy* was fallen down without in a swoon, for she fainted, and was afraid that no Gate would be opened to her.

Mercy faints

Then he took her by the hand, and said, Damsel, I bid thee arise.

Oh Sir, said she, I am faint; there is scarce life left in me. But he answered, That one once said, *When my soul fainted within me; I rememb'red the Lord, and my prayer came in unto thee, into thy Holy Temple.* Fear not, but stand upon thy feet, and tell me wherefore thou art come.

MERCY. I am come for that unto which I was never invited as my Friend *Christiana* was. Hers was from the King, and mine was but from her: wherefore I fear I presume.

The cause of her fainting

Did she desire thee to come with her to this Place?

MERCY. Yes; and as my Lord sees I am come. And if there is any grace or forgiveness of sins to spare, I beseech that I thy poor Handmaid may be partaker thereof.

Then he took her again by the hand, and led her gently in, and said, I pray for all them that believe on me, by what means soever they come unto me. Then said he to those that stood by, Fetch something, and give it to *Mercy* to smell on, thereby to stay her fainting. So they fetch'd her a bundle of *Myrrh*, and a while after she was revived.

Mark this

And now was *Christiana* and her Boys and *Mercy*, received of the Lord, at the head of the way, and spoke kindly unto by him.

Then said they yet further unto him, We are sorry for our sins, and beg of our Lord his Pardon, and further information what we must do.

I grant Pardon, said he, by word and deed; by word, in the promise of forgiveness; by deed, in the way I obtained it. Take the first from my lips with a kiss, and the other as it shall be revealed.

Christ crucified seen afar off

Now I saw in my Dream that he spake many good words unto them, whereby they were greatly gladded. He also had them up to the top of the Gate, and shewed them by what *deed* they were saved; and told them withal that that sight they would have again as they went along in the way, to their comfort.

Talk between the Christians

So he left them a while in a Summer Parlor below, where they entred into talk by themselves; and thus *Christiana* began: O Lord! how glad am I that we are got in hither.

MERCY. So you well may; but I of all have cause to leap for joy.

CHRIS. I thought one time, as I stood at the Gate (because I had knocked and none did answer) that all our labour had been lost, specially when that ugly Cur made such a heavy barking against us.

MERCY. But my worst fears was after I saw that you was taken into his favour and that I was left behind. Now thought I 'tis fulfilled which is written, *Two women shall be grinding together, the one shall be taken and the other left*. I had much ado to forbear crying out, Undone, undone.

First Part, p. 29

And afraid I was to knock any more; but when I looked up to what was written over the Gate, I took courage. I also thought that I must either knock again, or die; so I knocked, but I cannot tell how, for my spirit now struggled betwixt life and death.

CHRIS. Can you not tell how you knocked? I am

sure your knocks were so earnest, that the very sound of them made me start; I thought I never heard such knocking in all my life; I thought you would a come in by violent hands, or a took the Kingdom by storm.

Christiana thinks her companion prays better than she

MERCY. Alas, to be in my case, who that so was could but a done so? You saw that the Door was shut upon me, and that there was a most cruel Dog thereabout. Who, I say, that was so faint-hearted as I, that would not have knocked with all their might? But pray what said my Lord to my rudeness? was he not angry with me?

CHRIS. When he heard your lumbering noise, he gave a wonderful innocent smile; I believe what you did pleased him well enough, for he shewed no sign to the contrary. But I marvel in my heart why he keeps such a Dog; had I known that afore, I fear I should not have had heart enough to a ventured myself in this manner. But now we are in, we are in, and I am glad with all my heart.

Christ pleased with loud and restless praises

If the soul at first did know all it should meet with in its journey to heaven, it would hardly ever set out

MERCY. I will ask if you please next time he comes down, why he keeps such a filthy Cur in his yard; I hope he will not take it amiss.

Ay do, said the Children, and persuade him to hang him, for we are afraid he will bite us when we go hence.

The children are afraid of the dog

So at last he came down to them again, and *Mercy* fell to the ground on her face before him and worshipped, and said, Let my Lord accept of the sacrifice of Praise which I now offer unto him with the calves of my lips.

So he said unto her, *Peace be to thee, stand up.* But she continued upon her face and said, *Righteous art thou O Lord when I plead with thee, yet let me talk with thee of thy Judgments.* Wherefore dost thou keep so cruel a Dog in thy yard, at the sight of which such Women and Children as we are ready to fly from thy Gate for fear?

Mercy expostulates about the dog

He answered and said, That Dog has another owner; he also is kept close in another man's ground

Devil

only my Pilgrims hear his barking; he belongs to the Castle which you see there at a distance, but can come up to the walls of this place. He has frighted many an honest Pilgrim from worse to better, by the great voice of his roaring. Indeed he that owneth him doth not keep him of any good will to me or mine, but with intent to keep the Pilgrims from coming to me, and that they may be afraid to knock at this Gate for entrance. Sometimes also he has broken out, and has *worried* some that I love; but I take all at present patiently. I also give my Pilgrims timely help, so they are not delivered up to his power, to do to them what his doggish nature would prompt him to. But what! my purchased one, I tro, hadst thou known never so much beforehand, thou wouldest not have been afraid of a Dog.

First Part, p. 30

A check to the carnal fear of the pilgrims

The Beggars that go from Door to Door, will, rather than they will lose a supposed Alms, run the hazard of the bawling barking and biting too of a Dog; and shall a Dog, a Dog in another man's yard, a Dog whose barking I turn to the profit of Pilgrims, keep any from coming to me? I deliver them from the Lions, their Darling from the power of the Dog.

Christians, when wise enough, acquiesce in the wisdom of their Lord

MERCY. Then said *Mercy,* I confess my ignorance; I spake what I understood not; I acknowledge that thou doest all things well.

CHRIS. Then *Christiana* began to talk of their Journey, and to enquire after the way. So he fed them, and washed their feet, and set them in the way of his steps, according as he had dealt with her Husband before. So I saw in my Dream that they walk'd on their way, and had the weather very comfortable to them.

First Part, p. 32

Then *Christiana* began to sing, saying,

Bless'd be the Day that I began
A Pilgrim for to be;
And blessed also be that man
That thereto moved me.

'Tis true, 'twas long ere I began
To seek to live *for ever:*
But now I run fast as I can;
'Tis better late than never.

Our Tears to Joy, our Fears to Faith,
Are turned, as we see,
Thus our beginning (as one saith,)
Shews what our end will be.

Now there was, on the other side of the Wall that fenced in the way up which *Christiana* and her Companions were to go, a Garden, and that Garden belonged to him whose was that *barking Dog* of whom mention was made before. And some of the Fruit-Trees that grew in that Garden shot their branches over the Wall; and being mellow, they that found them did gather them up, and oft eat of them to their hurt. So *Christiana's* Boys, as Boys are apt to do, being pleas'd with the trees, and with the Fruit that did hang thereon, did plash[1] them, and began to eat. Their mother did also chide them for so doing, but still the Boys went on.

The devil's garden

The children eat of the enemy's fruit

Well, said she, my Sons, you transgress, for that Fruit is none of ours; but she did not know that they did belong to the Enemy; I'll warrant you if she had, she would a been ready to die for fear. But that passed, and they went on their way. Now by that they were gone about two bow-shots from the place that let them into the way, they espied two very *ill-favoured ones* coming down apace to meet them. With that *Christiana* and *Mercy* her Friend covered themselves with their Vails, and so kept on their Journey; the Children also went on before, so that at last they met together. Then they that came down to meet them, came just up to the Women as if they would embrace them; but *Christiana* said, Stand back, or go peaceably by as you should. Yet these two, as men that are deaf, regarded not *Christiana's* words, but began to lay hands upon them. At that *Christiana*

Two ill-favoured ones

They assault Christiana

The pilgrims struggle with them

[1] Bend them down with sticks.

waxing very wroth, spurned at them with her feet. *Mercy* also as well as she could, did what she could to shift them. *Christiana* again said to them, Stand back, and be gone, for we have no money to lose, being Pilgrims as ye see, and such too as live upon the Charity of our Friends.

ILL-FAV. Then said one of the two of the men, We make no assault upon you for your Money, but are come out to tell you, that if you will grant one small request which we shall ask, we will make Women of you for ever.

CHRIS. Now *Christiana* imagining what they should mean, made answer again, We will neither hear, nor regard, nor yield to what you shall ask. We are in haste, cannot stay, our business is a business of Life and Death. So again she and her Companions made a fresh assay to go past them, but they letted them in their way.

ILL-FAV. And they said, We intend no hurt to your lives, 'tis another thing we would have.

She cries out

CHRIS. Ah, quoth *Christiana,* you would have us Body and Soul, for I know 'tis for that you are come; but we will die rather upon the spot, than suffer ourselves to be brought into such snares as shall hazard our well-being hereafter. And with that they both shrieked out, and cried, Murder, murder: and so put themselves under those Laws that are provided for the Protection of Women. But the men still made their approach upon them, with design to prevail against them: they therefore cried out again.

It is good to cry out when we are assaulted

Now they being, as I said, not far from the Gate in at which they came, their voice was heard from where they was, thither. Wherefore some of the House came out, and knowing that it was *Christiana's* tongue they made haste to her relief. But by that they was got within sight of them, the Women was in a very great scuffle, the children also stood crying by. Then did he that came in for their relief call out to the Ruffians, saying, What is that thing that you

The Reliever comes

do? Would you make my Lord's people to transgress? He also attempted to take them, but they did make their escape over the Wall into the Garden of the man to whom the great Dog belonged; so the Dog became their Protector. This *Reliever* then came up to the Women, and asked them how they did. So they answered, We thank thy Prince, pretty well, only we have been somewhat affrighted; we thank thee also for that thou camest in to our help, for otherwise we had been overcome.

The ill ones fly to the devil for relief

RELIEVER. So after a few more words, this *Reliever* said as followeth; I marvelled much when you were entertained at the Gate above, being ye know that ye were but weak Women, that you petitioned not the Lord there for a Conductor; then might you have avoided these troubles and dangers, for he would have granted you one.

The Reliever talks to the women

CHRIS. Alas! said *Christiana*, we were so taken with our present blessing, that dangers to come were forgotten by us; besides, who could have thought that so near the King's Palace there should have lurked such naughty ones? Indeed it had been well for us, had we asked our Lord for one; but since our Lord knew 'twould be for our profit, I wonder he sent not one along with us!

Mark this

REL. It is not always necessary to grant things not asked for, lest by so doing they become of little esteem; but when the want of a thing is felt, it then comes under, in the eyes of him that feels it, that estimate that properly is its due, and so consequently will be thereafter used. Had my Lord granted you a Conductor, you would not neither so have bewailed that oversight of yours in not asking for one as now you have occasion to do. So all things work for good, and tend to make you more wary.

We lose for want of asking for

CHRIS. Shall we go back again to my Lord, and confess our folly, and ask one?

REL. Your confession of your folly I will present him with. To go back again you need not; for in all places where you shall come, you will find no want at all, for in every of my Lord's Lodgings which he has prepared for the reception of his Pilgrims, there is sufficient to furnish them against all attempts whatsoever. But as I said, he will be enquired of by them to do it for them: and 'tis a poor thing that is not worth asking for. When he had thus said, he went back to his place, and the Pilgrims went on their way.

The mistake of Mercy

MERCY. Then said *Mercy,* What a sudden blank is here! I made account we had now been past all danger, and that we should never see sorrow more.

Christiana's guilt

CHRIS. Thy *innocency,* My Sister, said *Christiana* to *Mercy,* may excuse thee much; but as for me, my fault is so much the greater, for that I saw this danger before I came out of the Doors, and yet did not provide for it where provision might a been had. I am therefore much to be blamed.

MERCY. Then said *Mercy,* How knew you this before you came from home? Pray open to me this riddle.

Christiana's dream repeated

CHRIS. Why, I will tell you. Before I set foot out of doors, one night as I lay in my bed, I had a Dream about this; for methought I saw two men as like these as ever the world they could look, stand at my bed's feet, plotting how they might prevent my Salvation. I will tell you their very words. They said ('twas when I was in my Troubles (*What shall we do with this Woman? for she cries out waking and sleeping, for forgiveness: if she be suffered to go on as she begins, we shall lose her as we have lost her Husband.* This you know might a made me take heed, and have provided when provision might a been had.

Mercy makes good use of their neglect of duty

MERCY. Well, said Mercy, as by this neglect we have an occasion ministred unto us to behold our own imperfections, so our Lord has taken occasion thereby to make manifest the riches of his Grace. For he, as we see, has followed us with unasked kindness, and has delivered us from their hands that were stronger than we, of his mere good pleasure.

Talk in the Interpreter's house about Christiana's going on pilgrimage

Thus now when they had talked away a little more time, they drew nigh to an House which stood in the way, which House was built for the relief of Pilgrims; as you will find more fully related in the First Part of these Records of the *Pilgrim's Progress.* So they drew on towards the House (the House of the *Interpreter*); and when they came to the door, they heard a great talk in the House. They then gave ear, and heard, as they thought, *Christiana* mentioned by name. For you must know that there went along, even before her, a talk of her and her Children's going on Pilgrimage. And this thing was the more pleasing to them, because they had heard that she was *Christian's Wife,* that Woman who was some time ago so unwilling to hear of going on Pilgrimage. Thus therefore they stood still and heard the good people within commending her, who they little thought stood at the door. At last *Christiana* knocked as she had done at the Gate before. Now when she had knocked, there came to the door a young Damsel, and opened the door and looked, and behold two Women was there.

She knocks at the door

The door is opened to them by Innocent

DAMSEL. Then said the Damsel to them, With whom would you speak in this place?

CHRIS. *Christiana* answered, We understand that this is a privileged place for those that are become Pilgrims, and we now at this door are such; wherefore we pray that we may be partakers of that for which we at this time are come; for the day, as thou seest, is very far spent, and we are loth to-night to go any further.

DAMSEL. Pray what may I call your name, that I may tell it to my Lord within?

CHRIS. My name is *Christiana;* I was the Wife of that Pilgrim that some years ago did travel this way, and these be his four Children. This Maiden also is my Companion, and is going on Pilgrimage too.

INNOCENT. Then ran *Innocent* in (for that was her name) and said to those within, Can you think who is at the door? There is *Christiana* and her

Joy in the house of the Interpreter that Christiana is turned pilgrim

Children and her Companion, all waiting for entertainment here. Then they leaped for joy, and went and told their Master. So he came to the door, and looking upon her, he said, Art thou that *Christiana* whom *Christian* the Good-man left behind him, when he betook himself to a Pilgrim's life?

CHRIS. I am that Woman that was so hard-hearted as to slight my Husband's Troubles, and that left him to go on in his Journey alone, and these are his four Children; but now I also am come, for I am convinced that no way is right but this.

INTER. Then is fulfilled that which is written of the man that said to his Son, Go work to-day in my Vine-yard; and he said to his Father, I will not; but afterwards repented and went.

CHRIS. Then said *Christiana,* So be it, *Amen.* God make it a true saying upon me, and grant that I may be found at the last of him in peace without spot and blameless.

INTER. But why standest thou thus at the door? Come in, thou Daughter of *Abraham.* We was talking of thee but now, for tidings have come to us before how thou art become a Pilgrim. Come Children, come in; come Maiden, come in. So he had them all into the House.

Old saints glad to see the young ones walk in God's ways

So when they were within, they were bidden sit down and rest them; the which when they had done, those that attended upon the Pilgrims in the House, came into the Room to see them. And one smiled, and another smiled, and they all smiled for joy that *Christiana* was become a Pilgrim. They also looked upon the Boys: they stroked them over the faces with the hand, in token of their kind reception of them. They also carried it lovingly to *Mercy,* and bid them all welcome into their Master's House.

The Significant Rooms

After a while, because Supper was not ready, the *Interpreter* took them into his *significant* Rooms, and shewed them what *Christian, Christiana's* Husband, had seen some time before. Here therefore they saw the Man in the Cage, the Man and his Dream, the Man that cut his way through his Enemies, and the Picture of the biggest of them all, together with the rest of those things that were then so profitable to *Christian*.

First Part, pp. 32-41

This done, and after these things had been somewhat digested by *Christiana* and her company, the *Interpreter* takes them apart again, and has them first into a Room where was a Man that could look no way but downwards, with a Muck-rake in his hand. There stood also one over his head with a Cœlestial Crown in his hand, and proffered him that Crown for his Muck-rake; but the man did neither look up, nor regard, but raked to himself the straws, the small sticks and dust of the floor.

The man with the muck-rake expounded

Then said *Christiana*, I persuade myself that I know something of the meaning of this; for this is a figure of a Man of this World, is it not, good Sir?

INTER. Thou hast said the right said he, and his Muck-rake doth shew his carnal mind. And whereas thou seest him rather give heed to rake up straws and sticks and the dust of the floor, than to what he says that calls to him from above with the Cœlestial Crown in his hand, it is to shew that Heaven is but as a fable to some, and that things here are counted the only things substantial. Now whereas it was also shewed thee that the man could look no way but downwards, it is to let thee know that earthly things when they are with power upon men's minds, quite carry their hearts away from God.

CHRIS. Then said *Christiana*, O deliver me from this Muck-rake.

Christiana's prayer against the muck-rake

INTER. That prayer, said the *Interpreter*, has lain by till 'tis almost rusty. *Give me not Riches*, is scarcely the prayer of one of ten thousand. Straws and sticks and dust with most are the great things now looked after.

With that *Mercy* and *Christiana* wept, and said, It is alas! too true.

When the *Interpreter* had shewed them this, he

had them into the very best Room in the House (a very brave Room it was) so he bid them look round about, and see if they could find anything profitable there. Then they looked round and round, for there was nothing there to be seen but a very great *Spider* on the wall, and that they overlook'd.

MER. Then said *Mercy,* Sir, I see nothing; but *Christiana* held her peace.

Of the spider

INTER. But said the *Interpreter,* Look again; she therefore look'd again and said, Here is not anything but an ugly *Spider,* who hangs by her hands upon the wall. Then said he, Is there but one *Spider* in all this spacious Room? Then the water stood in *Christiana's* eyes, for she was a woman quick of apprehension; and she said, Yes, Lord, there is here more than one. Yea, and *Spiders* whose Venom is far more destructive than that which is in her. The *Interpreter* then looked pleasantly upon her, and said, Thou hast said the truth. This made *Mercy* blush, and the Boys to cover their faces, for they all began now to understand the Riddle.

Talk about the spider

The interpretation

Then said the *Interpreter again, The Spider taketh hold with her hands as you see, and is in King's Palaces.* And wherefore is this recorded, but to shew you, that how full of the Venom of sin soever you be, yet you may by the hand of faith lay hold of and dwell in the best Room that belongs to the King's House above?

CHRIS. I thought, said *Christiana,* of some thing of this, but I could not imagine it all. I thought that we were like *Spiders,* and that we looked like ugly creatures, in what fine Room soever we were; but that by this *Spider,* this venomous and ill-favoured creature, we were to learn *how to act Faith,* came not into my mind. And yet she has taken hold with her hands, as I see, and dwells in the best Room in the House. God has made nothing in vain.

Then they seemed all to be glad, but the water

stood in their eyes; yet they looked one upon another, and also bowed before the *Interpreter.*

He had them then into another Room where was a Hen and Chickens, and bid them observe a while. So one of the Chickens went to the trough to drink, and every time she drank she lift up her head and her eyes towards Heaven. See, said he, what this little Chick doth, and learn of her to acknowledge whence your mercies come, by receiving them with looking up. Yet again, said he, observe and look; so they gave heed and perceived that the Hen did walk in a four-fold method towards her Chickens. 1. She had a *common call.* and that she hath all day long. 2. She had a *special call,* and that she had but sometimes. 3. She had a *brooding note.* And 4. She had an *out-cry.*

Of the hen and chickens

Now said he, compare this Hen to your King, and these Chickens to his obedient ones. For answerable to her, himself has his methods which he walketh in towards his People; by his *common call* he gives nothing; by his *special call* he always has something to give; he has also *a brooding voice* for them that are under his wing; and he has an *out-cry* to give the alarm when he seeth the Enemy come. I chose, my Darlings, to lead you into the Room where such things are, because you are Women, and they are easy for you.

CHRIS. And Sir, said *Christiana,* pray let us see some more. So he had them into the Slaughter-house, where was a Butcher a killing of a Sheep; and behold the Sheep was quiet, and took her death patiently. Then said the *Interpreter,* You must learn of this Sheep to suffer, and to put up wrongs without murmurings and complaints. Behold how quietly she taketh her death, and without objecting she suffereth her skin to be pulled over her ears. Your King doth call you his Sheep.

Of the butcher and the sheep

After this he led them into his Garden, where was great variety of Flowers, and he said, Do you

Of the garden

see all these? So *Christiana* said, Yes. Then said he again, Behold the Flowers are diverse in *stature,* in *quality* and *colour* and *smell* and *vertue,* and some are better than some; also where the Gardener has set them there they stand, and quarrel not with one another.

Of the field

Again, he had them into his Field, which he had sowed with Wheat and Corn; but when they beheld, the tops of all was cut off, only the straw remained. He said again, This ground was dunged and plowed and sowed, but what shall we do with the Crop? Then said *Christiana,* Burn some, and make muck of the rest. Then said the *Interpreter* again, Fruit you see is that thing you look for, and for want of that you condemn it to the fire, and to be trodden under foot of men; beware that in this you condemn not yourselves.

Of the robin and the spider

Then as they were coming in from abroad, they espied a little *Robin* with a great *Spider* in his mouth. So the *Interpreter* said, Look here. So they looked, and *Mercy* wondered; but *Christiana* said, What a disparagement is it to such a little pretty bird as the *Robin-red-breast* is, he being also a bird above many that loveth to maintain a kind of sociableness with man; I had thought they had lived upon crums of bread, or upon other such harmless matter. I like him worse than I did.

The *Interpreter* then replied, This *Robin* is an emblem very apt to set forth some Professors by; for to sight they are as this *Robin,* pretty of *note colour* and *carriage.* They seem also to have a very great love for Professors that are sincere; and above all other to desire to associate with, and to be in their company, as if they could live upon the good man's crums. They pretend also that therefore it is that they frequent the house of the godly, and the appointments of the Lord: but when they are by themselves, as the *Robin,* they can catch and gobble up *Spiders,* they can change their diet, drink Iniquity, and swallow down Sin like water.

So when they were come again into the house, because Supper as yet was not ready, *Christiana* again desired that the *Interpreter* would either shew or tell of some other things that are profitable.

Pray, and you will get at that which yet lies unrevealed

Then the *Interpreter* began and said, *The fatter the Sow is, the more she desires the Mire; the fatter the Ox is, the more gamesomely he goes to the slaughter; and the more healthy the lusty man is, the more prone he is unto evil.*

There is a desire in Woman to go neat and fine and it is a comely thing to be adorned with that that in God's sight is of great price.

'Tis easier watching a night or two, than to sit up a whole year together; so 'tis easier for one to begin to profess well, than to hold out as he should to the end.

Every Ship-master when in a Storm, will willingly cast that overboard that is of the smallest value in the vessel; but who will throw the best out first? None but he that feareth not God.

One Leak will sink a ship, and one sin will *destroy a Sinner.*

He that forgets his Friend is ungrateful unto him, but he that forgets his Saviour is unmerciful to himself.

He that lives in Sin, and looks for Happiness hereafter, is like him that soweth Cockle, and thinks to fill his Barn with Wheat or Barley.

If a man would live well, let him fetch his last day to him, and make it always his Company-keeper.

Whispering and change of thoughts proves that Sin is in the World.

If the World which God sets light by, is counted a thing of that worth with men, what is Heaven which God commendeth?

If the Life that is attended with so many Troubles, is so loth to be let go by us, what is the Life above?

Everybody will cry up the Goodness of Men; but who is there that is, as he should, affected with the goodness of God?

We seldom sit down to meat, but we eat and leave; so there is in Jesus Christ more Merit and Righteousness than the whole World has need of.

Of the tree that is rotten at heart

When the *Interpreter* had done, he takes them out into his Garden again, and had them to a Tree whose *inside* was all rotten and gone, and yet it grew and had Leaves. Then said *Mercy,* What means this? This Tree, said he, whose *outside* is fair, and whose *inside* is rotten, it is to which many may be compared that are in the Garden of God; who with their mouths speak high in behalf of God, but indeed will do nothing for him; whose Leaves are fair, but their heart good for nothing but to be *tinder* for the Devil's *tinder-box.*

They are at supper

Now Supper was ready, the Table spread, and all things set on the board; so they sate down and did eat when one had given thanks. And the *Interpreter* did usually entertain those that lodged with him with Musick at Meals, so the Minstrels played. There was also one that did sing, and a very fine voice he had. His Song was this:

The Lord is only my support,
And he that doth me feed;
How can I then want anything
Whereof I stand in need?

Talk at supper

When the Song and Musick was ended, the *Interpreter* asked *Christiana,* What it was that at first did move her to betake herself to a Pilgrim's life?

A repetition of Christiana's experience

Christiana answered, First, the loss of my Husband came into my mind, at which I was heartily grieved; but all that was but natural affection. Then after that came the Troubles and Pilgrimage of my Husband's into my mind, and also how like a churl I had carried it to him as to that. So guilt took hold of my mind, and would have drawn me into the Pond; but that opportunely I had a Dream of the well-being of my Husband, and a Letter sent me by the King of that Country where my

Husband dwells, to come to him. The Dream and the Letter together so wrought upon my mind, that they forced me to this way.

INTER. But met you with no opposition afore you set out of doors?

CHRIS. Yes, a Neighbor of mine, one Mrs. *Timorous* (she was akin to him that would have persuaded my Husband to go back for fear of the Lions). She all to-befooled[1] me for as she called it my intended desperate adventure; she also urged what she could to dishearten me to it, the hardship and Troubles that my Husband met with in the way: but all this I got over pretty well. But a Dream that I had of two ill-looked ones, that I thought did plot how to make me miscarry in my Journey, that hath troubled me much; yea, it still runs in my mind, and makes me afraid of every one that I meet, lest they should meet me to do me a mischief, and to turn me out of the way. Yea, I may tell my Lord, tho' I would not have everybody know it, that between this and the Gate by which we got into the way, we were both so sorely assaulted, that we were made to cry out Murder, and the two that made this assault upon us were like the two that I saw in my Dream.

Then said the *Interpreter,* Thy beginning is good, thy latter end shall greatly increase. So he addressed himself to *Mercy,* and said unto her, And what moved thee to come hither sweet heart? **A question put to Mercy**

Then *Mercy* blushed and trembled, and for a while continued silent.

INTER. Then said he, Be not afraid, only believe, and speak thy mind.

MERCY. So she began and said, Truly Sir, my want of Experience is that that makes me covet to be in silence, and that also that fills me with fears of coming short at last. I cannot tell of Visions and Dreams as my friend *Christiana* can, nor know **Mercy's answer**

[1] The force of the "to" is intensive.

I what it is to mourn for my refusing of the counsel of those that were good Relations.

INTER. What was it then, dear heart, that hath prevailed with thee to do as thou hast done?

MERCY. Why, when our friend here was packing up to be gone from our Town, I and another went accidently to see her. So we knocked at the door and went in. When we were within and seeing what she was doing, we asked what was her meaning. She said she was sent for to go to her Husband; and then she up and told us how she had seen him in a Dream, dwelling in a curious place among *Immortals*, wearing a Crown, playing upon a Harp, eating and drinking at his Prince's Table, and singing Praises to him for bringing him hither, *&c.* Now methought while she was telling these things unto us, my heart burned within me; and I said in my heart, If this be true, I will leave my Father and my Mother and the Land of my Nativity, and will, if I may, go along with *Christiana.*

So I asked her further of the truth of these things, and if she would let me go with her; for I saw now that there was no dwelling, but with the danger of ruine, any longer in our Town. But yet I came away with a heavy heart, not for that I was unwilling to come away, but for that so many of my Relations were left behind. And I am come with all the desire of my heart, and will go, if I may, with *Christiana,* unto her Husband and his King.

INTER. Thy setting out is good, for thou hast given credit to the truth. Thou art a *Ruth,* who did for the love she bore to *Naomi* and to the Lord her God, leave Father and Mother and the Land of her Nativity, to come out, and go with a people that she knew not heretofore. *The Lord recompense thy work, and a full reward be given thee of the Lord God of* Israel, *under whose Wings thou art come to trust.*

They address themselves for bed

Now Supper was ended, and Preparation was made for Bed; the Women were laid singly alone, and the Boys by themselves. Now when *Mercy* was in Bed, she could not sleep for joy, for that now her doubts of missing at last were removed further from her than ever they were before. So she lay blessing and praising God who had had such favour for her.

Mercy's good night's rest

The bath Sanctification

In the morning they arose with the Sun, and prepared themselves for their departure; but the *Interpreter* would have them tarry awhile, for said he, you must orderly go from hence. Then said he to the Damsel that at first opened unto them, Take them and have them into the Garden to the Bath, and there wash them, and make them clean from the soil which they gathered by travelling. Then *Innocent* the Damsel took them, and had them into the Garden, and brought them to the Bath; so she told them that there they must wash and be clean, for so her Master would have the Women to do that called at his house, as they were going on Pilgrimage. They then went in and washed, yea they and the Boys and all; and they came out of that Bath, not only sweet and clean, but also much enlivened and strengthened in their joints. So when they came in, they looked fairer a deal than when they went out to the washing.

They wash in it

They are sealed

When they were returned out of the Garden from the Bath, the *Interpreter* took them and looked upon them and said unto them, *Fair as the Moon.* Then he called for the *Seal* wherewith they used to be *sealed* that were washed in his Bath. So the *Seal* was brought, and he set his Mark upon them, that they might be known in the places whither they were yet to go. Now the *Seal* was the contents and sum of the Passover which the Children of *Israel* did eat when they came out from the land of *Egypt,* and the Mark was set between their eyes. This *Seal* greatly added to their beauty, for it was an ornament to their faces. It also added to their gravity, and made their countenances more like them of Angels.

They are clothed

Then said the *Interpreter* again to the Damsel that waited upon these Women, Go into the Vestry and fetch out Garments for these people; so she went and fetched out white Raiment, and laid it down before him; so he commanded them to put it on. *It was fine linen, white and clean.* When the Women were thus adorned, they seemed to be a terror one to the other, for that they could not see that glory each one on herself which they could see in each other. Now therefore they began to esteem each other better than themselves. For you are fairer than I am, said one; and you are more comely than I am, said another. The Children also stood amazed to see into what fashion they were brought.

True humility

The *Interpreter* then called for a Man-servant of his, one *Great-heart,* and bid him take *sword* and *helmet* and *shield;* and take these my Daughters, said he, and conduct them to the house called *Beautiful,* at which place they will rest next. So he took his Weapons and went before them, and the *Interpreter* said, God speed. Those also that belonged to the Family sent them away with many a good wish. So they went on their way and sung,

> This place has been our second stage,
> Here we have heard and seen
> Those good things that from age to age,
> To others hid have been.
> The Dunghill-raker, the Spider, Hen,
> The Chicken too to me
> Hath taught a lesson; let me then
> Conformed to it be.
> The Butcher, Garden, and the Field,
> The Robin and his bait,
> Also the Rotten Tree doth yield
> Me argument of weight,
> To move me for to watch and pray,
> To strive to be sincere,
> To take my Cross up day by day,
> And serve the Lord with fear.

Now I saw in my Dream that they went on, and *Great-heart* went before them; so they went and came to the place where *Christian's* Burden fell off his back and tumbled into a Sepulchre. Here then they made a pause, and here also they blessed God. Now said *Christiana*, it comes to my mind what was said to us at the Gate, to wit, that we should have pardon by *word* and *deed:* by *word*, that is, by the promise; by *deed*, to wit, in the way it was obtained. What the promise is, of that I know something; but what it is to have pardon by deed, or in the way that it was obtained, Mr *Great-heart*, I suppose you know; wherefore if you please let us hear your discourse thereof.

A comment upon what was said at the gate, or a discourse of our being justified by Christ

GREAT-HEART. Pardon by the deed done, is pardon obtained by some one for another that hath need thereof, not by the person pardoned, but in the way, *saith another*, in which I have obtained it. So then to speak to the question more large, the pardon that you and *Mercy* and these Boys have attained, was obtained by another, to wit, by him that let you in at the Gate; and he hath obtain'd it in this double way, he has performed Righteousness to cover you, and spilt Blood to wash you in.

CHRIS. But if he parts with his Righteousness to us, what will he have for himself?

GREAT-HEART. He has more Righteousness than you have need of, or than he needeth himself.

CHRIS. Pray make that appear.

GREAT-HEART. With all my heart; but first I must premise that he of whom we are now about to speak is one that has not his fellow. He has two Natures in one Person, plain to be *distinguished*, impossible to be *divided*. Unto each of these Natures a Righteousness belongeth, and each Righteousness is essential to that Nature; so that one may as easily cause the Nature to be extinct, as to separate its Justice or Righteousness from it. Of these Righteousnesses therefore we are not made partakers, so as that they, or any of them, should be put upon us that we might be made just, and live thereby. Besides these there is a Righteousness which this Person has, as these two Natures are joined in one. And this is not the Righteousness of the *Godhead,* as distinguished from the *Manhood;* nor the Righteousness of the *Manhood,* as distinguished from the *Godhead;* but a Righteousness which standeth in the union of both Natures, and may properly be called, the Righteousness that is essential to his being prepared of God to the capacity of the Mediatory Office which he was to be intrusted with. If he parts with his first Righteousness, he parts with his *Godhead;* if he parts with his second Righteousness, he parts with the purity of his *Manhood;* if he parts with this third, he parts with that perfection that capacitates him to the Office of Mediation. He has therefore another Righteousness, which standeth in performance, or obedience to a revealed will; and that is that he puts upon Sinners, and that by which their sins are covered. Wherefore he saith, *as by one man's disobedience many were made Sinners, so by the obedience of one shall many be made Righteous.*

CHRIS. But are the other Righteousnesses of no use to us?

GREAT-HEART. Yes, for though they are essential to his Natures and Office, and so cannot be communicated unto another, yet it is by vertue of them that the Righteousness that justifies is for that purpose efficacious. The Righteousness of his *Godhead* gives virtue to his Obedience; the Righteousness of his *Manhood* giveth capability to his obedience to justify; and the Righteousness that standeth in the union of these two Natures to his Office, giveth authority to that Righteousness to do the work for which it is ordained.

So then here is a Righteousness that Christ as God has no need of, for he is God without it; here is a Righteousness that Christ as Man has no need of to make him so, for he is perfect Man without it; again, here is a Righteousness that Christ as God-man has no need of, for he is perfectly so without it. Here then is a Righteousness that Christ, as God, as Man, as God-man, has no need of, with reference to himself, and therefore he can spare it; a justifying Righteousness that he for himself wanteth not, and therefore he giveth it away; hence 'tis called *the gift of Righteousness.* This Righteousness, since Christ Jesus the Lord has made himself under the Law, *must* be given away: for the Law doth not only bind him that is under it *to do justly,* but to use Charity. Wherefore he *must,* he *ought* by the Law, if he hath two Coats, to give one to him that hath none. Now our Lord indeed hath two Coats, one for himself, and one to spare; wherefore he freely bestows one upon those that have none. And thus *Christiana,* and *Mercy,* and the rest of you that are here, doth your pardon come by *deed,* or by the work of another man. Your Lord Christ is he that has worked, and has given away what he wrought for to the next poor beggar he meets.

But again, in order to pardon by *deed,* there must something be paid to God as a price, as well as something prepared to cover us withal. Sin has delivered us up to the just curse of a righteous Law; now from this curse we must be justified by way of redemption, a price being paid for the harms we have done; and this is by the Blood of your Lord, who came and stood in your place and stead, and died your death for your transgressions. Thus has he ransomed you from your transgressions by Blood, and covered your polluted and deformed souls with Righteousness. For the sake of which God passeth by you, and will not hurt you when he comes to judge the World.

Christiana affected with this way of redemption

CHRIS. This is brave. Now I see that there was something to be learned by our being pardoned by *word* and *deed.* Good *Mercy,* let us labour to keep this in mind, and my Children, do you remember it also. But Sir, was not this it that made my good *Christian's* Burden fall from off his shoulder, and that made him give three leaps for joy?

How the strings that bound Christian's burden to him were cut

GREAT-HEART. Yes, 'twas the belief of this that cut those strings that could not be cut by other means, and 'twas to give him a proof of the vertue of this, that he was suffered to carry his Burden to the Cross.

CHRIS. I thought so, for tho' my heart was lightful and joyous before, yet it is ten times more lightsome and joyous now. And I am persuaded by what I have felt, tho' I have felt but little as yet, that if the most burdened man in the world was here, and did see and believe as I now do, 'twould make his heart the more merry and blithe.

How affection to Christ is begot in the soul

GREAT-HEART. There is not only comfort, and the ease of a Burden brought to us, by the sight and consideration of these, but an indeared affection begot in us by it; for who can, if he doth but once think that pardon comes, not only by promise but thus, but be affected by the way and means of his redemption, and so with the man that hath wrought it for him?

First Part, p. 41.

CHRIS. True, methinks it makes my heart bleed to think that he should bleed for me. Oh! thou loving One. Oh! thou blessed One. Thou deservest to have me, thou hast bought me: thou deservest to have me all; thou hast paid for me ten thousand times more than I am worth. No marvel that this made the water stand in my Husband's eyes, and that it made him trudge so nimbly on; I am persuaded he wished me with him; but vile wretch that I was, I let him come all alone. O *Mercy,* that thy Father and Mother were here; yea, and Mrs *Timorous* also; nay, I wish now with all my heart, that here was Madam *Wanton* too. Surely, surely, their hearts would be affected; nor could the fear of the one, nor the powerful lusts of the other, prevail with them to go home again, and to refuse to become good Pilgrims.

Cause of admiration

GREAT-HEART. You speak now in the warmth of your affections: will it, think you, be always thus with you? Besides, this is not communicated to every one, nor to every one that did see your Jesus bleed. There was that stood by, and that saw the Blood run from his heart to the ground, and yet were so far off this, that instead of lamenting, they laughed at him; and instead of becoming his Disciples, did harden their hearts against him. So that all that you have, my Daughters, you have by a peculiar impression made by a divine contemplating upon what I have spoken to you. Remember that 'twas told you, that the *Hen* by her common call gives no meat to the *Chickens*. This you have therefore by a special Grace.

To be affected with Christ and with what he has done, is a thing special

Now I saw still in my Dream, that they went on until they were come to the place that *Simple* and *Sloth* and *Presumption* lay and slept in, when *Christian* went by on Pilgrimage. And behold they were hanged up in irons, a little way off on the other side.

Simple, and Sloth, and Presumption hanged, and why

MERCY. Then said *Mercy* to him that was their Guide and Conductor, What are those three men? and for what are they hanged there?

GREAT-HEART. These three men were men of very bad qualities, they had no mind to be Pilgrims themselves, and whosoever they could they hindered. They were for sloth and folly themselves, and whoever they could persuade with, they made so too, and withal taught them to presume that they should do well at last. They were asleep when *Christian* went by, and now you go by they are hanged.

Behold here how the slothful are a sign,
Hung up 'cause holy ways they did decline.
See here too how the child doth play the man,
And weak grow strong when *Great-heart* leads the van.

MERCY. But could they persuade any to be of their opinion?

GREAT-HEART. Yes, they turned several out of the

Their crimes

Who they prevailed upon to turn out of the way

way. There was *Slow-pace* that they persuaded to do as they. They also prevailed with one *Short-wind,* with one *No-heart,* with one *Linger-after-lust,* and with one *Sleepy-head,* and with a young woman her name was *Dull,* to turn out of the way and become as they. Besides they brought up an ill report of your Lord, persuading others that he was a Task-master. They also brought up an evil report of the good Land, saying 'twas not half so good as some pretend it was. They also began to vilify his Servants, and to count the very best of them meddlesome troublesome busy-bodies. Further, they would call the Bread of God *Husks,* the Comforts of his Children *Fancies,* the Travel and Labour of Pilgrims things to no purpose.

CHRIS. Nay, said *Christiana,* if they were such, they shall never be bewailed by me. They have but what they deserve, and I think it is well that they hang so near the High-way that others may see and take warning. But had it not been well if their crimes had been ingraven in some plate of iron or brass, and left here, even where they did their mischiefs, for a caution to other bad men?

GREAT-HEART. So it is, as you well may perceive if you will go a little to the Wall.

MERCY. No, no, let them hang, and their names rot, and their crimes live for ever against them. I think it a high favour that they were hanged afore we came hither, who knows else what they might a done to such poor women as we are? Then she turned it into a Song, saying,

> Now then you three, hang there and be a sign
> To all that shall against the truth combine.
> And let him that comes after fear this end,
> If unto Pilgrims he is not a Friend.
> And thou, my soul, of all such men beware,
> That unto holiness opposers are.

First Part, p. 46

Thus they went on, till they came at the foot of the Hill *Difficulty,* where again their good Friend Mr *Great-heart,* took an occasion to tell them of what happened there when *Christian* himself went by. So he had them first to the Spring. Lo, saith he, this is the Spring that *Christian* drank of before he went up this Hill, and then 'twas clear and good, but now 'tis dirty with the feet of some that are not desirous that Pilgrims here should quench their thirst. Thereat *Mercy* said, And why so envious, tro? But said the Guide, It will do, if taken up, and put into a vessel that is sweet and good; for then the dirt will sink to the bottom, and the water will come out by itself more clear. Thus therefore *Christiana* and her Companions were compelled to do. They took it up, and put it into an earthen pot, and so let it stand till the dirt was gone to the bottom, and then they drank thereof.

It is difficult getting of good doctrine in erroneous times

Next he shewed them the two *by-ways* that were at the foot of the Hill, where *Formality* and *Hypocrisy* lost themselves. And said he, these are dangerous Paths. Two were here cast away when *Christian* came by; and although, as you see, these ways are since stopped up with *chains posts* and a *ditch,* yet there are that will chuse to adventure here, rather than take the pains to go up this Hill.

By-paths, though barred up, will not keep all from going in them

CHRIS. The way of transgressors is hard. 'Tis a wonder that they can get into those ways without danger of breaking their necks.

GREAT-HEART. They will venture; yea, if at any time any of the King's servants doth happen to see them, and doth call unto them, and tell them that they are in the wrong ways, and do bid them beware the danger, then they will railingly return them answer and say, *As for the word that thou hast spoken unto us in the name of the King, we will not hearken unto thee; but we will certainly do whatsoever thing goeth out of our own mouths,* &c. Nay if you look a little farther, you shall see that these ways are made cautionary enough, not only by these *posts* and *ditch* and *chain,* but also by being hedged up; yet they will chuse to go there.

CHRIS. They are idle, they love not to take pains,

The reason why some do choose to go in by-ways

up-hill way is unpleasant to them. So it is fulfilled unto them as it is written, The way of the slothful man is a Hedge of Thorns. Yea, they will rather chuse to walk upon a Snare, than to go up this Hill, and the rest of this way to the City.

The hill puts the pilgrims to it

Then they set forward, and began to go up the Hill, and up the Hill they went; but before they got to the top, *Christiana* began to pant, and said, I dare say this is a breathing Hill. No marvel if they that love their ease more than their souls, chuse to themselves a smoother way. Then said *Mercy,* I must sit down; also the least of the Children began to cry. Come, come, said *Great-heart,* sit not down here, for a little above is the Prince's *Arbor.* Then took he the little Boy by the hand, and led him up thereto.

They sit in the arbor

When they were come to the *Arbor,* they were very willing to sit down, for they were all in a pelting heat. Then said *Mercy,* How sweet is rest to them that labour. And how good is the Prince of Pilgrims to provide such resting-places for them. Of this *Arbor* I have heard much, but I never saw it before. But here let us beware of sleeping; for as I have heard, for that it cost poor *Christian* dear.

First Part, pp. 47, 48

The little boy's answer to the guide, and also to Mercy

Then said Mr *Great-heart* to the little ones, Come my pretty Boys, how do you do? What think you now of going on Pilgrimage? Sir, said the least, I was almost beat out of heart, but I thank you for lending me a hand at my need. And I remember now what my Mother has told me, namely, That the way to Heaven is as up a Ladder, and the way to Hell is as down a Hill. But I had rather go up the Ladder to Life, than down the Hill to Death.

Which is hardest, up hill or down hill?

Then said *Mercy,* But the Proverb is, *To go down the Hill is easy.* But *James* said (for that was his name) The day is coming when in my opinion *going down Hill will be the hardest of all.* 'Tis a good Boy, said his Master, thou hast given her a right answer. Then *Mercy* smiled, but the little Boy did blush.

CHRIS. Come, said *Christiana,* will you eat a bit, a little to sweeten your mouths, while you sit here to rest your legs? For I have here a piece of Pomgranate, which Mr *Interpreter* put in my hand, just when I came out of his doors. He gave me also a piece of an Hony-comb, and a little Bottle of Spirits. I thought he gave you something, said *Mercy,* because he called you a to-side. Yes, so he did, said the other; but *Mercy,* it shall still be, as I said it should, when at first we came from home, thou shalt be a sharer in all the good that I have, because thou so willingly didst become my Companion. Then she gave to them, and they did eat, both *Mercy* and the Boys. And said *Christiana* to Mr *Great-heart,* Sir, will you do as we? But he answered, You are going on Pilgrimage, and presently I shall return: much good may what you have do to you, at home I eat the same every day. Now when they had eaten and drank, and had chatted a little longer, their Guide said to them, The day wears away, if you think good, let us prepare to be going. So they got up to go, and the little Boys went before. But *Christiana* forgat to take her Bottle of Spirits with her, so she sent her little Boy back to fetch it. Then said *Mercy,* I think this is a losing place. Here *Christian* lost his *Roll,* and here *Christiana* left her Bottle behind her. Sir, what is the cause of this? So their Guide made answer and said, The cause is *sleep* or *forgetfulness:* some *sleep* when they should keep *awake,* and some *forget* when they should *remember;* and this is the very cause, why often at the resting-places, some Pilgrims in some things come off losers. Pilgrims should watch, and remember what they have already received under their greatest enjoyment; but for want of doing so, oft-times their Rejoicing ends in Tears, and their Sun-shine in a Cloud: witness the story of *Christian* at this place.

They refresh themselves

Christiana forgets her bottle of spirits

Mark this

First Part, **pp. 47, 48**

When they were come to the place where *Mistrust* and *Timorous* met *Christian* to persuade him to go back for fear of the Lions, they perceived as it were a Stage, and before it towards the Road a broad plate with a Copy of Verses written thereon, and underneath, the reason of raising up of that Stage in that place rendered. The Verses were these:

> Let him that sees this Stage take heed
> Unto his Heart and Tongue;
> Lest if he do not, here he speed
> As some have long agone.

The words underneath the Verses were, *This Stage was built to punish such upon, who through* timorousness *or* mistrust, *shall be afraid to go further on Pilgrimage. Also on this Stage both* Mistrust *and* Timorous *were burned through the Tongue with an hot Iron, for endeavouring to hinder* Christian *in his Journey.*

Then said *Mercy,* This is much like to the saying of the Beloved, *What shall be given unto thee? or what shall be done unto thee, thou false Tongue? Sharp Arrows of the mighty, with coals of Juniper.*

First Part, p. 49

An emblem of those that go on bravely when there is no danger, but shrink when troubles come

So they went on, till they came within sight of the Lions. Now Mr *Great-heart* was a strong man, so he was not afraid of a Lion; but yet when they were come up to the place where the Lions were, the Boys that went before were glad to cringe behind, for they were afraid of the Lions; so they stept back, and went behind. At this their Guide smiled, and said, How now, my Boys, do you love to go before when no danger doth approach, and love to come behind so soon as the Lions appear?

Of Grim the Giant, and of his backing the lions

Now as they went up, Mr *Great-heart* drew his Sword, with intent to make a way for the Pilgrims in spite of the Lions. Then there appeared one, that it seems, had taken upon him to back the Lions; and he said to the Pilgrims' Guide, What is the cause of your coming hither? Now the name of that man was *Grim,* or *Bloody-man,* because of his slaying of Pilgrims, and he was of the race of the Giants.

GREAT-HEART. Then said the Pilgrims' Guide, These Women and Children are going on Pilgrimage, and this is the way they must go, and go it they shall in spite of thee and the Lions.

GRIM. This is not their way, neither shall they go therein. I am come forth to withstand them, and to that end will back the Lions.

Now to say truth, by reason of the fierceness of the Lions, and of the *grim* carriage of him that did back them, this way had of late lain much un-occupied, and was almost all grown over with Grass.

CHRIS. Then said *Christiana,* Tho' the High-ways have been un-occupied heretofore, and tho' the Travellers have been made in time past to walk through by-paths, it must not be so now I am risen, *now I am risen a Mother in* Israel.

GRIM. Then he swore *by the Lions,* but it should, and therefore bid them turn aside, for they should not have passage there.

GREAT-HEART. But their Guide made first his approach unto *Grim,* and laid so heavily at him with his Sword, that he forced him to a retreat.

GRIM. Then said he (that attempted to back the Lions) Will you slay me upon mine own ground?

GREAT-HEART. 'Tis the King's High-way that we are in, and in his way it is that thou hast placed thy Lions; but these Women and these Children, tho' weak, shall hold on their way in spite of thy Lions. And with that he gave him again a downright blow, and brought him upon his knees. With this blow he also broke his Helmet, and with the next he cut off an arm. Then did the Giant roar so hideously, that his voice frighted the Women, and yet they were glad to see him lie sprawling upon the ground. Now the Lions were chained, and so of themselves could do nothing. Wherefore when old *Grim* that intended to back them was dead, Mr *Great-heart* said to the Pilgrims, Come now and follow me, and no hurt shall happen to you from

A fight betwixt Grim and Great-heart

The victory

They pass by the lions the Lions. They therefore went on, but the Women trembled as they passed by them; the Boys also looked as if they would die, but they all got by without further hurt.

They come to the porter's lodge Now then they were within sight of the Porter's Lodge, and they soon came up unto it; but they made the more haste after this to go thither, because 'tis dangerous travelling there in the Night. So when they were come to the Gate, the Guide knocked, and the Porter cried, *Who is there?* But as soon as the Guide had said, *It is I,* he knew his voice, and came down (for the Guide had oft before that come thither as a Conductor of Pilgrims). When he was come down, he opened the Gate, and seeing the Guide standing just before it (for he saw not the Women, for they were behind him) he said unto him, How now, Mr *Great-heart,* what is your business here so late to-night? I have brought, said he, some Pilgrims hither, where by my Lord's commandment they must lodge. I had been here some time ago, had I not been opposed by the Giant that did use to back the Lions; but I after a long and tedious combat with him, have cut him off, and have brought the Pilgrims hither in safety.

Great-heart attempts to go back

PORTER. Will you not go in, and stay till morning?

GREAT-HEART. No, I will return to my Lord to-night.

The pilgrims implore his company still

CHRIS. Oh Sir, I know not how to be willing you should leave us in our Pilgrimage, you have been so faithful and so loving to us, you have fought so stoutly for us, you have been so hearty in counselling of us, that I shall never forget your favour towards us.

MERCY. Then said *Mercy,* O that we might have thy company to our Journey's end. How can such poor Women as we hold out in a way so full of troubles as this way is, without a Friend and Defender?

JAMES. Then said *James,* the youngest of the

Boys, Pray Sir, be persuaded to go with us, and help us, because we are so weak, and the way so dangerous as it is.

GREAT-HEART. I am at my Lord's commandment. If he shall allot me to be your Guide quite through, I will willingly wait upon you. But here you failed at first; for when he bid me come thus far with you, then you should have begged me of him to have gone quite through with you, and he would have granted your request. However at present I must withdraw, and so, good *Christiana, Mercy,* and my brave Children, Adieu.

Help lost for want of asking for

Then the Porter, Mr *Watchful,* asked *Christiana* of her Country, and of her Kindred. And she said, I came from the City of Destruction, I am a Widow woman, and my Husband is dead, his name was *Christian* the Pilgrim. How, said the Porter, was he your Husband? Yes, said she, and these are his Children; and this, pointing to *Mercy,* is one of my Towns-women. Then the Porter rang his bell, as at such times he is wont, and there came to the door one of the Damsels, whose name was *Humble-mind.* And to her the Porter said, Go tell it within that *Christiana* the Wife of *Christian,* and her Children, are come hither on Pilgrimage. She went in therefore and told it. But O what a noise for gladness was there within, when the Damsel did but drop that word out of her mouth.

First Part, p. 50

Christiana makes herself known to the porter; he tells it to a damsel

Joy at the noise of the pilgrims coming

So they came with haste to the Porter, for *Christiana* stood still at the door. Then some of the most grave said unto her, *Come in* Christiana, *come in thou Wife of that good man, come in thou blessed woman, come in with all that are with thee.* So she went in, and they followed her that were her Children and her Companions. Now when they were gone in, they were had into a very large room, where they were bidden to sit down; so they sat down, and the Chief of the house was called to see and welcome the Guests. Then they came in, and understanding who they were, did salute each other

Christians' love is kindled at the sight of one another

with a kiss, and said, Welcome ye Vessels of the Grace of God, welcome to us your Friends.

Now because it was somewhat late, and because the Pilgrims were weary with their Journey, and also made faint with the sight of the Fight and of the terrible Lions, therefore they desired as soon as might be, to prepare to go to rest. Nay, said those of the Family, refresh yourselves first with a morsel of Meat. For they had prepared for them a Lamb, with the accustomed Sauce belonging thereto; for the Porter had heard before of their coming, and had told it to them within. So when they had supped, and ended their Prayer with a Psalm, they desired they might go to rest. But let us, said *Christiana,* if we may be so bold as to chuse, be in that Chamber that was my Husband's when he was here. So they had them up thither, and they lay all in a room. When they were at rest, *Christiana* and *Mercy* entred into discourse about things that were convenient.

First Part, p. 57

Christ's bosom is for all pilgrims

CHRIS. Little did I think once, that when my Husband went on Pilgrimage, I should ever a followed.

MERCY. And you as little thought of lying in his Bed and in his Chamber to rest, as you do now.

CHRIS. And much less did I ever think of seeing his face with comfort, and of worshipping the Lord the King with him, and yet now I believe I shall.

MERCY. Hark, don't you hear a noise?

Music

CHRIS. Yes, 'tis as I believe, a noise of Musick for joy that we are here.

MERCY. Wonderful! Musick in the House, Musick in the Heart, and Musick also in Heaven, for joy that we are here.

Thus they talked awhile, and then betook themselves to sleep. So in the morning, when they were awake, *Christiana* said to *Mercy:*

Mercy did laugh in her sleep

CHRIS. What was the matter that you did laugh in your sleep to-night. I suppose you was in a Dream.

MERCY. So I was, and a sweet Dream it was, but are you sure I laughed?

CHRIS. Yes, you laughed heartily; but prithee *Mercy,* tell me thy dream.

MERCY. I was a dreamed that I sat all alone in a solitary place, and was bemoaning of the hardness of my Heart.

Mercy's dream

Now I had not sat there long, but methought many were gathered about me, to see me, and to hear what it was that I said. So they hearkened, and I went on bemoaning the hardness of my Heart. At this some of them laughed at me, some called me Fool, and some began to thrust me about. With that, methought I looked up, and saw one coming with Wings towards me. So he came directly to me, and said, *Mercy,* what aileth thee? Now when he had heard me make my complaint, he said, *Peace be to thee.* He also wiped mine eyes with his Handkerchief, and clad me in Silver and Gold: he put a Chain about my Neck, and Ear-rings in mine Ears, and a beautiful Crown upon my Head. Then he took me by the Hand, and said *Mercy,* come after me. So he went up, and I followed, till we came at a Golden Gate. Then he knocked; and when they within had opened, the man went in, and I followed him up to a Throne, upon which one sat, and he said to me, *Welcome Daughter.* The place looked bright and twinkling like the Stars, or rather like the Sun, and I thought that I saw your Husband there. So I awoke from my Dream. But did I laugh?

What her dream was

CHRIS. Laugh: ay, and well you might, to see yourself so well. For you must give me leave to tell you, that I believe it was a good Dream, and that as you have begun to find the first part true, so you shall find the second at last. *God speaks once, yea twice, yet man perceiveth it not. In a Dream, in a Vision of the night, when deep sleep falleth upon men, in slumbring upon the bed.* We need not, when a-bed, lie awake to talk with God.

He can visit us while we sleep, and cause us then to hear his voice. Our heart oft-times wakes when we sleep; and God can speak to that, either by words, by Proverbs, by Signs and Similitudes, as well as if one was awake.

Mercy glad of her dream

MERCY. Well, I am glad of my Dream, for I hope ere long to see it fulfilled, to the making of me laugh again.

CHRIS. I think it is now high time to rise, and to know what we must do.

MERCY. Pray, if they invite us to stay a while, let us willingly accept of the proffer. I am the willinger to stay a while here, to grow better acquainted with these Maids. Methinks *Prudence Piety* and *Charity* have very comely and sober countenances.

CHRIS. We shall see what they will do. So when they were up and ready, they came down. And they asked one another of their rest, and if it was comfortable or not.

MERCY. Very good, said *Mercy;* it was one of the best night's Lodging that ever I had in my life.

They stay here some time

Then said *Prudence* and *Piety,* If you will be persuaded to stay here a while, you shall have what the house will afford.

Prudence desires to catechise Christiana's children

CHAR. Ay, and that with a very good will, said *Charity.* So they consented, and stayed there about a month or above, and became very profitable one to another. And because *Prudence* would see how *Christiana* had brought up her Children, she asked leave of her to catechise them. So she gave her free consent. Then she began at the youngest, whose name was *James.*

James catechised

PRUDENCE. And she said, Come *James,* canst thou tell who made thee?

JAMES. God the Father, God the Son, and God the Holy Ghost.

PRUD. Good Boy. And canst thou tell me who saves thee?

JAMES. God the Father, God the Son, and God the Holy Ghost.

PRUD. Good Boy still. But how doth God the Father save thee?

JAMES. By his Grace.

PRUD. How doth God the Son save thee?

JAMES. By his Righteousness, Death, and Blood, and Life.

PRUD. And how doth God the Holy Ghost save thee?

JAMES. By his Illumination, by his Renovation, and by his Preservation.

Then said *Prudence* to *Christiana,* You are to be commended for thus bringing up your Children. I suppose I need not ask the rest these questions, since the youngest of them can answer them so well. I will therefore now apply myself to the youngest next.

PRUD. Then she said, Come *Joseph* (for his name was *Joseph*) will you let me catechise you?

Joseph catechised

JOSEPH. With all my heart.

PRUD. What is Man?

JOSEPH. A Reasonable Creature, so made by God, as my Brother said.

PRUD. What is supposed by this word *saved?*

JOSEPH. That Man by Sin has brought himself into a state of Captivity and Misery.

PRUD. What is supposed by his being saved by the Trinity?

JOSEPH. That Sin is so great and mighty a Tyrant, that none can pull us out of its clutches but God; and that God is so good and loving to man, as to pull him indeed out of this miserable state.

PRUD. What is God's design in saving of poor Men?

JOSEPH. The glorifying of his Name, of his Grace and Justice, *&c.* and the everlasting Happiness of his Creature.

PRUD. Who are they that must be saved.

JOSEPH. Those that accept of his Salvation.

PRUD. Good Boy, *Joseph,* thy Mother has taught thee well, and thou hast hearkened to what she hath said unto thee.

Then said *Prudence* to *Samuel,* who was the eldest but one.

Samuel catechised

PRUD. Come *Samuel,* are you willing that I should catechise you also?

SAMUEL. Yes, forsooth, if you please.

PRUD. What is Heaven?

SAM. A place and state most blessed, because God dwelleth there.

PRUD. What is Hell?

SAM. A place and state most woful, because it is the dwelling place of Sin, the Devil, and Death.

PRUD. Why wouldst thou go to Heaven?

SAM. That I may see God, and serve him without weariness; that I may see Christ, and love him everlastingly; that I may have that fulness of the Holy Spirit in me that I can by no means here enjoy.

PRUD. A very good Boy also, and one that has learned well.

Matthew catechised

Then she addressed herself to the eldest, whose name was *Matthew;* and she said to him, Come *Matthew,* shall I also catechise you?

MATTHEW. With a very good will.

PRUD. I ask then, if there was ever anything that had a being antecedent to or before God,

MATT. No, for God is eternal, nor is there anything excepting himself that had a being until the beginning of the first day. *For in six days the Lord made Heaven and Earth, the Sea and all that in them is.*

PRUD. What do you think of the Bible?

MATT. It is the Holy Word of God.

PRUD. Is there nothing written therein but what you understand?

MATT. Yes a great deal.

PRUD. What do you do when you meet with such places therein that you do not understand?

MATT. I think God is wiser than I. I pray also that he will please to let me know all therein that he knows will be for my good.

PRUD. How believe you as touching the Resurrection of the Dead?

MATT. I believe they shall rise, the same that was buried, the same in *nature,* tho' not in *corruption.* And I believe this upon a double account. First, because God has promised it. Secondly, because he is able to perform it.

Prudence's conclusion upon the catechising of the boys

Then said *Prudence* to the Boys, You must still hearken to your Mother, for she can learn you more. You must also diligently give ear to what good talk you shall hear from others, for for your sakes do they speak good things. Observe also and that with carefulness, what the Heavens and the Earth do teach you; but especially be much in the meditation of that Book that was the cause of your Father's becoming a Pilgrim. I for my part, my Children, will teach you what I can while you are here, and shall be glad if you will ask me Questions that tend to godly edifying.

Mercy has a sweetheart

Now by that these Pilgrims had been at this place a week, *Mercy* had a visitor that pretended some good will unto her, and his name was Mr *Brisk.* A man of some breeding, and that pretended to Religion, but a man that stuck very close to the World. So he came once or twice or more to *Mercy,* and offered love unto her. Now *Mercy* was of fair countenance, and therefore the more alluring.

Mercy's temper

Her mind also was, to be always busying of herself in doing, for when she had nothing to do for herself, she would be making of Hose and Garments for others, and would bestow them upon them that had need. And Mr *Brisk* not knowing where or how she disposed of what she made, seemed to be greatly taken for that he found her never idle. I will warrant her a good housewife, quoth he to himself.

Mercy inquires of the maids concerning Mr Brisk

Mercy then revealed the business to the Maidens that were of the house, and enquired of them concerning him, for they did know him better than she. So they told her that he was a very busy young man, and one that pretended to Religion, but was as they feared, a stranger to the Power of that which was good.

Nay then, said *Mercy,* I will look no more on him, for I purpose never to have a clog to my soul.

Prudence then replied, That there needed no great matter of discouragement to be given to him, her continuing so as she had began to do for the poor, would quickly cool his courage.

Talk betwixt Mercy and Mr Brisk

So the next time he comes, he finds her at her old work, a making of things for the poor. Then said he, What, always at it? Yes, said she, either for myself or for others. And what canst thou earn a day? quoth he. I do these things, said she, *that I may be rich in Good Works, laying up in store a good Foundation against the time to come, that I may lay hold on Eternal Life.* Why prithee what dost thou with them? said he. Cloath the naked, said she. With that his countenance fell. So he forbore to come at her again. And when he was asked the reason why, he said *that Mercy was a pretty lass, but troubled with ill conditions.*

He forsakes her, and why

Mercy in the practice of mercy rejected; while Mercy in the name of mercy is liked

When he had left her, *Prudence* said, Did I not tell thee, that Mr *Brisk* would soon forsake thee? yea, he will raise up an ill report of thee; for notwithstanding his pretence to Religion, and his seeming love to *Mercy,* yet *Mercy* and he are of tempers so different, that I believe they will never come together.

MERCY. I might a had Husbands afore now, tho' I spake not of it to any; but they were such as did not like my Conditions, though never did any of them find fault with my Person. So they and I could not agree.

PRUD. *Mercy* in our days is little set by any

further than as to its Name; the Practice, which is set forth by thy Conditions, there are but few that can abide.

Mercy's resolution

MERCY. Well, said *Mercy,* if nobody will have me, I will die a Maid, or my Conditions shall be to me as a Husband. For I cannot change my nature, and to have one that lies cross to me in this, that I purpose never to admit of as long as I live. I had a Sister named *Bountiful,* that was married to one of these churls; but he and she could never agree; but because my Sister was resolved to do as she had began, that is, to shew kindness to the poor, therefore her Husband first cried her down at the Cross,[1] and then turned her out of his doors.

How Mercy's sister was served by her husband

PRUD. And yet he was a Professor, I warrant you.

MERCY. Yes, such a one as he was, and of such as he the world is now full: but I am for none of them at all.

Matthew falls sick

Now *Matthew* the eldest Son of *Christiana* fell sick, and his sickness was sore upon him, for he was much pained in his Bowels, so that he was with it at times, pulled as 'twere both ends together. There dwelt also not far from thence, one Mr *Skill,* an antient and well-approved Physician. So *Christiana* desired it, and they sent for him, and he came. When he was entred the room, and had a little observed the Boy, he concluded that he was sick of the Gripes. Then he said to his Mother, What diet has *Matthew* of late fed upon? Diet, said *Christiana,* nothing but that which is wholesome. The Physician answered, This Boy has been tampering with something that lies in his maw undigested, and that will not away without means. And I tell you he must be purged, or else he will die.

Gripes of conscience

The physician's judgment

SAM. Then said *Samuel,* Mother, Mother, what was that which my Brother did gather up and eat, so soon as we were come from the Gate that is at

[1] Gave notice that he would not be responsible for debts contracted by his wife.

Samuel puts his mother in mind of the fruit his brother did eat

the head of this way, You know that there was an Orchard on the left hand, on the other side of the wall, some of the trees hung over the wall, and my Brother did plash and did eat.

CHRIS. True my Child, said *Christiana,* he did take thereof and did eat, naughty Boy as he was. I did chide him, and yet he would eat thereof.

SKILL. I knew he had eaten something that was not wholesome food, and that food, to wit, that Fruit, is even the most hurtful of all. It is the Fruit of *Beelzebub's* Orchard. I do marvel that none did warn you of it; many have died thereof.

CHRIS. Then *Christiana* began to cry, and she said, O naughty Boy, and O careless Mother, what shall I do for my Son?

SKILL. Come, do not be too much dejected; the Boy may do well again, but he must purge and vomit.

CHRIS. Pray Sir, try the utmost of your skill with him whatever it costs.

Potion prepared

SKILL. Nay, I hope I shall be reasonable. So he made him a Purge, but it was too weak. 'Twas said it was made of the Blood of a Goat, the Ashes of a Heifer, and with some of the Juice of Hyssop, *&c.* When Mr *Skill* had seen that that Purge was too weak, he made him one to the purpose, 'twas made *Ex Carne & Sanguine Christi.* (You know Physicians give strange Medicines to their Patients.) And it was made up into Pills, with a Promise or two, and a proportionable quantity of Salt. Now he was to take them three at a time fasting, in half a quarter of a pint of the Tears of Repentance.

The Latin I borrow

The boy loath to take the physick

When this Potion was prepared and brought to the Boy he was loth to take it, tho' torn with the Gripes as if he should be pulled in pieces. Come, come, said the Physician, you must take it. It goes against my stomach, said the Boy. I must have you take it, said his Mother. I shall vomit it up again, said the Boy. Pray Sir, said *Christiana* to Mr *Skill,* how does it taste? It has no ill taste, said the Doctor, and with that she touched one of the Pills with the tip of her tongue. Oh *Matthew,* said she, this Potion is sweeter than Hony. If thou lovest thy Mother, if thou lovest thy Brothers, if thou lovest *Mercy,* if thou lovest thy Life, take it. So with much ado, after a short prayer for the blessing of God upon it, he took it, and it wrought kindly with him. It caused him to purge, it caused him to sleep and rest quietly, it put him into a fine heat and breathing sweat, and did quite rid him of his Gripes.

The mother tastes it, and persuades him

So in little time he got up and walked about with a staff, and would go from room to room, and talk with *Prudence Piety* and *Charity* of his Distemper, and how he was healed.

A word of God in the hand of his faith

So when the Boy was healed, *Christiana* asked Mr *Skill,* saying Sir, what will content you for your pains and care to and of my Child? And he said, You must pay the Master of the College of Physicians, according to rules made in that case and provided.

CHRIS. But Sir, said she, what is this Pill good for else?

SKILL. It is a universal Pill, it is good against all the diseases that Pilgrims are incident to, and when it is well prepared, it will keep good time out of mind.

This pill an universal remedy

CHRIS. Pray Sir, make me up twelve boxes of them, for if I can get these, I will never take other Physick.

SKILL. These Pills are good to prevent diseases, as well as to cure when one is sick. Yea, I dare say it, and stand to it, that if a man will but use this Physick as he should, *it will make him live for ever.* But good *Christiana,* thou must give these Pills no other way but as I have prescribed, for if you do, they will do no good. So he gave unto *Christiana* Physick for herself and her Boys and for *Mercy,* and bid *Matthew* take heed how he eat any more green Plums, and kissed them and went his way.

In a glass of the tears of repentance

It was told you before that *Prudence* bid the Boys, that if at any time they would, they should ask her some Questions that might be profitable, and she would say something to them.

Of physick

MATT. Then *Matthew* who had been sick, asked her, *Why for the most part Physick should be bitter to our palates?*

PRUD. To shew how unwelcome the Word of God and the effects thereof are to a Carnal Heart.

Of the effects of physick

MATT. Why does Physick, if it does good, purge, and cause that we vomit?

PRUD. To shew that the Word, when it works effectually, cleanseth the Heart and Mind. For look, what the one doth to the Body the other doth to the Soul.

Of fire and of the sun

MATT. What should we learn by seeing the Flame of our Fire go upwards? and by seeing the Beams and sweet Influences of the Sun strike downwards?

PRUD. By the going up of the Fire we are taught to ascend to Heaven by fervent and hot desires; and by the Sun his sending his Heat Beams and sweet Influences downwards, we are taught that the Saviour of the world, tho' high, reaches down with his Grace and Love to us below.

Of the clouds

MATT. Where have the Clouds their water?

PRUD. Out of the Sea.

MATT. What may we learn from that?

PRUD. That Ministers should fetch their Doctrine from God.

MATT. Why do they empty themselves upon the Earth?

PRUD. To shew that Ministers should give out what they know of God to the World.

Of the rainbow

MATT. Why is the Rainbow caused by the Sun?

PRUD. To shew that the covenant of God's Grace is confirmed to us in Christ.

MATT. Why do the Springs come from the Sea to us through the Earth?

PRUD. To shew that the Grace of God comes to us through the Body of Christ.

MATT. Why do some of the Springs rise out of the tops of high Hills? Of the springs

PRUD. To shew that the Spirit of Grace shall spring up in *some* that are Great and Mighty, as well as in *many* that are Poor and Low.

MATT. Why doth the Fire fasten upon the Candle-wick? Of the candle

PRUD. To shew that unless Grace doth kindle upon the Heart, there will be no true Light of Life in us.

MATT. Why is the Wick and Tallow and all, spent to maintain the light of the Candle?

PRUD. To shew that Body and Soul and all, should be at the service of, and spend themselves to maintain in good condition, that Grace of God that is in us.

MATT. Why doth the Pelican pierce her own Breast with her Bill? Of the pelican

PRUD. To nourish her young ones with her Blood, and thereby to shew that Christ the blessed so loved his young, his people, as to save them from Death by his Blood.

MATT. What may one learn by hearing the Cock to crow? Of the cock

PRUD. Learn to remember *Peter's* sin, and *Peter's* repentance. The Cock's crowing shews also that Day is coming on; let then the crowing of the Cock put thee in mind of that last and terrible Day of Judgment.

Now about this time their month was out, wherefore they signified to those of the house that 'twas convenient for them to up and be going. Then said *Joseph* to his Mother, It is convenient that you forget not to send to the house of Mr *Interpreter*, to pray him to grant that Mr *Great-heart* should be sent unto us, that he may be our Conductor the rest of our way. Good Boy, said she, I had almost forgot. So she drew up a Petition, and prayed Mr *Watchful* the Porter to send it by some fit man to her good Friend Mr *Interpreter*; who when it was

The weak may sometimes call the strong to prayers

come, and he had seen the contents of the Petition, said to the Messenger, Go tell them that I will send him.

They provide to be gone on their way

When the Family where *Christiana* was, saw that they had a purpose to go forward, they called the whole house together, to give thanks to their King for sending of them such profitable Guests as these. Which done, they said to *Christiana,* And shall we not shew thee something, according as our custom is to do to Pilgrims, on which thou mayest meditate when thou art upon the way? So they took *Christiana* her Children and *Mercy,* into the closet, and shewed them one of the Apples that *Eve* did eat of, and that she also did give to her Husband, and that for the eating of which they both were turned out of Paradise, and asked her what she thought that was? Then *Christiana* said, 'Tis Food or Poison, I know not which. So they opened the matter to her, and she held up her hands and wondered.

Eve's apple

A sight of sin is amazing

Jacob's ladder

Then they had her to a place, and shewed her *Jacob's* Ladder. Now at that time there were some Angels ascending upon it. So *Christiana* looked and looked, to see the Angels go up, and so did the rest of the Company. Then they were going in to another place to shew them something else, but *James* said to his Mother, Pray bid them stay here a little longer, for this is a curious sight. So they turned again, and stood feeding their eyes with this so pleasant a prospect. After this they had them into a place where did hang up a Golden Anchor, so they bid *Christiana* take it down, For, said they, you shall have it with you, for 'tis of absolute necessity that you should, that you may lay hold of that within the vail, and stand steadfast, in case you should meet with turbulent weather. So they were glad thereof. Then they took them, and had them to the Mount upon which *Abraham* our Father had offered up *Isaac* his Son, and shewed them the Altar, the Wood, the Fire, and the Knife, for they remain to be seen to this very day. When they had seen

A sight of Christ is taking

Golden anchor

Of Abraham offering up Isaac

it, they held up their hands and blest themselves, and said, Oh what a man for love to his Master, and for denial to himself was *Abraham*. After they had shewed them all these things, *Prudence* took them into the Dining-room, where stood a pair of excellent Virginals, so she played upon them, and turned what she had shewed them into this excellent song, saying,

Prudence's virginals

Eve's Apple we have shew'd you,
  Of that be you aware;
You have seen *Jacob's* Ladder too,
  Upon which Angels are.
An Anchor you received have,
  But let not these suffice,
Until with *Abr'am* you have gave
  Your best a Sacrifice.

Mr Great-heart come again

Now about this time, one knocked at the door; so the Porter opened, and behold Mr *Great-heart* was there; but when he was come in, what joy was there? For it came now fresh again into their minds, how but a while ago he had slain old *Grim Bloody-man* the Giant, and *delivered* them from the Lions.

He brings a token from his Lord with him

Then said Mr *Great-heart* to *Christiana* and to *Mercy*, My Lord has sent each of you a Bottle of Wine, and also some parched Corn, together with a couple of Pomgranates. He has also sent the Boys some Figs and Raisins to refresh you on your way.

Then they addressed themselves to their Journey, and *Prudence* and *Piety* went along with them. When they came at the gate, *Christiana* asked the Porter if any of late went by? He said, No, only one some time since, who also told me that of late there had been a great robbery committed on the King's Highway, as you go; but he saith the thieves are taken, and will shortly be tried for their lives. Then *Christiana* and *Mercy* were afraid, but *Matthew* said, Mother fear nothing, as long as Mr *Great-heart* is to go with us and to be our Conductor.

Robbery

Then said *Christiana* to the Porter, Sir, I am

Christiana takes her leave of the Porter

much obliged to you for all the kindnesses that you have shewed me since I came hither, and also for that you have been so loving and kind to my Children. I know not how to gratify your kindness. Wherefore pray as a token of my respects to you, accept of this small mite. So she put a gold Angel in his hand, and he made her a low obeisance, and said, Let thy Garments be always white, and let thy Head want no Ointment. Let *Mercy* live and not die, and let not her works be few. And to the Boys he said, Do you fly youthful lusts, and follow after Godliness with them that are grave and wise, so shall you put gladness into your Mother's heart, and obtain praise of all that are sober-minded. So they thanked the Porter and departed.

The Porter's blessing

Now I saw in my Dream that they went forward until they were come to the brow of the Hill, where *Piety* bethinking herself, cried out, Alas! I have forgot what I intended to bestow upon *Christiana* and her Companions, I will go back and fetch it. So she ran and fetched it. While she was gone, *Christiana* thought she heard in a Grove a little way off on the right hand, a most curious, melodious note, with words much like these,

> Through all my Life thy Favour is
> So frankly shew'd to me,
> That in thy House for evermore
> My dwelling-place shall be.

And listening still she thought she heard another answer it, saying,

> For why? The Lord our God is good,
> His Mercy is for ever sure;
> His Truth at all times firmly stood,
> And shall from age to age endure.

So *Christiana* asked *Prudence* what 'twas that made those curious notes? They are, said she, our Country Birds; they sing these notes but seldom, except it be at the Spring, when the Flowers appear, and the Sun shines warm, and then you may hear them all day long. I often, said she, go out to hear them, we also oft-times keep them tame in our house. They are very fine company for us when we are melancholy, also they make the Woods and Groves and Solitary places, places desirous to be in.

By this time Piety was come again; so she said to *Christiana*, Look here, I have brought thee a scheme of all those things that thou hast seen at our house, upon which thou mayest look when thou findest thyself forgetful, and call those things again to remembrance for thy edification and comfort.

Piety bestoweth something on them at parting

Now they began to go down the Hill into the Valley of *Humiliation*. It was a steep Hill, and the way was slippery; but they were very careful, so they got down pretty well. When they were down in the Valley, *Piety* said to *Christiana*, This is the place where *Christian* your Husband met with that foul Fiend *Apollyon*, and where they had that Fight that they had; I know you cannot but have heard thereof. But be of good courage; as long you have here Mr *Great-heart* to be your Guide and Conductor, we hope you will fare the better. So when these two had committed the Pilgrims unto the conduct of their Guide, he went forward and they went after.

First Part, p. 60

GREAT-HEART. Then said Mr *Great-heart*, we need not to be so afraid of this Valley, for here is nothing to hurt us unless we procure it to ourselves. 'Tis true, *Christian* did here meet with *Apollyon*, with whom he also had a sore Combat; but that *fray* was the fruit of those slips that he got in his going down the Hill; for they that get *slips* there, must look for *combats* here. And hence it is that this Valley has got so hard a name; for the common people when they hear that some frightful thing has befallen such a one in such a place, are of an opinion that that place is haunted with some foul Fiend or evil Spirit; when alas it is for the fruit of their doing, that such things do befall them there.

Mr Great-heart at the Valley of Humiliation

First Part, p. 61

This Valley of *Humiliation* is of itself as fruitful

The reason why Christian was so beset here

a place as any the Crow flies over; and I am persuaded if we could hit upon it, we might find somewhere hereabouts, something that might give us an account why *Christian* was so hardly beset in this place.

A pillar with an inscription on it

Then *James* said to his Mother, Lo, yonder stands a Pillar, and it looks as if something was written thereon, let us go and see what it is. So they went, and found there written, *Let* Christian's *slips before he came hither, and the Battles that he met with in this place, be a warning to those that come after.* Lo, said their Guide, did not I tell you that there was something hereabouts that would give intimation of the reason why *Christian* was so hard beset in this place? Then turning himself to *Christiana,* he said, No disparagement to *Christian* more than to many others whose hap and lot his was; for 'tis easier going *up* than *down* this Hill, and that can be said but of few Hills in all these parts of the world. But we will leave the good man, he is at rest, he also had a brave Victory over his Enemy, let him grant that dwelleth above, that we fare no worse when we come to be tried than he.

This valley a brave place

But we will come again to this Valley of *Humiliation.* It is the best and most fruitful piece of ground in all those parts. It is fat ground, and as you see, consisteth much in meadows; and if a man was to come here in the Summer-time, as we do now, if he knew not anything before thereof, and if he also delighted himself in the sight of his eyes, he might see that that would be delightful to him. Behold how green this Valley is, also how beautified with *Lillies.* I have also known many labouring men that have got good estates in this Valley of *Humiliation* (for God resisteth the Proud, but gives more Grace to the Humble) for indeed it is a very fruitful soil, and doth bring forth by handfuls. Some also have wished that the next way to their Father's house were here, that they might be troubled no more with either Hills or Mountains,

Men thrive in the Valley of Humiliation

to go over; but the way is the way, and there's an end.

Now as they were going along and talking, they espied a Boy feeding his Father's Sheep. The Boy was in very mean cloaths, but of a very fresh and well-favoured countenance, and as he sate by himself, he sung. Hark, said Mr *Great-heart*, to what the Shepherd's Boy saith. So they hearkened, and he said,

He that is down needs fear no fall,
He that is low no pride; Phil. iv. 12, 13
He that is humble, ever shall
Have God to be his Guide.
I am content with what I have,
Little be it, or much:
And Lord, contentment still I crave,
Because thou savest such.
Fulness to such a burden is
That go on Pilgrimage; Heb. xiii. 5
Here little, and hereafter Bliss,
Is best from age to age.

Then said their Guide, Do you hear him? I will dare to say, that this Boy lives a merrier life, and wears more of that Herb called *Heart's-ease* in his bosom, than he that is clad in Silk and Velvet; but we will proceed in our discourse.

In this Valley our Lord formerly had his Country-house; he loved much to be here; he loved also to walk these Meadows, for he found the air was pleasant. Besides here a man shall be free from the noise, and from the hurryings of this life. All states are full of Noise and Confusion, only the Valley of *Humiliation* is that empty and solitary place. Here a man shall not be so let and hindred in his Contemplation, as in other places he is apt to be. This is a Valley that nobody walks in, but those that love a Pilgrim's life. And tho' *Christian* had the hard hap to meet here with *Apollyon*, and to enter with him a brisk encounter, yet I must tell you, that in former times men have met with Angels here, have found Pearls here, and have in this place found the words of Life.

Christ, when in the flesh, had his country-house in the Valley of Humiliation

Did I say our Lord had here in former days his Country-house, and that he loved here to walk? I will add, in this place, and to the people that live and trace these Grounds, he has left a yearly revenue to be faithfully payed them at certain seasons, for their maintenance by the way, and for their further encouragement to go on in their Pilgrimage.

SAMUEL. Now as they went on, *Samuel* said to Mr. *Great-heart,* Sir, I perceive that in this Valley my Father and *Apollyon* had their Battle, but whereabout was the Fight, for I perceive this Valley is large?

Forgetful Green

GREAT-HEART. Your Father had that Battle with *Apollyon* at a place yonder before us, in a narrow passage just beyond *Forgetful Green.* And indeed that place is the most dangerous place in all these parts. For if at any time the Pilgrims meet with any brunt, it is when they forget what favours they have received, and how unworthy they are of them. This is the place also where others have been hard put to it; but more of the place when we are come to it; for I persuade myself that to this day there remains either some sign of the Battle, or some Monument to testify that such a Battle there was fought.

Humility a sweet grace

MERCY. Then said *Mercy,* I think I am as well in this Valley as I have been anywhere else in all our Journey, the place methinks suits with my spirit. I love to be in such places where there is no rattling with Coaches, nor rumbling with Wheels. Methinks here one may without much molestation, be thinking what he is, whence he came, what he has done, and to what the King has called him. Here one may think, and break at heart, and melt in one's spirit, until one's eyes become like *the Fishpools of* Heshbon. They that go rightly through this Valley of Baca make it a Well, the Rain that God sends down from Heaven upon them that are here also filleth the Pools. This Valley is that from whence also the King will give to their vineyards, and they that go through it shall sing, as *Christian* did for all he met with *Apollyon*.

GREAT-HEART. 'Tis true, said their Guide, I have gone through this Valley many a time, and never was better than when here.

An experiment of it

I have also been a Conduct to several Pilgrims, and they have confessed the same, *To this man will I look*, saith the King, *even to him that is Poor, and of a Contrite Spirit, and that trembles at my Word.*

Now they were come to the place where the afore mentioned Battle was fought. Then said the Guide to *Christiana* her Children and *Mercy*, This is the place, on this ground *Christian* stood, and up there came *Apollyon* against him. And look, did not I tell you? Here is some of your Husband's Blood upon these stones to this day; behold also how here and there are yet to be seen upon the place some of the shivers of *Apollyon's* broken Darts. See also how they did beat the ground with their feet as they fought, to make good their places against each other, how also with their by-blows they did split the very stones in pieces. Verily *Christian* did here play the man, and shewed himself as stout, as could, had he been there, even *Hercules* himself. When *Apollyon* was beat, he made his retreat to the next Valley, that is called the Valley of the *Shadow of Death*, unto which we shall come anon.

The place where Christian and the fiend did fight.

Some signs of the battle remain

Lo yonder also stands a Monument, on which is engraven this Battle, and *Christian's* Victory, to his fame throughout all ages. So because it stood just on the way-side before them, they stept to it and read the writing, which word for word was this.

A monument of the battle

Hard by here was a Battle fought,
  Most strange, and yet most true;
Christian and *Apollyon* sought
  Each other to subdue.
The Man so bravely play'd the Man,
  He made the *Fiend* to fly;
Of which a Monument I stand,
  The same to testify.

A monument of Christian's victory

First Part, p. 65

When they had passed by this place, they came upon the borders of the *Shadow of Death;* and this Valley was longer than the other; a place also most strangely haunted with evil things, as many are able to testify. But these Women and Children went the better through it because they had daylight, and because Mr *Great-heart* was their Conductor.

Groanings heard

When they were entred upon this Valley, they thought that they heard a groaning as of dead men, a very great groaning. They thought also they did hear words of Lamentation spoken, as of some in extreme Torment. These things made the Boys to quake, the Women also looked pale and wan; but their Guide bid them be of good comfort.

The ground shakes

So they went on a little further, and they thought that they felt the ground begin to shake under them, as if some hollow place was there; they heard also a kind of hissing as of Serpents, but nothing as yet appeared. Then said the Boys, Are we not yet at the end of this doleful place? But the Guide also bid them be of good courage, and look well to their feet, lest haply, said he, you be taken in some Snare.

James sick with fear

Now *James* began to be sick, but I think the cause thereof was fear; so his Mother gave him some of that glass of Spirits that she had given her at the *Interpreter's* house, and three of the Pills that Mr *Skill* had prepared, and the Boy began to revive. Thus they went on till they came to about the middle of the Valley, and then *Christiana* said, Methinks I see something yonder upon the road before us, a thing of such a shape such as I have not seen. Then said *Joseph,* Mother, what is it? An ugly thing, Child, an ugly thing, said she. But Mother, what is it like? said he. 'Tis like I cannot tell what, said she. And now it was but a little way off. Then said she, It is nigh.

The fiend appears

The Pilgrims are afraid

Well, well, said Mr *Great-heart,* Let them that are most afraid keep close to me. So the Fiend came on, and the Conductor met it; but when it was just come to him, it vanished to all their sights. Then remembred they what had been said some time ago, *Resist the Devil, and he will fly from you.*

Great-heart encourages them

They went therefore on, as being a little refreshed; but they had not gone far, before *Mercy* looking behind her, saw, as she thought, something most like a Lion, and it came a great padding pace after; and it had a hollow Voice of Roaring, and at every Roar that it gave it made all the Valley echo, and their hearts to ake, save the heart of him that was their Guide. So it came up, and Mr *Great-heart* went behind, and put the Pilgrims all before him. The Lion also came on apace, and Mr *Great-heart* addressed himself to give him Battle. But when he saw that it was determined that resistance should be made, he also drew back and came no further.

A lion

Then they went on again, and their Conductor did go before them, till they came at a place where was cast up a Pit the whole breadth of the way, and before they could be prepared to go over that, a great Mist and a Darkness fell upon them, so that they could not see. Then said the Pilgrims, Alas! now what shall we do? But their Guide made answer, Fear not, stand still and see what an end will be put to this also. So they stayed there because their path was marr'd. They then also thought that they did hear more apparently the noise and rushing of the Enemies, the fire also and the smoke of the Pit was much easier to be discerned. Then said *Christiana* to *Mercy,* Now I see what my poor Husband went through, I have heard much of this place, but I never was here afore now. Poor man, he went here all alone in the night; he had night almost quite through the way; also these Fiends were busy about him as if they would have torn him in pieces. Many have spoke of it, but none can tell what the Valley of the *Shadow of Death* should mean, until they come in it themselves. *The heart*

A pit and darkness

Christiana now knows what her husband felt

knows its own Bitterness, and a stranger intermeddleth not with its Joy. To be here is a fearful thing.

Great-heart's reply

GREAT-HEART. This is like doing business in great Waters, or like going down into the deep; this is like being in the heart of the Sea, and like going down to the bottoms of the Mountains; now it seems as if the Earth with its bars were about us for ever. *But let them that walk in Darkness and have no Light, trust in the name of the Lord, and stay upon their God.* For my part, as I have told you already, I have gone often through this Valley, and have been much harder put to it than now I am, and yet you see I am alive. I would not boast, for that I am not mine own saviour, but I trust we shall have a good Deliverance. Come let us pray for Light to him that can lighten our Darkness, and that can rebuke not only these, but all the Satans in Hell.

They pray

So they cried and prayed, and God sent Light and Deliverance, for there was now no let in their way, no not there where but now they were stopt with a Pit. Yet they were not got through the Valley; so they went on still, and behold great stinks and loathsome smells, to the great annoyance of them. Then said *Mercy* to *Christiana,* There is not such pleasant being here as at the Gate, or at the *Interpreter's,* or at the house where we lay last.

One of the boys' reply

Oh but, said one of the Boys, it is not so bad to go through here as it is to *abide* here always, and for ought I know, one reason why we must go this way to the house prepared for us, is, that our home might be made the sweeter to us.

Well said *Samuel,* quoth the Guide, thou hast now spoke like a man. Why, if ever I get out here again, said the Boy, I think I shall prize light and good way better than ever I did in all my life. Then said the Guide, We shall be out by and by.

Heedless is slain, and Take-heed preserved

So on they went, and *Joseph* said, Cannot we see to the end of this Valley as yet? Then said the Guide, Look to your feet, for you shall presently be among the Snares. So they looked to their feet and went on, but they were troubled much with the Snares. Now when they were come among the Snares, they espied a man cast into the Ditch on the left hand, with his flesh all rent and torn. Then said the Guide, That is one *Heedless,* that was a going this way, he has lain there a great while. There was one *Take-heed* with him when he was taken and slain, but he escaped their hands. You cannot imagine how many are killed hereabouts, and yet men are so foolishly venturous, as to set out lightly on Pilgrimage, and to come without a Guide. Poor *Christian,* it was a wonder that he here escaped; but he was beloved of his God, also he had a good heart of his own, or else he could never a done it. Now they drew towards the end of the way, and just there where *Christian* had seen the Cave when he went by, out thence came forth *Maul* a Giant. This *Maul* did use to spoil young Pilgrims with Sophistry; and he called *Great-heart* by his name, and said unto him, How many times have you been forbidden to do these things? Then said Mr *Great-heart,* What things? What things? quoth the Giant, you know what things, but I will put an end to your trade. But pray, said Mr *Great-heart,* before we fall to it, let us understand wherefore we must fight. Now the Women and Children stood trembling, and knew not what to do. Quoth the Giant, You rob the Country, and rob it with the worst of thefts. These are but generals, said Mr *Great-heart,* come to particulars, man.

First Part, p. 70

Maul, a giant

He quarrels with Great-heart

Then said the Giant, Thou practisest the craft of a Kidnapper, thou gatherest up Women and Children, and carriest them into a strange Country, to the weakening of my master's Kingdom. But now *Great-heart* replied, I am a servant of the God of Heaven, my business is to persuade sinners to repentance, I am commanded to do my endeavour to turn Men Women and Children, from darkness to light, and from the power of Satan to God; and

God's ministers counted as kidnappers

The giant and Mr Great-heart must fight

if this be indeed the ground of thy quarrel, let us fall to it as soon as thou wilt.

Then the Giant came up, and Mr *Great-heart* went to meet him; and as he went he drew his Sword, but the Giant had a Club. So without more ado they fell to it, and at the first blow the Giant stroke Mr *Great-heart* down upon one of his knees; with that the Women and Children cried out; so Mr *Great-heart* recovering himself, laid about him in full lusty manner, and gave the Giant a wound in his arm; thus he fought for the space of an hour to that height of heat, that the breath came out of the Giant's nostrils, as the heat doth out of a boiling Caldron.

Weak folks' prayers do sometimes help strong folks' cries

Then they sat down to rest them, but Mr *Great-heart* betook him to prayer; also the Women and Children did nothing but sigh and cry all the time that the Battle did last.

The giant struck down

When they had rested them, and taken breath, they both fell to it again, and Mr *Great-heart* with a full blow fetched the Giant down to the ground. Nay hold and let me recover, quoth he. So Mr *Great-heart* fairly let him get up. So to it they went again, and the Giant missed but little of all to breaking Mr *Great-heart's* skull with his Club.

Mr *Great-heart* seeing that, runs to him in the full heat of his spirit, and pierceth him under the fifth rib; with that the Giant began to faint, and could hold up his Club no longer. Then Mr *Great-heart* seconded his blow, and smit the head of the Giant from his shoulders. Then the Women and Children rejoiced, and Mr *Great-heart* also praised God for the deliverance he had wrought.

He is slain, and his head disposed of

When this was done, they among them erected a Pillar, and fastned the Giant's head thereon, and wrote underneath in letters that Passengers might read,

He that did wear this head, was one
That Pilgrims did misuse;
He stopt their way, he spared none,

But did them all abuse;
Until that I *Great-heart* arose,
The Pilgrim's Guide to be;
Until that I did him oppose
That was their Enemy.

Now I saw that they went to the Ascent that was a little way off cast up to be a Prospect for Pilgrims, (that was the place from whence *Christian* had the first sight of *Faithful* his Brother) wherefore here they sat down and rested, they also here did eat and drink and make merry, for that they had gotten deliverance from this so dangerous an Enemy. As they sat thus and did eat, *Christiana* asked the Guide if he had caught no hurt in the Battle. Then said Mr *Great-heart,* No, save a little on my flesh; yet that also shall be so far from being to my determent, that it is at present a proof of my love to my Master and you, and shall be a means by Grace to increase my reward at last.

First Part, p. 71

CHRIS. But was you not afraid, good Sir, when you see him come out with his club?

Discourse of the fight

GREAT-HEART. It is my duty, said he, to distrust mine own ability, that I may have reliance on him that is stronger than all.

CHRIS. But what did you think when he fetched you down to the ground at the first blow?

GREAT-HEART. Why I thought, quoth he, that so my Master himself was served, and yet he it was that conquered at the last.

MATT. When you all have thought what you please, I think God has been wonderful good unto us, both in bringing us out of this Valley, and in delivering us out of the hand of this Enemy; for my part I see no reason why we should distrust our God any more, since he has *now,* and in *such* a place as this, given us such testimony of his love as this.

Matthew here admires goodness

Then they got up and went forward. Now a little before them stood an Oak, and under it when they came to it, they found an old Pilgrim fast

Old Honest asleep under an oak

asleep; they knew that he was a Pilgrim by his Cloaths and his Staff and his Girdle.

So the Guide Mr *Great-heart* awaked him, and the old Gentleman as he lift up his eyes, cried out, What's the matter? who are you? and what is your business here?

GREAT-HEART. Come man be not so hot, here is none but Friends: yet the old man gets up and stands upon his guard, and will know of them what they were. Then said the Guide, My name is *Great-heart,* I am the Guide of these Pilgrims which are going to the Cœlestial Country.

One saint sometimes takes another for his enemy

HONEST. Then said Mr *Honest,* I cry you mercy, I fear'd that you had been of the company of those that some time ago did rob *Little-faith* of his money; but now I look better about me, I perceive you are honester people.

Talk between Great-heart and he

GREAT-HEART. Why what would or could you a done to a helped yourself, if we indeed had been of that company?

HON. Done! why I would a fought as long as breath had been in me; and had I so done, I am sure you could never have given me the worst on't; for a Christian can never be overcome, unless he shall yield of himself.

GREAT-HEART. Well said, Father *Honest,* quoth the Guide, for by this I know thou art a cock of the right kind, for thou hast said the truth.

HON. And by this also I know that thou knowest what true Pilgrimage is, for all others do think that we are the soonest overcome of any.

Whence Mr Honest came

GREAT-HEART. Well now we are so happily met, pray let me crave your name, and the name of the place you came from.

HON. My name I cannot, but I came from the Town of *Stupidity,* it lieth about four degrees beyond the City of *Destruction.*

GREAT-HEART. Oh! are you that Countryman then? I deem I have half a guess of you, your name is Old *Honesty,* is it not, So the old Gentleman blushed, and said, Not *Honesty* in the abstract, but *Honest* is my name, and I wish that my *nature* shall agree to what I am called.

HON. But Sir, said the old Gentleman, how could you guess that I am such a man, since I came from such a place?

GREAT-HEART. I had heard of you before, by my Master, for he knows all things that are done on the Earth; but I have often wondered that any should come from your place, for your Town is worse than is the City of *Destruction* itself.

Stupefied ones are worse than those merely carnal

HON. Yes, we lie more off from the Sun, and so are more cold and senseless; but was a man in a Mountain of Ice, yet if the Sun of Righteousness will arise upon him, his frozen heart shall feel a thaw; and thus it hath been with me.

GREAT-HEART. I believe, it, Father *Honest,* I believe it, for I know the thing is true.

Then the old Gentleman saluted all the Pilgrims with a holy kiss of charity, and asked them of their names, and how they had fared since they set out on their Pilgrimage.

CHRIS. Then said *Christiana,* My name I suppose you have heard of, good *Christian* was my Husband, and these four were his Children. But can you think how the old Gentleman was taken, when she told them who she was! He skipped, he smiled, and blessed them with a thousand good wishes, saying,

Old Honest and Christiana talk

HON. I have heard much of your Husband, and of his travels and Wars which he underwent in his days. Be it spoken to your comfort, the name of your Husband rings over all these parts of the world: his Faith, his Courage, his Enduring, and his Sincerity under all, has made his name famous. Then he turned him to the Boys, and asked them of their names, which they told him. And then said he unto them, *Matthew,* be thou like *Matthew* the Publican, not in *vice* but in *vertue. Samuel,* said he, be thou like *Samuel* the Prophet, a man of

He also talks with the boys.

Old Mr Honest's blessing on them

faith and *prayer. Joseph,* said he, be thou like *Joseph* in *Potiphar's* house, *chaste,* and *one that flies from temptation.* And *James* be thou like *James the Just* and like *James* the Brother of our Lord.

He blesseth Mercy

Then they told him of *Mercy,* and how she had left her Town and her Kindred to come along with *Christiana* and with her Sons. At that the old *honest* man said, *Mercy* is thy name? by Mercy shalt thou be sustained, and carried through all those difficulties that shall assault thee in thy way, till thou shalt come thither where thou shalt look the Fountain of Mercy in the face with comfort.

All this while the Guide Mr *Great-heart* was very much pleased, and smiled upon his Companion.

Talk of one Mr Fearing

Now as they walked along together, the Guide asked the old Gentleman if he did not know one Mr *Fearing,* that came on Pilgrimage out of his parts?

HON. Yes, very well, said he. He was a man that had the root of the matter in him, but he was one of the most troublesome Pilgrims that ever I met with in all my days.

GREAT-HEART. I perceive you knew him, for you have given a very right character of him.

HON. Knew him! I was a great Companion of his; I was with him most an end; when he first began to think of what would come upon us hereafter, I was with him.

GREAT-HEART. I was his Guide from my Master's house to the gates of the Cœlestial City.

HON. Then you knew him to be a troublesome one.

GREAT-HEART. I did so, but I could very well bear it, for men of my calling are oftentimes intrusted with the conduct of such as he was.

HON. Well then, pray let us hear a little of him, and how he managed himself under your conduct.

GREAT-HEART. Why, he was always afraid that he should come short of whither he had a desire to go. Everything frightned him that he heard anybody speak of, that had but the least appearance of opposition in it. I hear that he lay roaring at the Slough of *Dispond* for above a month together, nor durst he, for all he saw several go over before him, venture, tho' they, many of them, offered to lend him their hand. He would not go back again neither. The Cœlestial City, he said, he should die if he came not to it, and yet was dejected at every difficulty, and stumbled at every Straw that anybody cast in his way. Well, after he had lain at the Slough of *Dispond* a great while, as I have told you; one Sun-shine morning, I do not know how, he ventured, and so got over. But when he was over, he would scarce believe it. He had, I think, a Slough of *Dispond* in his mind, a Slough that he carried everywhere with him, or else he could never have been as he was. So he came up to the Gate, you know what I mean, that stands at the head of this way, and there also he stood a good while before he would adventure to knock. When the Gate was opened he would give back, and give place to others, and say that he was not worthy; for for all he gat before some to the Gate, yet many of them went in before him. There the poor man would stand shaking and shrinking, I dare say it would have pitied one's heart to have seen him, nor would he go back again. At last he took the Hammer that hanged on the Gate in his hand, and gave a small Rap or two; then one opened to him, but he shrank back as before. He that opened stept out after him, and said, Thou trembling one, what wantest thou? With that he fell down to the ground. He that spoke to him wondered to see him so faint. So he said to him, Peace be to thee, up, for I have set open the door to thee, come in, for thou art blest. With that he gat up, and went in trembling, and when he was in, he was ashamed to shew his face. Well, after he had been entertained there a while, as you know how the manner is, he

Mr Fearing's troublesome pilgrimage

His behaviour at the Slough of Dispond

His behaviour at the gate

His behaviour at the Interpreter's door

was bid go on his way, and also told the way he should take. So he came till he came to our house. But as he behaved himself at the Gate, so he did at my Master the *Interpreter's* door. He lay thereabout in the cold a good while, before he would adventure to call, yet he would not go back, and the nights were long and cold then. Nay he had a Note of Necessity in his bosom to my Master, to receive him and grant him the comfort of his house, and also to allow him a stout and valiant Conduct because he was himself so *chickin-hearted* a man; and yet for all that he was afraid to call at the door. So he lay up and down thereabouts till, poor man, he was almost starved. Yea so great was his Dejection, that tho' he saw several others for knocking got in, yet he was afraid to venture. At last, I think I looked out of the window, and perceiving a man to be up and down about the door, I went out to him, and asked what he was; but, poor man, the water stood in his eyes; so I perceived what he wanted. I went therefore in and told it in the house, and we shewed the thing to our Lord. So he sent me out again, to entreat him to come in; but I dare say I had hard work to do it. At last he came in, and I will say that for my Lord, he carried it wonderful lovingly to him. There were but few good bits at the Table but some of it was laid upon his trencher. Then he presented the Note, and my Lord looked thereon, and said his desire should be granted. So when he had been there a good while, he seemed to get some heart, and to be a little more comfortable; for my Master, you must know, is one of very tender bowels, specially to them that are afraid; wherefore he carried it so towards him as might tend most to his encouragement. Well, when he had had a sight of the things of the place, and was ready to take his Journey to go to the City, my Lord, as he did to *Christian* before, gave him a Bottle of Spirits, and some comfortable things to eat. Thus we set forward, and

How he was entertained there

He is a little encouraged at the Interpreter's house

I went before him; but the man was but of few words, only he would sigh aloud.

When we were come to where the three fellows were hanged, he said that he doubted that that would be his end also. Only he seemed glad when he saw the Cross and the Sepulchre. There I confess he desired to stay a little to look, and he seemed for a while after to be a little cheery. When we came to the Hill *Difficulty,* he made no stick at that, nor did he much fear the Lions; for you must know that his trouble was not about such things as those, his fear was about his acceptance at last.

He was greatly afraid when he saw the gibbet; cheery when he saw the cross

I got him in at the House *Beautiful,* I think, before he was willing. Also when he was in, I brought him acquainted with the Damsels that were of the place, but he was ashamed to make himself much for company. He desired much to be alone, yet he always loved good talk, and often would get behind the Screen to hear it. He also loved much to see antient things, and to be pondering them in his mind. He told me afterwards that he loved to be in those two houses from which he came last, to wit, at the Gate, and that of the *Interpreter's,* but that he durst not be so bold to ask.

Dumpish at the House Beautiful

When we went also from the House *Beautiful,* down the Hill into the Valley of *Humiliation,* he went down as well as ever I saw man in my life; for he cared not how mean he was, so he might be happy at last. Yea, I think there was a kind of sympathy betwixt that Valley and him, for I never saw him better in all his Pilgrimage than when he was in that Valley.

He went down into, and was very pleasant in the Valley of Humiliation

Here he would lie down, embrace the ground and kiss the very Flowers that grew in this Valley. He would now be up every morning by break of day, tracing and walking to and fro in this Valley.

But when he was come to the entrance of the Valley of the *Shadow of Death,* I thought I should have lost my man; not for that he had any inclination to go back, that he always abhorred. but he

Much perplexed in the Valley of the Shadow of Death

was ready to die for fear. O, the *Hobgoblins* will have me, the *Hobgoblins* will have me, cried he, and I could not beat him out on't. He made such a noise and such an outcry here, that, had they but heard him, 'twas enough to encourage them to come and fall upon us.

But this I took very great notice of, that this Valley was as quiet while he went through it, as ever I knew it before or since. I suppose these Enemies here had now a special check from our Lord, and a command not to meddle until Mr *Fearing* was past over it.

His behaviour at Vanity Fair

It would be too tedious to tell you of all. We will therefore only mention a passage or two more. When he was come at *Vanity Fair,* I thought he would have fought with all the men in the Fair. I feared there we should both have been knock'd o' the head, so hot was he against their fooleries. Upon the Inchanted Ground he was also very wakeful. But when he was come at the River where was no Bridge, there again he was in a heavy case. Now, now, he said, he should be drowned for ever, and so never see that face with comfort that he had come so many miles to behold.

His boldness at last

And here also I took notice of what was very remarkable, the Water of that River was lower at this time than ever I saw it in all my life. So he went over at last, not much above wet-shod. When he was going up to the Gate, Mr *Great-heart* began to take his leave of him, and to wish him a good reception above. So he said, *I shall, I shall.* Then parted we asunder, and I saw him no more.

HON. Then it seems he was well at last.

GREAT-HEART. Yes, yes; I never had doubt about him; he was a man of a choice spirit, only he was always kept very low, and that made his life so burdensome to himself, and so troublesome to others. He was above many tender of sin. He was so afraid of doing injuries to others, that he often would deny himself of that which was lawful, because he would not offend.

HON. But what should be the reason that such a good man should be all his days so much in the dark?

GREAT-HEART. There are two sorts of reasons for it. One is, the wise God will have it so, some must *pipe* and some must *weep*. Now Mr *Fearing* was one that played upon this *Base;* he and his fellows sound the *sackbut,* whose notes are more doleful than the notes of other Musick are; though indeed some say the Base is the Ground of Musick. And for my part I care not at all for that profession that begins not in heaviness of mind. The first string that the Musician usually touches is the Base, when he intends to put all in tune. God also plays upon this string first, when he sets the soul in tune for himself. Only here was the imperfection of Mr *Fearing,* he could play upon no other Musick but this, till towards his latter end.

Reasons why good men are so in the dark

I make bold to talk thus metaphorically, for the ripening of the Wits of young Readers; and because in the Book of the Revelations, the saved are compared to a company of Musicians that play upon their Trumpets and Harps, and sing their Songs before the Throne.

HON. He was a very zealous man, as one may see by what relation you have given of him. Difficulties, Lions or *Vanity Fair,* he feared not at all. 'Twas only Sin Death and Hell that was to him a terror, because he had some doubts about his interest in that Cœlestial Country.

GREAT-HEART. You say right. *Those* were the things that were his troublers, and they, as you have well observed, arose from the weakness of his mind there-about, not from weakness of spirit as to the practical part of a Pilgrim's life. I dare believe that, as the Proverb is, *he could have bit a Fire-brand, had it stood in his way;* but the things with which he was oppressed, no man ever yet could shake off with ease.

A close about him

Christiana's sentence

CHRIS. Then said *Christiana,* This relation of Mr *Fearing* has done me good. I thought nobody had been like me, but I see there was some semblance 'twixt this good man and I, only we differed in two things. His troubles were so great, they brake out, but mine I kept within. His also lay so hard upon him, they made him that he could not knock at the houses provided for Entertainment, but my trouble was always such as made me knock the louder.

Mercy's sentence

MERCY. If I might also speak my heart, I must say that something of him has also dwelt in me; for I have ever been more afraid of the Lake and the loss of a place in *Paradise,* than I have been of the loss of other things. Oh, thought I, may I have the happiness to have a habitation *there,* 'tis enough, though I part with all the world to win it.

Matthew's sentence

MATT. Then said *Matthew,* Fear was one thing that made me think that I was far from having that within me that accompanies Salvation, but if it was so with such a good man as he, why may it not also go well with me?

James's sentence

JAMES. No fears, no Grace, said *James.* Tho' there is not always Grace where there is the fear of Hell, yet to be sure there is no Grace where there is no fear of God.

GREAT-HEART. Well said, *James,* thou hast hit the mark, for the fear of God is the beginning of Wisdom, and to be sure they that want the *beginning* have neither *middle* nor *end.* But we will here conclude our discourse of Mr *Fearing,* after we have sent after him this farewell.

Their farewell about him

Well, Master *Fearing,* thou didst fear
Thy God, and wast afraid
Of doing anything while here
That would have thee betray'd.

And didst thou fear the Lake and Pit?
Would others do so too.
For as for them that want thy wit,
They do themselves undo.

Now I saw that they still went on in their talk; for after Mr *Great-heart* had made an end with Mr *Fearing*, Mr *Honest* began to tell them of another, but his name was Mr *Self-will*. He pretended himself to be a Pilgrim, said Mr *Honest*, but I persuade myself he never came in at the Gate that stands at the head of the way. Of Mr Self-will

GREAT-HEART. Had you ever any talk with him about it?

HON. Yes, more than once or twice, but he would always be like himself, self-willed. He neither cared for man, nor argument, nor yet example; what his mind prompted him to do, that he would do, and nothing else could he be got to. Old Honest had talked with him

GREAT-HEART. Pray what principles did he hold? for I suppose you can tell.

HON. He held that a man might follow the Vices as well as the Vertues of the Pilgrims, and that if he did both he should be certainly saved. Self-will's opinions

GREAT-HEART. How? if he had said 'tis possible for the best to be guilty of the Vices, as well as to partake of the Vertues of Pilgrims, he could not much have been blamed. For indeed we are exempted from no Vice absolutely, but on condition that we watch and strive. But this I perceive is not the thing; but if I understand you right, your meaning is, that he was of that opinion, that it was allowable so to be?

HON. Ay, ay, so I mean, and so he believed and practised.

GREAT-HEART. But what Ground had he for his so saying?

HON. Why, he said he had the Scripture for his Warrant.

GREAT-HEART. Prithee, Mr *Honest*, present us with a few particulars.

HON. So I will. He said to have to do with other men's Wives had been practised by *David*, God's beloved, and therefore he could do it. He said to have more Women than one, was a thing that *Solomon* practised, and therefore he could do it. He said that *Sarah* and the godly Midwives of *Egypt* lied, and so did save *Rahab,* and therefore he could do it. He said that the Disciples went at the bidding of their Master, and took away the owner's Ass, and therefore he could do so too. He said that *Jacob* got the Inheritance of his Father in a way of Guile and Dissimulation, and therefore he could do so too.

GREAT-HEART. High base indeed, and you are sure he was of this opinion?

HON. I have heard him plead for it, bring Scripture for it, bring Argument for it, *&c.*

GREAT-HEART. An opinion that is not fit to be with any allowance in the world.

HON. You must understand me rightly. He did not say that any man might do this, but that those that had the Vertues of those that did such things, might also do the same.

GREAT-HEART. But what more false than such a conclusion? for this is as much as to say, that because good men heretofore have sinned of infirmity, therefore he had allowance to do it of a presumptuous mind. Or if because a Child by the Blast of the Wind, or for that it stumbled at a Stone, fell down and defiled itself in mire, therefore he might wilfully lie down and wallow like a Boar therein. Who could a thought that any one could so far a been blinded by the power of Lust? But what is written must be true, They stumble at the word being disobedient, whereunto also they were appointed.

His supposing that such may have the godly man's Vertues, who addict themselves to their Vices, is also a delusion as strong as the other. 'Tis just as if the Dog should say, I have or may have the qualities of the Child, because I lick up its stinking Excrements. To eat up the Sin of God's People, is no sign of one that is possessed with their Vertues. Nor can I believe that one that is of this opinion can at present have Faith or Love in him. But I know you have made strong objections against him, prithee what can he say for himself?

HON. Why, he says, To do this by way of opinion, seems abundance more honest than to do it, and yet hold contrary to it in opinion.

GREAT-HEART. A very wicked answer, for tho' to let loose the Bridle to Lusts while our opinions are against such things, is bad; yet to sin and plead a toleration so to do, is worse. The one stumbles Beholders accidentally, the other pleads them into the Snare.

HON. There are many of this man's mind, that have not this man's mouth, and *that* makes going on Pilgrimage of so little esteem as it is.

GREAT-HEART. You have said the truth, and it is to be lamented. But he that feareth the King of *Paradise* shall come out of them all.

CHRIS. There are strange opinions in the world, I know one that said, 'Twas time enough to repent when they come to die.

GREAT-HEART. Such are not over wise. That man would a been loth, might he have had a Week to run twenty mile in for his life, to have deferred that Journey to the last hour of that Week.

HON. You say right, and yet the generality of them that count themselves Pilgrims do indeed do thus. I am, as you see, an old man, and have been a traveller in this road many a day, and I have taken notice of many things.

I have seen some that have set out as if they would drive all the world afore them, who yet have in few days died as they in the Wilderness, and so never gat sight of the Promised Land.

I have seen some that have promised nothing at first setting out to be Pilgrims, and that one would a thought could not have lived a day, that have yet proved very good Pilgrims.

I have seen some who have spoke very well of

that again have after a little time run as fast just back again.

I have seen some who have spoke very well of a Pilgrim's life at first, that after a while have spoken as much against it.

I have heard some when they first set out for *Paradise,* say positively there is such a place, who when they have been almost there, have come back again and said there is none.

I have heard some vaunt what they would do in case they should be opposed, that have even at a false alarm fled Faith, the Pilgrim's way, and all.

Fresh news of trouble

Now as they were thus in their way, there came one running to meet them, and said, Gentlemen and you of the weaker sort, if you love Life shift for yourselves, for the Robbers are before you.

First Part, p. 130

Great-heart's resolution

GREAT-HEART. Then said Mr *Great-heart,* They be the three that set upon *Little-faith* heretofore. Well, said he, we are ready for them. So they went on their way. Now they looked at every turning, when they should a met with the Villains; but whether they heard of Mr *Great-heart,* or whether they had some other game, they came not up to the Pilgrims.

Christiana wisheth for an inn

Gaius

They enter into his house

Christiana then wished for an Inn for herself and her Children, because they were weary. Then said Mr *Honest,* There is one a little before us, where a very honorable Disciple, one *Gaius,* dwells. So they all concluded to turn in thither, and the rather because the old Gentleman gave him so good a report. So when they came to the door, they went in, not knocking, for Folks use not to knock at the door of an Inn. Then they called for the Master of the house, and he came to them. So they asked if they might lie there that night?

Gaius entertains them, and how

GAIUS. Yes Gentlemen, if you be true men, for my house is for none but Pilgrims. Then was *Christiana, Mercy* and the Boys the more glad, for that the Innkeeper was a lover of Pilgrims. So they called for Rooms, and he shewed them one for *Christiana* and her Children and *Mercy,* and another for Mr *Great-heart* and the old Gentleman.

GREAT-HEART. Then said Mr *Great-heart,* Good *Gaius,* what hast thou for Supper? for these Pilgrims have come far to-day, and are weary.

GAIUS. It is late, said *Gaius,* so we cannot conveniently go out to seek food, but such as we have you shall be welcome to, if that will content.

GREAT-HEART. We will be content with what thou hast in the house, forasmuch as I have proved thee, thou art never destitute of that which is convenient.

Then he went down and spake to the Cook, whose name was *Taste-that-which-is-good,* to get ready Supper for so many Pilgrims. This done, he comes up again, saying, Come my good Friends, you are welcome to me, and I am glad that I have a house to entertain you; and while Supper is making ready, if you please, let us entertain one another with some good discourse. So they all said, Content.

Gaius's cook

GAIUS. Then said *Gaius,* Whose Wife is this aged Matron? and whose Daughter is this young Damsel?

Talk between Gaius and his guests

GREAT-HEART. The Woman is the Wife of one *Christian* a Pilgrim of former times, and these are his four Children. The Maid is one of her Acquaintance, one that she hath persuaded to come with her on Pilgrimage. The Boys take all after their Father, and covet to tread in his steps; yea, if they do but see any place where the old Pilgrim hath lain, or any print of his foot, it ministreth joy to their hearts, and they covet to lie or tread in the same.

Mark this

GAIUS. Then said *Gaius,* Is this *Christian's* Wife? and are these *Christian's* Children? I knew your Husband's Father, yea, also his Father's Father. Many have been good of this stock, their Ancestors dwelt first at *Antioch. Christian's* Progenitors (I suppose you have heard your Husband talk of them) were very worthy men. They have above any that I know, shewed themselves men of great Vertue

Of Christian's ancestors

and Courage for the Lord of Pilgrims, his ways, and them that loved him. I have heard of many of your Husband's Relations that have stood all trials for the sake of the Truth. *Stephen* that was one of the first of the Family from whence your Husband sprang, was knocked o' the head with Stones. *James,* another of this Generation, was slain with the edge of the Sword. To say nothing of *Paul* and *Peter,* men antiently of the Family from whence your Husband came, there was *Ignatius* who was cast to the Lions, *Romanus* whose flesh was cut by pieces from his bones, and *Polycarp* that played the man in the Fire. There was he that was hanged up in a Basket in the Sun for the Wasps to eat, and he whom they put into a Sack and cast him into the Sea to be drowned. 'Twould be impossible utterly to count up all of that Family that have suffered Injuries and Death for the love of a Pilgrim's life. Nor can I but be glad to see that thy Husband has left behind him four such Boys as these. I hope they will bear up their Father's *name,* and tread in their Father's *steps,* and come to their Father's *end.*

GREAT-HEART. Indeed Sir, they are likely Lads, they seem to chuse heartily their Father's ways.

Advice to Christiana about her boys

GAIUS. That is it that I said, wherefore *Christian's* Family is like still to spread abroad upon the face of the ground, and yet to be numerous upon the face of the earth. Wherefore let *Christiana* look out some Damsels for her Sons, to whom they may be betrothed, *&c.* that the name of their Father and the house of his Progenitors may never be forgotten in the world.

HON. 'Tis pity this Family should fall and be extinct.

GAIUS. Fall it cannot, but be diminished it may; but let *Christiana* take my advice, and that's the way to uphold it.

And *Christiana,* said this Innkeeper, I am glad to see thee and thy friend *Mercy* together here, a lovely couple. And may I advise, take *Mercy* into a nearer Relation to thee. If she will, let her be given to *Matthew* thy eldest Son, 'tis the way to preserve you a Posterity in the earth. So this match was concluded, and in process of time they were married. But more of that hereafter.

Mercy and Matthew marry

Gaius also proceeded and said, I will now speak on the behalf of Women, to take away their Reproach. For as Death and the Curse came into the world by a Woman, so also did Life and Health: *God sent forth his Son, made of a Woman.* Yea, to shew how much those that came after did abhor the act of their Mother, this sex in the Old Testament coveted Children, if happily this or that Woman might be the Mother of the Saviour of the World.

Why women of old so much desired children

I will say again, that when the Saviour was come, Women rejoiced in him before either Man or Angel. I read not, that ever any Man did give unto Christ so much as one Groat, but the Women followed him and ministered to him of their Substance. 'Twas a Woman that washed his Feet with Tears, and a Woman that anointed his Body to the Burial. They were Women that wept when he was going to the Cross, and Women that followed him from the Cross, and that sat by his Sepulchre when he was buried. They were Women that was first with him at his Resurrection-morn, and Women that brought tiding first to his Disciples that he was risen from the Dead. Women therefore are highly favoured, and shew by these things that they are sharers with us in the Grace of Life.

Now the Cook sent up to signify that Supper was almost ready, and sent one to lay the Cloath, the Trenchers, and to set the Salt and Bread in order.

Supper ready

Then said *Matthew*, The sight of this Cloath and of this forerunner of the Supper, begetteth in me a greater Appetite to my food than I had before.

GAIUS. So let all ministring doctrines *to* thee in this life, beget *in* thee a greater desire to sit at the

What to be gathered from laying of the board with the cloth and trenchers

Supper of the great King in his Kingdom; for all Preaching Books and Ordinances here, are but as the laying of the Trenchers and as setting of Salt upon the Board, when compared with the Feast that our Lord will make for us when we come to his House.

So Supper came up, and first a Heave-shoulder and a Wave-breast was set on the Table before them, to shew that they must begin their meal with Prayer and Praise to God. The Heave-shoulder *David* lifted his Heart up to God with, and with the Wave-breast, where his Heart lay, with that he used to lean upon his Harp when he played. These two Dishes were very fresh and good, and they all eat heartily well thereof.

The next they brought up was a Bottle of Wine, red as Blood. So *Gaius* said to them, Drink freely, this is the Juice of the true Vine that makes glad the heart of God and Man. So they drank and were merry.

A dish of milk

The next was a dish of Milk well crumbed. But *Gaius* said, Let the Boys have that, that they may grow thereby.

Of hony and butter

Then they brought up in course a dish of Butter and Hony. Then said *Gaius,* Eat freely of this, for this is good to cheer up and strengthen your Judgments and Understandings. This was our Lord's dish when he was a Child, *Butter and Hony shall he eat, that he may know to refuse the Evil and chuse the Good.*

A dish of apples

Then they brought them up a dish of Apples, and they were very good tasted Fruit. Then said *Matthew,* May we eat Apples, since they were such, by and with which the Serpent beguiled our first Mother?

Then said *Gaius,*

Apples were they with which we were beguil'd,
Yet *sin,* not Apples, hath our souls defil'd.
Apples forbid, if eat, corrupts the Blood;
To eat such when commanded, does us good.

Drink of *his* Flagons, then, thou Church, his Dove,
And eat *his* Apples, who are sick of Love.

Then said *Matthew,* I made the scruple because I a while since was sick with eating of Fruit.

GAIUS. Forbidden Fruit will make you sick, but not what our Lord has tolerated.

While they were thus talking, they were presented with another dish, and 'twas a dish of Nuts. Then said some at the Table, Nuts spoil tender Teeth, specially the Teeth of Children; which when *Gaius* heard, he said,

A dish of nuts

Hard Texts are Nuts (I will not call them cheaters)
Whose Shells do keep their Kernels from the Eaters.
Ope then the Shells, and you shall have the Meat,
They here are brought for you to crack and eat.

Then were they very merry, and sat at the Table a long time, talking of many things. Then said the old Gentleman, My good Landlord, while we are cracking your Nuts, if you please, do you open this Riddle:

A riddle put forth by Old Honest

A man there was, tho' some did count him mad,
The more he cast away the more he had.

Then they all gave good heed, wondring what good *Gaius* would say; so he sat still a while, and then thus replied:

Gaius opens it

He that bestows his Goods upon the Poor,
Shall have as much again, and ten times more.

Joseph wonders

Then said *Joseph,* I dare say Sir, I did not think you could a found it out.

Oh, said *Gaius,* I have been trained up in this way a great while, nothing teaches like experience. I have learned of my Lord to be kind, and have found by experience that I have gained thereby. *There is that scattereth, yet increaseth, and there is that withholdeth more than is meet, but it tendeth to Poverty. There is that maketh himself Rich, yet hath nothing, there is that maketh himself Poor, yet hath great Riches.*

Then *Samuel* whispered to *Christiana* his Mother, and said, Mother, this is a very good man's house, let us stay here a good while, and let my Brother *Matthew* be married here to *Mercy* before we go any further.

The which *Gaius* the Host overhearing said, With a very good will, my Child.

Matthew and Mercy are married

So they stayed there more than a month, and *Mercy* was given to *Matthew* to Wife.

While they stayed here, *Mercy,* as her custom was, would be making Coats and Garments to the Poor, by which she brought up a very good report upon the Pilgrims.

The boys go to bed, the rest sit up

But to return again to our Story. After Supper the Lads desired a Bed, for that they were weary with travelling. Then *Gaius* called to shew them their chamber, but said *Mercy,* I will have them to Bed. So she had them to Bed, and they slept well. But the rest sat up all night, for *Gaius* and they were such suitable Company that they could not tell how to part. Then after much talk of their Lord, themselves, and their Journey, old Mr *Honest,* he that put forth the Riddle to *Gaius,* began to nod. Then said *Great-heart,* What Sir, you begin to be drowsy, come, rub up, now here's a Riddle for you. Then said Mr *Honest,* Let's hear it.

Old Honest nods

Then said Mr *Great-heart:*

A riddle

He that will kill, must first be overcome;
Who live abroad would, first must die at home.

Hah, said Mr. *Honest,* it is a hard one, hard to expound, and harder to practise. But come Landlord, said he, I will if you please, leave my part to you, do you expound it, and I will hear what you say.

No said *Gaius,* 'twas put to you, and 'tis expected that you should answer it.

Then said the old Gentleman,

He first by Grace must conquer'd be,
That Sin would mortify;
And who, that lives, would convince me,
Unto himself must die.

The riddle opened

It is right, said *Gaius,* good Doctrine and Experience teaches this. For *First,* until Grace displays itself, and overcomes the soul with its Glory, it is altogether without heart to oppose Sin. Besides, if Sin is Satan's Cords by which the soul lies bound, how should it make resistance before it is loosed from that infirmity?

Secondly, Nor will any that knows either Reason or Grace, believe that such a man can be a living Monument of Grace that is a Slave to his own Corruptions.

A question worth the minding

And now it comes in my mind, I will tell you a Story worth the hearing. There were two men that went on Pilgrimage, the one began when he was young, the other when he was old. The young man had strong Corruptions to grapple with, the old man's were decayed with the decays of nature. The young man trod his steps as even as did the old one, and was every way as light as he. Who now, or which of them, had their Graces shining clearest, since both seemed to be alike?

A comparison

HON. The young man's, doubtless. For that which heads it against the greatest opposition, gives best demonstration that it is strongest. Specially when it also holdeth pace with that that meets not with half so much, as to be sure old age does not.

A mistake

Besides, I have observed that old men have blessed themselves with this mistake, namely, taking the decays of Nature for a gracious Conquest over Corruptions, and so have been apt to beguile themselves. Indeed old men that are gracious are best able to give advice to them that are young, because they have seen most of the emptiness of things. But yet, for an old and a young to set out both together, the young one has the advantage of the fairest discovery of a work of Grace within him, tho' the old man's Corruptions are naturally the weakest.

Another question

Thus they sat talking till break of day. Now when the Family was up, *Christiana* bid her Son *James* that he should read a Chapter, so he read the 53d of *Isaiah*. When he had done, Mr *Honest* asked, why it was said *that the Saviour is said to come out of a dry ground, and also that he had no form nor comeliness in him?*

GREAT-HEART. Then said Mr *Great-heart*, To the First I answer, Because the Church of the Jews, of which Christ came, had then lost almost all the Sap and Spirit of Religion. To the Second I say, the words are spoken in the person of the Unbelievers, who because they want that Eye that can see into our Prince's Heart, therefore they judge of him by the meanness of his Outside. Just like those that know not that Precious Stones are covered over with a homely Crust, who when they have found one, because they know not what they have found, cast it again away as men do a common Stone.

Giant Slay-good assaulted and slain

Well, said *Gaius*, now you are here, and since, as I know, Mr *Great-heart* is good at his Weapons, if you please, after we have refreshed ourselves, we will walk into the Fields to see if we can do any good. About a mile from hence there is one *Slay-good*, a Giant that doth much annoy the King's High-way in these parts; and I know whereabout his Haunt is. He is Master of a number of Thieves. 'Twould be well if we could clear these parts of him.

So they consented and went, Mr *Great-heart* with his Sword, Helmet and Shield, and the rest with Spears and Staves.

He is found with one Feeble-mind in his hands

When they came to the place where he was, they found him with one *Feeble-mind* in his hands, whom his Servants had brought unto him, having taken him in the way. Now the Giant was rifling of him, with a purpose after that to pick his Bones, for he was of the nature of Flesh-eaters.

Well, so soon as he saw Mr *Great-heart* and his Friends at the Mouth of his cave with their Weapons, he demanded what they wanted?

GREAT-HEART. We want thee, for we are come to revenge the quarrel of the many that thou hast slain of the Pilgrims, when thou hast dragged them out of the King's High-way, wherefore come out of thy Cave. So he armed himself and came out, and to a Battle they went, and fought for above an hour and then stood still to take wind.

SLAY. Then said the Giant, Why are you here on my ground?

One Feeble-mind rescued from the giant

GREAT-HEART. To revenge the Blood of Pilgrims, as I also told thee before. So they went to it again, and the Giant made Mr *Great-heart* give back; but he came up again, and in the greatness of his mind he let fly with such stoutness at the Giant's head and sides, that he made him let his Weapon fall out of his hand. So he smote him and slew him, and cut off his Head, and brought it away to the Inn. He also took *Feeble-mind* the Pilgrim, and brought him with him to his Lodgings. When they were come home, they shewed his head to the Family, and then set it up, as they had done others before, for a terror to those that should attempt to do as he hereafter.

Then they asked Mr *Feeble-mind* how he fell into his hands?

How Feeble-mind came to be a pilgrim

FEEBLE-MIND. Then said the poor man, I am a sickly man as you see, and, because Death did usually once a day knock at my door, I thought I should never be well at home; so I betook myself to a Pilgrim's life, and have travelled hither from the Town of *Uncertain*, where I and my Father were born. I am a man of no strength at all of body, nor yet of mind; but would if I could, tho' I can but *crawl*, spend my life in the Pilgrim's way. When I came at the Gate that is at the head of the way, the Lord of that place did entertain me freely, neither objected he against my weekly looks, nor against my feeble mind; but gave me such things that were necessary for my Journey, and bid me hope to the end. When I came to the house of the *Interpreter*, I received much kindness there, and because the Hill *Difficulty* was judged too hard for me, I was carried up that by one of his servants. Indeed I have found much relief from Pilgrims, tho' none was willing to go so softly as I am forced to do; yet still as they came on, they bid me be of good cheer, and said that it was the will of their Lord that comfort should be given to the *feeble-minded*, and so went on their own pace. When I was come up to *Assault* Lane, then this Giant met with me, and bid me prepare for an Encounter; but alas, feeble one that I was, I had more need of a Cordial.

Mark this

So he came up and took me. I conceited he should not kill me. Also when he had got me into his Den, since I went not with him willingly, I believed I should come out alive again; for I have heard that not only any Pilgrim that is taken captive by violent hands, if he keeps heart-whole towards his Master, is by the Laws of Providence to die by the hand of the Enemy. Robbed I looked to be, and robbed to be sure I am; but I am, as you see, escaped with Life, for the which I thank my King as Author, and you as the Means. Other brunts I also look for,

Mark this

but this I have resolved on, to wit, to *run* when I can, to *go* when I cannot *run*, and to *creep* when I cannot *go*. As to the main, I thank him that loves me, I am fixed. My way is before me, my Mind is beyond the River that has no Bridge, tho' I am, as you see, but of a *feeble* Mind.

Hon. Then said old Mr *Honest*, Have you not some time ago been acquainted with one Mr *Fearing* a Pilgrim?

Mr Fearing, Mr Feeble-mind's uncle

Feeble. Acquainted with him, Yes. He came from the Town of *Stupidity*, which lieth four degrees to the northward of the City of *Destruction*, and as many off of where I was born; yet we were well acquainted, for indeed he was mine Uncle, my

Father's Brother. He and I have been much of a temper. He was a little shorter than I, but yet we were much of a complexion.

HON. I perceive you know him, and I am apt to believe also that you were related one to another; for you have his whitely Look, a Cast like his with your eye, and your Speech is much alike.

Feeble-mind has some of Mr Fearing's features

FEEBLE. Most have said so that have known us both, and besides, what I have read in him, I have for the most part found in myself.

GAIUS. Come Sir, said good *Gaius,* be of good cheer, you are welcome to me and to my house, and what thou hast a mind to, call for freely; and what thou would'st have my servants to do for thee, they will do it with a ready mind.

Gaius comforts him

Then said Mr *Feeble-mind,* This is unexpected Favour, and as the Sun shining out of a very dark Cloud. Did Giant *Slay-good* intend me this favour when he stopped me, and resolved to let me go no further? Did he intend that after he had rifled my Pockets, I should go to *Gaius* mine Host? Yet so it is.

Notice to be taken of Providence

Now just as Mr *Feeble-mind* and *Gaius* was thus in talk, there comes one running and called at the door, and told, That about a mile and a half off there was one Mr *Not-right* a Pilgrim struck dead upon the place where he was with a Thunderbolt.

Tidings how one Not-right was slain with a thunderbolt, and Mr Feeble-mind's comments upon it

FEEBLE. Alas, said Mr *Feeble-mind,* is he slain? He overtook me some days before I came so far as hither, and would be my Company-keeper. He also was with me when *Slay-good* the Giant took me, but he was nimble of his heels and escaped. But it seems he escaped to die, and I was took to live.

What one would think doth seek to slay outright,
Ofttimes delivers from the saddest plight.
That very Providence whose face is Death,
Doth ofttimes to the lowly Life bequeath.
I taken was, he did escape and flee,
Hands cross'd gives Death to him, and Life to me.

Now about this time *Matthew* and *Mercy* were married. Also *Gaius* gave his Daughter *Phebe* to

James, Matthew's Brother, to Wife; after which time they yet stayed above ten days at *Gaius's* house, spending their time and the seasons like as Pilgrims use to do.

The pilgrims prepare to go forward

When they were to depart, *Gaius* made them a Feast, and they did eat and drink and were merry. Now the hour was come that they must be gone, wherefore Mr *Great-heart* called for a Reckoning. But *Gaius* told him that at his house it was not the custom for Pilgrims to pay for their Entertainment. He boarded them by the year, but looked for his pay from the good *Samaritan,* who had promised him at his return, whatsoever charge he was at with them faithfully to repay him. Then said Mr *Great-heart* to him,

How they greet one another at parting

GREAT-HEART. *Beloved, thou dost faithfully whatsoever thou dost to the Brethren and to Strangers, which have borne witness of thy Charity before the Church; whom if thou (yet) bring forward on their Journey after a Godly sort, thou shalt do well.*

Gaius, his last kindness to Feeble-mind

Then *Gaius* took his leave of them all, and of his Children, and particularly of Mr *Feeble-mind.* He also gave him something to drink by the way.

Now Mr *Feeble-mind,* when they were going out of the door, made as if he intended to linger. The which when Mr *Great-heart* espied, he said, Come Mr *Feeble-mind*, pray do you go along with us, I will be your Conductor, and you shall fare as the rest.

Feeble-mind for going behind

FEEBLE. Alas, I want a suitable Companion, you are all lusty and strong, but I, as you see, am weak. I chuse therefore rather to come behind, lest by reason of my many Infirmities I should be both a Burden to myself and to you. I am, as I said, a man of a weak and feeble mind, and shall be offended and made weak at that which others can bear. I shall like no Laughing, I shall like no gay Attire, I shall like no unprofitable Questions. Nay I am so weak a man, as to be offended with that which others have a liberty to do. I do not yet know all the Truth. I am a very ignorant *Christian man.* Sometimes if I hear some rejoice in the Lord, it troubles me because I cannot do so too. It is with me as it is with a weak man among the strong, or as with a sick man among the healthy, or as a Lamp despised, (*He that is ready to slip with his feet, is as a Lamp despised in the thought of him that is at ease.*) So that I know not what to do.

His excuse for it

GREAT-HEART. But Brother, said Mr *Great-heart,* I have it in Commission to comfort the *feeble-minded,* and to support the weak. You must needs go along with us; we will wait for you, we will lend you our help, we will deny ourselves of some things both opinionative and practical for your sake, we will not enter into doubtful disputations before you, we will be made all things to you rather than you shall be left behind.

Great-heart's commission

A Christian spirit

Now all this while they were at *Gaius's* door; and behold as they were thus in the heat of their discourse Mr *Ready-to-halt* came by with his Crutches in his hand, and he also was going on Pilgrimage.

Promises

FEEBLE. Then said Mr *Feeble-mind* to him, Man, how camest thou hither? I was but just now complaining that I had not a suitable Companion, but thou art according to my wish. Welcome, welcome, good Mr *Ready-to-halt,* I hope thee and I may be some help.

Feeble-mind glad to see Ready-to-halt come by

READY-TO-HALT. I shall be glad of thy Company, said the other; and good Mr *Feeble-mind,* rather than we will part, since we are thus happily met, I will lend thee one of my Crutches.

FEEBLE. Nay, said he, tho' I thank thee for thy good will, I am not inclined to halt before I am lame. Howbeit, I think when occasion is, it may help me against a Dog.

READY. If either myself or my Crutches can do thee a pleasure, we are both at thy command, good Mr *Feeble-mind.*

Thus therefore they went on, Mr *Great-heart* and Mr *Honest* went before, *Christiana* and her Children went next, and Mr *Feeble-mind* and Mr *Ready-to-halt* came behind with his Crutches. Then said Mr *Honest,*

New talk

Hon. Pray Sir, now we are upon the Road, tell us some profitable things of some that have gone on Pilgrimage before us.

First Part, pp. 59-69

Great-heart. With a good will. I suppose you have heard how *Christian* of old did meet with *Apollyon* in the Valley of *Humiliation,* and also what hard work he had to go through the Valley of the *Shadow of Death.* Also I think you cannot but have heard how *Faithful* was put to it with Madam *Wanton,* with *Adam* the First, with one *Discontent,* and *Shame,* four as deceitful Villains as a man can meet with upon the road.

Hon. Yes, I have heard of all this; but indeed good *Faithful* was hardest put to it with *Shame,* he was an unwearied one.

Great-heart. Ay, for as the Pilgrim well said, he of all men had the wrong name.

First Part, p. 79

Hon. But pray Sir, where was it that *Christian* and *Faithful* met *Talkative?* That same was also a notable one.

Great-heart. He was a confident Fool, yet many follow his ways.

Hon. He had like to a beguiled *Faithful.*

First Part p. 82

Great-heart. Ay, but *Christian* put him into a way quickly to find him out. Thus they went on till they came at the place where *Evangelist* met with *Christian* and *Faithful,* and prophesied to them of what should befall them at *Vanity Fair.*

Great-heart. Then said their Guide, Hereabouts did *Christian* and *Faithful* meet with *Evangelist,* who prophesied to them of what Troubles they should meet with at *Vanity Fair.*

Hon. Say you so? I dare say it was a hard Chapter that then he did read unto them.

Great-heart. 'Twas so; but he gave them encouragement withal. But what do we talk of them? they were a couple of lion-like men, they had set their faces like flint. Don't you remember how undaunted they were when they stood before the Judge? First Part, p. 91

HON. Well, *Faithful* bravely suffered.

GREAT-HEART. So he did, and as brave things came on't, for *Hopeful* and some others, as the Story relates it, were converted by his Death.

HON. Well, but pray go on, for you are well acquainted with things.

GREAT-HEART. Above all that *Christian* met with after he had passed through *Vanity Fair,* one *By-ends* was the arch one. First Part, p. 103

HON. *By-ends,* What was he?

GREAT-HEART. A very arch Fellow, a downright Hypocrite. One that would be religious which way ever the World went, but so cunning that he would be sure neither to lose nor suffer for it. He had his mode of Religion for every fresh occasion, and his Wife was as good at it as he. He would turn and change from opinion to opinion, yea, and plead for so doing too. But so far as I could learn, he came to an ill end with his *by-ends,* nor did I ever hear that any of his Children were ever of any esteem with any that truly feared God.

They are come within sight of Vanity

Now by this time they were come within sight of the Town of *Vanity* where *Vanity Fair* is kept. So when they saw that they were so near the Town, they consulted with one another how they should pass through the Town, and some said one thing and some another. At last Mr *Great-heart* said, I have, as you may understand, often been a Conductor of Pilgrims through this Town, now I am acquainted with one Mr *Mnason,* a *Cyprusian* by Nation, an old Disciple, at whose house we may lodge. If you think good, said he, we will turn in there.

They enter into one Mr Mnason's to lodge

Content, said old *Honest,* Content, said *Christiana,* Content said Mr *Feeble-mind,* and so they said all. Now you must think it was eventide by that they got to the outside of the Town, but Mr *Great-heart* knew the way to the old man's house. So thither they came; and he called at the door, and the old man within knew his tongue so soon as ever he heard it; so he opened, and they all came in. Then said *Mnason* their Host, How far have ye come to-day? so they said, From the house of *Gaius* our Friend. I promise you, said he, you have gone a good stitch, you may well be a weary, sit down. So they sat down.

They are glad of entertainment

GREAT-HEART. Then said their Guide, Come, what cheer Sirs? I dare say you are welcome to my Friend.

MNASON. I also, said Mr *Mnason,* do bid you welcome, and whatever you want, do but say, and we will do what we can to get it for you.

HON. Our great want a while since was Harbour and good Company, and now I hope we have both.

MNASON. For Harbour, you see what it is, but for good Company, that will appear in the trial.

GREAT-HEART. Well, said Mr *Great-heart,* will you have the Pilgrims up into their Lodging?

MNASON. I will, said Mr *Mnason.* So he had them to their respective places; and also shewed them a very fair Dining-room, where they might be and sup together, until time was come to go to Rest.

Now when they were set in their places, and were a little cheery after their Journey, Mr *Honest* asked his Landlord if there were any store of good people in the Town?

MNASON. We have a few, for indeed they are but a few when compared with them on the other side.

They desire to see some of the good people of the town

HON. But how shall we do to see some of them? for the sight of good men to them that are going on Pilgrimage, is like to the appearing of the Moon and the Stars to them that are sailing upon the Seas.

Then Mr *Mnason* stamped with his foot, and

his daughter *Grace* came up; so he said unto her, *Grace*, go you tell my Friends, Mr *Contrite*, Mr *Holy-man*, Mr *Love-saint*, Mr *Dare-not-lye*, and Mr *Penitent*, that I have a Friend or two at my house that have a mind this evening to see them.

Some sent for

So *Grace* went to call them, and they came and after Salutation made, they sat down together at the Table.

Then said Mr *Mnason* their Landlord, My Neighbors, I have, as you see, a Company of Strangers come to my house, they are Pilgrims, they come from afar, and are going to Mount *Sion*. But who, quoth he, do you think this is, pointing with his finger to *Christiana*, it is *Christiana* the Wife of *Christian* that famous Pilgrim, who with *Faithful* his Brother were so shamefully handled in our Town. At that they stood amazed, saying, We little thought to see *Christiana*, when *Grace* came to call us, wherefore this is a very comfortable surprise. Then they asked her of her welfare, and if these young men were her Husband's Sons? And when she had told them they were, they said, The King whom you love and serve, make you as your Father, and bring you where he is in Peace.

HON. Then Mr *Honest* (when they were all sat down) asked Mr *Contrite* and the rest in what posture their Town was at present?

Some talk betwixt Mr Honest and Contrite

CONTRITE. You may be sure we are full of hurry in Fair-time. 'Tis hard keeping our hearts and spirits in any good order, when we are in a cumbered condition. He that lives in such a place as this is, and that has to do with such as we have, has need of an Item, to caution him to take heed every moment of the day.

The fruit of watchfulness

HON. But how are your Neighbors for quietness?

CONTRITE. They are much more moderate now than formerly. You know how *Christian* and *Faithful* were used at our Town; but of late, I say, they have been far more moderate. I think the blood of *Faithful* lieth with load upon them till

Persecution not so hot at Vanity Fair as formerly

now, for since they burned him they have been ashamed to burn any more. In *those* days we were afraid to walk the Streets, but *now* we can shew our heads. *Then* the name of a Professor was odious, *now,* specially in some parts of our Town (for you know our Town is large) Religion is counted honourable.

Then said Mr *Contrite* to them, Pray how fareth it with you in your Pilgrimage? How stands the Country affected towards you?

HON. It happens to us as it happeneth to Wayfaring men; sometimes our way is clean, sometimes foul, sometimes up hill, sometimes down hill. We are seldom at a certainty, the Wind is not always on our backs, nor is every one a Friend that we meet with in the way. We have met with some notable Rubs already, and what are yet behind we know not, but for the most part we find it true that has been talked of of old, *A good man must suffer Trouble.*

CONTRITE. You talk of Rubs, what Rubs have you met withal?

HON. Nay, ask Mr *Great-heart* our Guide, for he can give the best account of that.

GREAT-HEART. We have been beset three or four times already. First *Christiana* and her Children were beset with two Ruffians, that they feared would a took away their lives. We was beset with Giant *Bloody-man,* Giant *Maul* and Giant *Slay-good.* Indeed we did rather beset the last, than were beset of him. And thus it was: After we had been some time at the house of *Gaius, mine Host and of the whole Church,* we were minded upon a time to take our Weapons with us, and so go see if we could light upon any of those that were Enemies to Pilgrims, (for we heard that there was a notable one thereabouts.) Now *Gaius* knew his Haunt better than I, because he dwelt thereabout, so we looked and looked till at last we discerned the Mouth of his Cave, then we were glad and plucked up our

Spirits. So we approached up to his Den, and lo when we came there, he had dragged by mere force into his Net this poor Man Mr *Feeble-mind,* and was about to bring him to his end. But when he saw us, supposing as we thought he had had another Prey, he left the poor man in his Hole, and came out. So we fell to it full sore, and he lustily laid about him; but in conclusion he was brought down to the ground, and his Head cut off, and set up by the Way-side for a terror to such as should after practise such Ungodliness. That I tell you the truth, here is the man himself to affirm it, who was as a Lamb taken out of the Mouth of the Lion.

FEEBLE-MIND. Then said Mr *Feeble-mind,* I found this true to my Cost and Comfort, to my Cost when he threatened to pick my Bones every moment, and to my Comfort when I saw Mr *Great-heart* and his Friends with their Weapons approach so near for my Deliverance.

HOLY-MAN. Then said Mr *Holy-man,* There are two things that they have need to be possessed with that go on Pilgrimage, *courage,* and an *unspotted life.* If they have not *courage,* they can never hold on their way, and if their Lives be *loose,* they will make the very name of a Pilgrim stink.

Mr Holy-man's speech

LOVE-SAINT. Then said Mr *Love-saint,* I hope this caution is not needful amongst you. But truly there are many that go upon the road, that rather declare themselves Strangers to Pilgrimage than Strangers and Pilgrims in the Earth.

Mr Love-saint's speech

DARE-NOT-LYE. Then said Mr *Dare-not-lye,* 'Tis true, they neither have the Pilgrim's Weed, nor the Pilgrim's Courage; they go not uprightly, but all awry with their feet; one Shoe goes *inward,* another *outward,* and their Hosen out behind; there a Rag, and there a Rent, to the Disparagement of their Lord.

Mr Dare-not-lye's speech

PENITENT. These things, said Mr *Penitent,* they ought to be troubled for, nor are the Pilgrims like to have that Grace put upon them and their

Mr Penitent's speech

Pilgrim's Progress as they desire, until the way is cleared of such Spots and Blemishes.

Thus they sat talking and spending the time, until Supper was set upon the Table; unto which they went and refreshed their weary bodies; so they went to Rest. Now they stayed in this Fair a great while at the house of this Mr *Mnason,* who in process of time gave his daughter *Grace* unto *Samuel Christiana's* Son to Wife, and his Daughter *Martha* to *Joseph.*

The time as I said, that they lay here was long, (for it was not now as in former times.) Wherefore the Pilgrims grew acquainted with many of the good people of the Town, and did them what service they could. *Mercy,* as she was wont, laboured much for the Poor, wherefore their Bellies and Backs blessed her, and she was there an Ornament to her Profession. And to say the truth for *Grace Phebe* and *Martha,* they were all of a very good Nature, and did much good in their place. They were also all of them very Fruitful, so that *Christian's* name, as was said before, was like to live in the World.

A monster

While they lay here, there came a Monster out of the Woods, and slew many of the people of the Town. It would also carry away their Children, and teach them to suck its Whelps. Now no man in the Town durst so much as face this Monster, but all men fled when they heard of the Noise of his coming.

His shape, his nature

The Monster was like unto no one Beast upon the earth; its Body was like the Dragon, and it had seven Heads and ten Horns. It made great havock of Children, and yet it was governed by a Woman. This Monster propounded Conditions to men, and such men as loved their Lives more than their Souls, accepted of those Conditions. So they came under.

Now this Mr *Great-heart,* together with these that came to visit the Pilgrims at Mr *Mnason's* house, entered into a Covenant to go and engage this Beast, if perhaps they might deliver the people of this Town from the Paws and Mouth of this so devouring a Serpent.

Then did Mr *Great-heart,* Mr *Contrite,* Mr *Holy-man,* Mr *Dare-not-lye,* and Mr *Penitent,* with their Weapons go forth to meet him. Now the Monster at first was very rampant, and looked upon these Enemies with great Disdain, but they so belaboured him, being sturdy men at Arms, that they made him make a Retreat. So they came home to Mr *Mnason's* house again.

How he is engaged

The Monster, you must know, had his certain Seasons to come out in, and to make his Attempts upon the Children of the people of the Town; also these Seasons did these valiant Worthies watch him in, and did still continually assault him; insomuch that in process of time he became not only wounded but lame, also he has not made that havock of the Towns-men's Children as formerly he has done. And it is verily believed by some, that this Beast will die of his Wounds.

This therefore made Mr *Great-heart* and his Fellows of great Fame in this Town, so that many of the people that wanted their taste of things, yet had a reverend Esteem and Respect for them. Upon this account therefore it was that these Pilgrims got not much hurt here. True there were some of the baser sort, that could see no more than a Mole, nor understand more than a Beast, these had no reverence for these men, nor took they notice of their Valour or Adventures.

Well the time grew on that the Pilgrims must go on their way, wherefore they prepared for their Journey. They sent for their Friends, they conferred with them, they had some time set apart therein to commit each other to the Protection of their Prince. There was again that brought them of such things as they had, that was fit for the Weak and the Strong, for the Women and the

Men, and so laded them with such things as was necessary.

Then they set forwards on their way, and their Friends accompanying them so far as was convenient, they again committed each other to the Protection of their King, and parted.

They therefore that were of the Pilgrims' Company went on, and Mr *Great-heart* went before them. Now the Women and Children being weakly, they were forced to go as they could bear, by this means Mr *Ready-to-halt* and Mr *Feeble-mind* had more to sympathize with their Condition.

When they were gone from the Towns-men, and when their Friends had bid them farewell they quickly came to the place where *Faithful* was put to Death. There therefore they made a stand, and thanked Him that had enabled him to bear his Cross so well, and the rather because they now found that they had a benefit by such a manly Suffering as his was.

They went on therefore after this a good way further, talking of *Christian* and *Faithful,* and how *Hopeful* joined himself to *Christian* after that *Faithful* was dead.

First Part, p. 111

Now they were come up with the Hill *Lucre,* where the Silver-mine was, which took *Demas* off from his Pilgrimage, and into which, as some think, *By-ends* fell and perished; wherefore they considered that. But when they were come to the old Monument that stood over against the Hill *Lucre,* to wit, to the Pillar of Salt that stood also within view of *Sodom* and its stinking Lake, they marvelled, as did *Christian* before, that men of that Knowledge and ripeness of Wit as they was, should be so blinded as to turn aside here. Only they considered again that Nature is not affected with the Harms that others have met with, especially if that thing upon which they look has an attracting vertue upon the foolish eye.

I saw now that they went on till they came at

the River that was on this side of the Delectable Mountains. To the River where the fine Trees grow on both sides, and whose Leaves, if taken inwardly, are good against Surfeits, where the Meadows are green all the year long, and where they might lie down safely. First Part, p. 59

By this River side in the Meadow there were Cotes and Folds for Sheep, an House built for the nourishing and bringing up of those Lambs, the Babes of those Women that go on Pilgrimage. Also there was here one that was intrusted with them who could have Compassion, and that could gather these Lambs with his Arm and carry them in his Bosom, and that could gently lead those that were with young. Now to the care of *this Man, Christiana* admonished her four Daughters to commit their little ones, that by these Waters they might be housed, harboured, suckered, and nourished, and that none of them might be lacking in time to come. This Man, if any of them go astray or be lost, he will bring them again: he will also bind up that which was broken, and will strengthen them that are sick. Here they will never want Meat and Drink and Cloathing, here they will be kept from Thieves and Robbers, for this Man will die before one of those committed to his trust shall be lost. Besides, here they shall be sure to have good Nurture and Admonition, and shall be taught to walk in right paths, and that you know is a Favour of no small account. Also here, as you see, are delicate Waters, pleasant Meadows, dainty Flowers, variety of Trees, and such as bear wholesome Fruit, Fruit not like that that *Matthew* eat of, that fell over the Wall out of *Beelzebub's* Garden, but Fruit that procureth Health where there is none, and that continueth and increaseth it where it is.

So they were content to commit their little ones to him; and that which was also an encouragement to them so to do, was, for that all this was to be at the Charge of the King, and so was as an Hospital for young Children and Orphans.

First Part, p. 116

Now they went on; and when they were come to *By-path* Meadow, to the Stile over which *Christian* went with his Fellow *Hopeful,* when they were taken by Giant *Despair* and put into *Doubting* Castle, they sat down and consulted what was best to be done; to wit, now they were so strong, and had got such a man as Mr *Great-heart* for their Conductor, whether they had not best make an attempt upon the Giant, demolish his Castle, and if there were any Pilgrims in it, to set them at liberty before they went any further. So one said one thing, and another said the contrary. One questioned if it was lawful to go upon *unconsecrated* ground, another said they might provided their end was good, but Mr *Great-heart* said, Though that Assertion offered last cannot be universally true, yet I have a Commandment to resist Sin, to overcome Evil, to fight the good Fight of Faith, and I pray, with whom should I fight this good Fight, if not with Giant *Despair?* I will therefore attempt the taking away of his Life, and the demolishing of *Doubting* Castle. Then said he, who will go with me? Then said old *Honest,* I will. And so will we too, said *Christiana's four Sons, Matthew Samuel James* and *Joseph,* for they were young men and strong. So they left the Women in the Road, and with them Mr *Feeble-mind* and Mr *Ready-to-halt* with his Crutches to be their Guard, until they came back; for in that place, tho' Giant *Despair* dwelt so near, they keeping in the Road, a little Child might lead them.

They being come to By-path stile, have a mind to have a pluck with Giant Despair

So Mr *Great-heart,* old *Honest* and the four young men went to go up to *Doubting* Castle to look for Giant *Despair.* When they came at the Castle-gate, they knocked for entrance with an unusual Noise. At that the old Giant comes to the Gate, and *Diffidence* his Wife follows. Then said he, Who and what is he that is so hardy as after this manner to molest the Giant *Despair?* Mr *Great-heart* replied, It is I, *Great-heart,* one of the King of the Cœlestial Country's Conductors of Pilgrims to their place, and I demand of thee that thou open thy Gates for my Entrance. Prepare thyself also to fight, for I am come to take away thy Head, and to demolish *Doubting* Castle.

Now Giant *Despair,* because he was a Giant, thought no man could overcome him; and again, thought he, since heretofore I have made a Conquest of Angels, shall *Great-heart* make me afraid? So he harnessed himself and went out. He had a Cap of Steel upon his Head, a Breast-plate of Fire girded to him, and he came out in Iron Shoes, with a great Club in his Hand. Then these six men made up to him, and beset him behind and before. Also when *Diffidence* the Giantess came up to help him, old Mr *Honest* cut her down at one Blow. Then they fought for their Lives, and Giant *Despair* was brought down to the Ground, but was very loth to die. He struggled hard, and had, as they say, as many Lives as a Cat, but *Great-heart* was his Death, for he left him not till he had severed his Head from his Shoulders.

Despair has overcome angels

Despair is loath to die

Then they fell to demolishing *Doubting* Castle, and that you know might with ease be done since Giant *Despair* was dead. They were seven days in destroying of that; and in it of Pilgrims they found one Mr *Dispondency,* almost starved to Death, and one *Much-afraid* his Daughter; these two they saved alive. But it would a made you a wondered to have seen the dead Bodies that lay here and there in the Castle-yard, and how full of dead men's Bones the Dungeon was.

Doubting Castle demolished

When Mr *Great-heart* and his Companions had performed this exploit, they took Mr *Dispondency* and his Daughter *Much-afraid* into their protection, for they were honest people tho' they were Prisoners in *Doubting* Castle to that Tyrant Giant *Despair.* They therefore I say, took with them the Head of

They have music and dancing for joy

the Giant (for his Body they had buried under a heap of Stones) and down to the Road and to their Companions they came, and shewed them what they had done. Now when *Feeble-mind* and *Ready-to-halt* saw that it was the Head of Giant *Despair* indeed, they were very jocund and merry. Now *Christiana,* if need was, could play upon the Vial, and her Daughter *Mercy* upon the Lute; so since they were so merry disposed, she played them a Lesson, and *Ready-to-halt* would dance. So he took *Dispondency's* Daughter named *Much-afraid* by the hand, and to dancing they went in the Road. True he could not dance without one Crutch in his hand, but I promise you he footed it well. Also the Girl was to be commended, for she answered the Musick handsomely.

As for Mr *Dispondency,* the Musick was not much to him, he was for feeding rather than dancing, for that he was almost starved. So *Christiana* gave him some of her Bottle of Spirits for present relief, and then prepared him something to eat; and in little time the old Gentleman came to himself, and began to be finely revived.

Now I saw in my Dream, when all these things were finished, Mr *Great-heart* took the Head of Giant *Despair,* and set it upon a Pole by the Highway side, right over against the Pillar that *Christian* erected for a Caution to Pilgrims that came after, to take heed of entering into his grounds.

Though *Doubting* Castle be demolished,
And the Giant *Despair* hath lost his Head,
Sin can rebuild the Castle, make't remain,
And make *Despair* the Giant live again.

Then he writ under it upon a Marble-stone these verses following:

A monument of deliverance

This is the Head of him, whose Name only
In former times did Pilgrims terrify.
His Castle's down, and *Diffidence* his Wife
Brave Master *Great-heart* has bereft of Life.
Dispondency, his Daughter *Much-afraid,*

> *Great-heart* for them also the Man has play'd.
> Who hereof doubts, if he'll but cast his eye
> Up hither, may his scruples satisfy:
> This Head also, when doubting Cripples dance,
> Doth shew from Fears they have Deliverance.

When these men had thus bravely shewed themselves against *Doubting* Castle, and had slain Giant *Despair,* they went forward, and went on till they came to the *Delectable* Mountains, where *Christian* and *Hopeful* refreshed themselves with the varieties of the place. They also acquainted themselves with the Shepherds there, who welcomed them, as they had done *Christian* before, unto the *Delectable* Mountains.

Now the Shepherds seeing so great a Train follow Mr *Great-heart,* (for with him they were well acquainted) they said unto him, Good Sir, you have got a goodly Company here, pray where did you find all these?

Then Mr *Great-heart* replied,

The Guide's speech to the Shepherds

> First here is *Christiana* and her Train,
> Her Sons, and her Sons' Wives, who like the *Wain,*
> Keep by the Pole, and do by Compass steer
> From Sin to Grace, else they had not been here;
> Next here's old *Honest* come on Pilgrimage,
> *Ready-to-halt* too, who I dare engage
> True-hearted is, and so is *Feeble-mind,*
> Who willing was not to be left behind;
> *Dispondency,* good man, is coming after,
> And so also is *Much-afraid* his Daughter.
> May we have entertainment here, or must
> We further go? Let's know whereon to trust.

Their entertainment

Then said the Shepherds, This is a comfortable Company. You are welcome to us, for we have comfort for the *feeble* as for the *strong.* Our Prince has an eye to what is done to the least of these, therefore Infirmity must not be a block to our Entertainment. So they had them to the Palace door, and then said unto them, Come in Mr *Feeble-mind,* Come in Mr *Ready-to-halt,* Come in Mr

A description of false shepherds

Dispondency, and Mr *Much-afraid* his Daughter. *These,* Mr *Great-heart,* said the Shepherds to the Guide, we call in by name, for that they are most subject to draw back, but as for you and the rest that are *strong,* we leave you to your wonted Liberty. Then said Mr *Great-heart,* This day I see that Grace doth shine in your Faces, and that you are my Lord's Shepherds indeed; for that you have not *pushed* these diseased neither with Side nor Shoulder, but have rather strewed their way into the Palace with Flowers, as you should.

So the feeble and weak went in, and Mr *Great-heart* and the rest did follow. When they were also set down, the Shepherds said to those of the weakest sort, What is it that you would have? for, said they, all things must be managed here to the supporting of the weak, as well as the warning of the unruly.

So they made them a Feast of things easy of Digestion, and that were pleasant to the Palate, and nourishing; the which when they had received, they went to the Rest, each one respectively unto his proper place. When Morning was come, because the Mountains were high, and the day clear, and because it was the custom of the Shepherds to shew to the Pilgrims before their departure, some Rarities; therefore after they were ready, and had refreshed themselves, the Shepherds took them out into the Fields, and shewed them first what they had shewed to *Christian* before.

Mount Marvel

Then they had them to some new places. The first was to Mount *Marvel,* where they looked, and beheld a man at a distance, *that tumbled the Hills about with Words.* Then they asked the Shepherds what that should mean? So they told them, that that man was the Son of one *Greatgrace,* of whom you read in the First Part of the Records of the Pilgrim's Progress. And he is set there to teach Pilgrims how to believe down or to tumble out of their ways what Difficulties they shall meet with,

First Part, p. 130

by Faith. Then said Mr *Great-heart,* I know him, he is a man above many.

Mount Innocent

Then they had them to another place called Mount *Innocent,* and there they saw a man cloathed all in White, and two men *Prejudice* and *Ill-will* continually casting Dirt upon him. Now behold the Dirt whatsoever they cast at him would in a little time fall off again, and his Garment would look as clear as if no Dirt had been cast thereat.

Then said the Pilgrims, What means this? The Shepherds answered, This man is named *Godly-man,* and this Garment is to shew the Innocency of his life. Now those that throw Dirt at him, are such as hate his *well-doing,* but as you see the Dirt will not stick upon his Cloaths, so it shall be with him that liveth truly innocently in the World. Whoever they be that would make such men dirty, they labour all in vain; for God, by that a little time is spent, will cause that their Innocence shall break forth as the Light, and their Righteousness as the Noon-day.

Mount Charity

Then they took them, and had them to Mount *Charity,* where they shewed them a man that had a bundle of cloth lying before him, out of which he cut Coats and Garments for the Poor that stood about him; yet his Bundle or Roll of Cloth was never the less.

Then said they, What should this be? This is, said the Shepherds, to shew you, that he that has a heart to give of his Labour to the Poor, shall never want where-withal. He that watereth shall be watered himself. And the Cake that the Widow gave to the Prophet did not cause that she had ever the less in her Barrel.

The work of one Fool, and one Want-wit

They had them also to a place where they saw one *Fool* and one *Want-wit* washing of an *Ethiopian* with intention to make him white, but the more they washed him the blacker he was. They then asked the Shepherds what that should mean. So they told them, saying, Thus shall it be with the vile person. All means used to get such an one a good name shall in conclusion tend but to make him more abominable. Thus it was with the *Pharisees,* and so shall it be with all Hypocrites.

Mercy has a mind to see the hole in the hill

Then said *Mercy* the Wife of *Matthew* to *Christiana* her Mother, Mother, I would, if it might be, see the Hole in the Hill, or that commonly called the By-way to Hell. So her Mother brake her mind to the Shepherds. Then they went to the Door. It was in the side of a Hill, and they opened it, and Bid *Mercy* hearken awhile. So she hearkened, and heard one saying, *Cursed be my Father for holding of my feet back from the way of Peace and Life;* and another said, *O that I had been torn in pieces before I had, to save my Life, lost my Soul;* and another said, *If I were to live again, how would I deny myself, rather than come to this place.* Then there was as if the very Earth had groaned and quaked under the feet of this young Woman for fear. So she looked white, and came trembling away, saying, Blessed be he and she that is delivered from this place.

First Part, p. 126

Mercy longeth, and for what

Now when the Shepherds had shewed them all these things, then they had them back to the Palace, and entertained them with what the house would afford. But *Mercy* being a young and breeding Woman, longed for something that she saw there, but was ashamed to ask. Her Mother-in-law then asked her what she ailed, for she looked as one not well. Then said *Mercy,* There is a looking-glass hangs up in the Dining-room, off of which I can not take my mind, if therefore I have it not, I think I shall miscarry. Then said her Mother, I will mention thy wants to the Shepherds, and they will not deny it thee. But she said, I am ashamed that these men should know that I longed. Nay my Daughter, said she, it is no Shame, but a Vertue, to long for such a thing as that, So *Mercy* said, Then Mother, if you please, ask the Shepherds if they are willing to sell it.

Now the Glass was one of a thousand. It would present a man, one way, with his own Feature exactly, and, turn it but another way, and it would shew one the very Face and Similitude of the Prince of Pilgrims himself. Yea I have talked with them that can tell, and they have said that they have seen the very Crown of Thorns upon his Head, by looking in that Glass, they have therein also seen the Holes in his Hands, in his Feet, and his Side. Yea such an excellency is there in that Glass, that it will shew him to one where they have a mind to see him, whether living or dead, whether in Earth or Heaven, whether in a state of Humiliation or in his Exaltation, whether coming to Suffer or coming to Reign.

It was the Word of God

Christiana therefore went to the Shepherds apart (now the names of the Shepherds are *Knowledge, Experience, Watchful,* and *Sincere*) and said unto them, There is one of my Daughters, a breeding Woman, that I think doth long for something she hath seen in this house, and she thinks she shall miscarry if she should by you be denied.

First Part, p. 125

EXPERIENCE. Call her, call her, she shall assuredly have what we can help her to. So they called her, and said to her, *Mercy,* what is that thing thou wouldest have? Then she blushed, and said, The great Glass that hangs up in the Dining-room. So *Sincere* ran and fetched it, and with a joyful consent it was given her. Then she bowed her head, and gave thanks, and said, By this I know that I have obtained favour in your eyes.

She doth not lose her longing

They also gave to the other young Women such things as they desired, and to their Husbands great Commendations for that they joined with Mr *Great-heart* to the slaying of Giant *Despair* and the demolishing of *Doubting* Castle.

About *Christiana's* Neck the Shepherds put a Bracelet, and so they did about the Necks of her four Daughters, also they put Ear-rings in their Ears, and Jewels on their Fore-heads.

How the Shepherds adorn the pilgrims

First Part, p. 127

When they were minded to go hence, they let them go in peace, but gave not to them those certain Cautions which before were given to *Christian* and his Companion. The reason was for that these had *Great-heart* to be their Guide, who was one that was well acquainted with things, and so could give them their Cautions more seasonably, to wit, even then when the Danger was nigh the approaching.

First Part, p. 127

What Cautions *Christian* and his Companions had received of the Shepherds, they had also lost by that the time was come that they had need to put them in practice. Wherefore here was the advantage that this Company had over the other.

From hence they went on singing, and they said,

> Behold, how fitly are the stages set
> For their Relief that Pilgrims are become;
> And how they us receive without one let,
> That make the other life our mark and home!
> What Novelties they have to us they give,
> That we, tho' Pilgrims, joyful lives may live;
> They do upon us too such things bestow,
> That shew we Pilgrims are where'er we go.

First Part, p. 129

When they were gone from the Shepherds, they quickly came to the place where *Christian* met with one *Turn-away,* that dwelt in the town of *Apostacy.* Wherefore of him Mr *Great-heart* their Guide did now put them in mind, saying, This is the place where *Christian* met with one *Turn-away,* who carried with him the character of his Rebellion at his back. And this I have to say concerning this man, he would hearken to no counsel, but once a falling, persuasion could not stop him.

How one Turn-away managed his apostacy

When he came to the place where the Cross and the Sepulchre was, he did meet with one that did bid him look there; but he gnashed with his teeth, and stamped, and said he was resolved to go back to his own Town. Before he came to the Gate, he met with *Evangelist,* who offered to lay hands on him to turn him into the way again. But this

Turn-away resisted him, and having done much despite unto him, he got away over the Wall, and so escaped his hand.

Then they went on; and just at the place where *Little-faith* formerly was robbed, there stood a man with his Sword drawn, and his Face all bloody. Then said Mr *Great-heart,* What art thou? The man made answer, saying, I am one whose name is *Valiant-for-truth.* I am a Pilgrim, and am going to the Cœlestial City. Now as I was in my way, there were three men did beset me and propounded unto me these three things: 1. Whether I would become one of them? 2. Or go back from whence I came? 3. Or die upon the place? To the first I answered, I had been a true man a long season, and therefore it could not be expected that I now should cast in my Lot with Thieves. Then they demanded what I would say to the second. So I told them that the place from whence I came, had I not found Incommodity there, I had not forsaken it at all; but finding it altogether unsuitable to me, and very unprofitable for me, I forsook it for this way. Then they asked me what I said to the third. And I told them, My life cost more dear far than that I should lightly give it away. Besides, you have nothing to do thus to put things to my Choice, wherefore at your Peril be it if you meddle. Then these three, to wit *Wild-head, Inconsiderate* and *Pragmatick,* drew upon me, and I also drew upon them.

One Valiant-for-truth beset with thieves

So we fell to it, one against three, for the space of above three hours. They have left upon me, as you see, some of the marks of their Valour, and have also carried away with them some of mine. They are but just now gone. I suppose they might, as the saying is, hear your Horse dash, and so they betook them to flight.

How he behaved himself, and put them to flight

GREAT-HEART. But here was great odds, three against one.

Great-heart wonders at his valour

VALIANT. 'Tis true, but little or more are nothing

to him that has the Truth on his side. *Tho' an Host encamp against me,* said one, *my heart shall not fear; tho' War should rise against me, in this will I be confident,* &c. Besides, saith he, I have read in some Records, that one man has fought an Army; and how many did *Samson* slay with the Jaw-bone of an Ass?

GREAT-HEART. Then said the Guide, Why did you not cry out, that some might a come in for your succour?

VALIANT. So I did, to my King, who I knew could hear, and afford invisible help, and that was sufficient for me.

GREAT-HEART. Then said *Great-heart* to Mr *Valiant-for-truth,* Thou hast worthily behaved thyself. Let me see thy Sword. So he shewed it him. When he had taken it in his hand, and looked thereon a while, he said, Ha, *it is a right* Jerusalem *Blade.*

VALIANT. It is so. Let a man have one of these Blades, with a Hand to wield it and Skill to use it, and he may venture upon an Angel with it. He need not fear its holding, if he can but tell how to lay on. Its edges will never blunt. It will cut *flesh* and *bones* and *soul* and *spirit* and all.

GREAT-HEART. But you fought a great while, I wonder you was not weary.

The Word The Faith Blood

VALIANT. I fought till my Sword did cleave to my Hand; and when they were joined together, as if a Sword grew out of my Arm, and when the Blood ran through my Fingers, then I fought with most courage.

GREAT-HEART. Thou hast done well. Thou hast resisted unto Blood, striving against Sin. Thou shalt abide by us, come in and go out with us, for we are thy Companions.

Then they took him and washed his Wounds, and gave him of what they had to refresh him, and so they went on together. Now as they went on, because Mr. *Great-heart* was delighted in him (for he loved one greatly that he found to be a man of his hands) and because there were with his Company them that was feeble and weak, therefore he questioned with him about many things, as first, what Country-man he was?

VALIANT. I am of *Dark-land,* for there I was born, and there my Father and Mother are still.

GREAT-HEART. *Dark-land,* said the Guide, doth not that lie upon the same Coast with the City of *Destruction?*

VALIANT. Yes it doth. Now that which caused me to come on Pilgrimage was this; we had one Mr *Tell-true* came into our parts, and he told it about what *Christian* had done, that went from the City of *Destruction,* namely, how he had forsaken his Wife and Children, and had betaken himself to a Pilgrim's life. It was also confidently reported how he had killed a Serpent that did come out to resist him in his Journey, and how he got through to whither he intended. It was also told what Welcome he had at all his Lord's Lodgings, especially when he came to the Gates of the Cœlestial City, for there, said the man, he was received with sound of Trumpet by a company of Shining Ones. He told it also, how all the Bells in the City did ring for joy at his reception, and what Golden Garments he was cloathed with, with many other things that now I shall forbear to relate. In a word, that man so told the story of *Christian* and his Travels, that my heart fell into a burning haste to be gone after him, nor could Father or Mother stay me: so I got from them, and am come thus far on my way.

How Mr Valiant came to go on pilgrimage

GREAT-HEART. You came in at the Gate, did you not?

VALIANT. Yes, yes, for the same man also told us that all would be nothing, if we did not begin to enter this way at the Gate.

He begins right

GREAT-HEART. Look you, said the Guide to *Christiana,* the Pilgrimage of your Husband, and what he has gotten thereby, is spread abroad far and near.

Christian's name famous

VALIANT. Why, is this *Christian's* wife?

GREAT-HEART. Yes, that it is, and these are also her four Sons.

VALIANT. What, and going on Pilgrimage too?

GREAT-HEART. Yes verily they are following after.

He is much rejoiced to see Christian's wife

VALIANT. It glads me at heart. Good man, how joyful will he be when he shall see them that would not go with him, yet to enter after him in at the Gates into the City.

GREAT-HEART. Without doubt it will be a comfort to him; for next to the joy of seeing himself there, it will be a joy to meet there his Wife and his Children.

VALIANT. But now you are upon that, pray let me hear your opinion about it. Some make a question, Whether we shall know one another when we are there?

GREAT-HEART. Do they think they shall know themselves then, or that they shall rejoice to see themselves in that Bliss? and if they think they shall know and do these, why not know others, and rejoice in their Welfare also?

Again, since Relations are our second self, though that state will be dissolved there, yet why may it not be rationally concluded that we shall be more glad to see them there than to see they are wanting?

VALIANT. Well, I perceive whereabouts you are as to this. Have you any more things to ask me about my beginning to come on Pilgrimage?

GREAT-HEART. Yes. Was your Father and Mother willing that you should become a Pilgrim?

VALIANT. Oh no. They used all means imaginable to persuade me to stay at home.

GREAT-HEART. What could they against it?

The great stumbling-blocks that by his friends were laid in his way

VALIANT. They said it was an *idle* life, and if I myself were not inclined to Sloth and Laziness, I would never countenance a Pilgrim's condition.

GREAT-HEART. And what did they say else?

VALIANT. Why, they told me that it was a dangerous way; yea, the most dangerous way in the World, said they, is that which the Pilgrims go.

GREAT-HEART. Did they shew wherein this way is so dangerous?

VALIANT. Yes, and that in many particulars.

GREAT-HEART. Name some of them.

VALIANT. They told me of the Slough of *Dispond,* where *Christian* was well nigh smothered. They told me that there were Archers standing ready in *Beelzebub-castle* to shoot them that should knock at the Wicket-gate for entrance. They told me also of the Wood and dark Mountains, of the Hill *Difficulty,* of the Lions, and also of the three Giants, *Bloody-man, Maul* and *Slay-good.* They said moreover that there was a foul Fiend haunted the Valley of *Humiliation,* and that *Christian* was by him almost bereft of Life. Besides, say they, you must go over the Valley of the *Shadow of Death,* where the Hobgoblins are, where the Light is Darkness, where the way is full of Snares, Pits, Traps, and Gins. They told me also of Giant *Despair,* of *Doubting* Castle and of the ruin that the Pilgrims met with there. Further, they said I must go over the Inchanted Ground, which was dangerous. And that after all this, I should find a River, over which I should find no Bridge, and that that River did lie betwixt me and the Cœlestial Country.

The first stumbling-block

GREAT-HEART. And was this all?

VALIANT. No. They also told me that this way was full of Deceivers, and of persons that laid await there, to turn good men out of the Path.

The second

GREAT-HEART. But how did they make that out?

VALIANT. They told me that Mr *Worldly Wiseman* did there lie in wait to deceive. They also said that there was *Formality* and *Hypocrisy* continually on the road. They said also that *By-ends, Talkative* or *Demas* would go near to gather me up, that the *Flatterer* would catch me in his Net, or that with green-headed *Ignorance* I would presume to go on to the Gate, from whence he always was sent back to the Hole that was in the side of the Hill, and made to go the By-way to Hell.

GREAT-HEART. I promise you this was enough to discourage, but did they make an end here?

The third

VALIANT. No, stay. They told me also of many that had tried that way of old, and that had gone a great way therein, to see if they could find something of the Glory there that so many had so much talked of from time to time; and how they came back again, and befooled themselves for setting a foot out of doors in that Path, to the satisfaction of all the Country. And they named several that did so, as *Obstinate* and *Pliable, Mistrust* and *Timorous, Turnaway* and old *Atheist,* with several more, who, they said, had some of them gone far to see if they could find, but not one of them found so much advantage by going as amounted to the weight of a Feather.

GREAT-HEART. Said they anything more to discourage you?

The fourth

VALIANT. Yes. They told me of one Mr *Fearing* who was a Pilgrim, and how he found this way so solitary that he never had comfortable hour therein. Also that Mr *Dispondency* had like to have been starved therein; yea, and also, which I had almost forgot, that *Christian* himself, about whom there has been such a noise, after all his ventures for a Cœlestial Crown, was certainly drowned in the black River, and never went foot further, however it was smothered up.

GREAT-HEART. And did none of these things discourage you?

VALIANT. No, they seemed but as so many nothings to me.

GREAT-HEART. How came that about?

How he got over these stumbling-blocks

VALIANT. Why I still believed what Mr *Tell-true* had said, and that carried me beyond them all.

GREAT-HEART. Then this was your Victory, even your Faith.

VALIANT. It was so; I believed, and therefore came out, got into the Way, fought all that set themselves against me, and by believing am come to this place.

Who would True valour see,
Let him come hither;
One here will constant be,
Come Wind, come Weather.
There's no Discouragement
Shall make him once relent
His first avow'd intent
To be a Pilgrim.

Who so beset him round
With dismal Stories,
Do but themselves confound,
His Strength the more is;
No Lion can him fright,
He'll with a Giant fight,
But he will have a right
To be a Pilgrim.

Hobgoblin nor foul Fiend
Can daunt his spirit;
He knows he at the end
Shall Life inherit.
Then Fancies fly away,
He'll fear not what men say,
He'll labour night and day
To be a Pilgrim.

By this time they were got to the Inchanted Ground, where the air naturally tended to make one *drowsy,* and that place was all grown over with Briars and Thorns, excepting here and there where was an Inchanted Arbor, upon which if a man sits, or in which if a man sleeps, 'tis a question, say some, whether ever he shall rise or wake again in this world. Over this Forest therefore they went, both one with another, and Mr *Great-heart* went before for that he was the Guide, and Mr *Valiant-for-truth* he came behind, being there a Guard for fear lest peradventure some Fiend or Dragon or Giant or Thief should fall upon their Rear, and so do mischief. They went on here each man with his Sword drawn in his hand, for they knew it was

First Part, p. 140

a dangerous place. Also they cheered up one another as well as they could; *Feeble-mind*, Mr *Great-heart* commanded should come up after him, and Mr *Dispondency* was under the eye of Mr *Valiant*.

Now they had not gone far, but a great Mist and a Darkness fell upon them all, so that they could scarce for a great while see the one the other. Wherefore they were forced for some time to feel for one another by Words, for they walked not by Sight.

But any one must think that here was but sorry going for the best of them all, but how much worse for the Women and Children, who both of *feet* and *heart* were but tender. Yet so it was, that through the encouraging words of him that led in the front, and of him that brought them up behind, they made a pretty good shift to wag along.

The way also was here very wearisome through Dirt and Slabbiness. Nor was there on all this ground so much as one Inn or Victualling-house, therein to refresh the feebler sort. Here therefore was grunting and puffing and sighing. While one tumbleth over a Bush, another sticks fast in the Dirt; and the Children, some of them, lost their Shoes in the Mire. While one cries out, I am down; and another, Ho, where are you? and a third, The Bushes have got such fast hold on me, I think I cannot get away from them.

An arbor on the Inchanted Ground

Then they come at an Arbor, warm, and promising much refreshing to the Pilgrims; for it was finely wrought above head, beautified with Greens, furnished with Benches and Settles. It also had in it a soft Couch whereon the weary might lean. This you must think, all things considered, was tempting, for the Pilgrims already began to be foiled with the badness of the way, but there was not one of them that made so much as a motion to stop there. Yea, for ought I could perceive, they continually gave so good heed to the advice of their Guide, and he did so faithfully tell them of Dangers, and of the nature of Dangers, when they were at them, that usually when they were nearest to them they did most pluck up their Spirits, and hearten one another to deny the Flesh. This Arbor was called the *Slothful's Friend,* on purpose to allure, if it might be, some of the Pilgrims there to take up their Rest when weary.

The name of the arbor

I saw then in my Dream, that they went on in this their solitary ground, till they came to a place at which a man is apt to lose his way. Now tho' when it was *light,* their Guide could well enough tell how to miss those ways that led wrong, yet in the *dark* he was put to a stand; but he had in his Pocket a Map of all ways leading to or from the Cœlestial City; wherefore he struck a Light (for he never goes also without his Tinder-box) and takes a view of his Book or Map, which bids him be careful in that place to turn to the right-hand way. And had he not here been careful to look in his Map, they had all in probability been smothered in the Mud, for just a little before them, and that at the end of the cleanest way too, was a Pit, none knows how deep, full of nothing but Mud, there made on purpose to destroy the Pilgrims in.

The way difficult to find

The guide has a map of all ways leading to or from the city

Then thought I with myself, who that goeth on Pilgrimage but would have one of these Maps about him, that he may look when he is at a stand, which is the way he must take?

God's Book

They went on then in this Inchanted Ground till they came to where there was another Arbor, and it was built by the High-way side. And in that Arbor there lay two men whose names were *Heedless* and *Too-bold.* These two went thus far on Pilgrimage, but here being wearied with their Journey, they sat down to rest themselves, and so fell asleep. When the Pilgrims saw them, they stood still, and shook their heads, for they knew that the sleepers were in a pitiful case. Then they consulted what to do, whether to go on and leave them in their

An arbor and two asleep therein

sleep, or to step to them and try to awake them. So they concluded to go to them and awake them, that is, if they could; but with this caution, namely, to take heed that themselves did not sit down nor imbrace the offered benefit of that Arbor.

The pilgrims try to wake them

So they went in and spake to the men, and called each by his name, (for the Guide it seems did know them) but there was no voice nor answer. Then the Guide did shake them, and do what he could to disturb them. Then said one of them, *I will pay you when I take my Mony.* At which the Guide shook his Head. *I will fight so long as I can hold my Sword in my hand,* said the other. At that one of the Children laughed.

Their endeavor is fruitless

Then said *Christiana,* What is the meaning of this? The Guide said, *They talk in their Sleep.* If you strike them, beat them, or whatever else you do to them, they will answer you after this fashion; or as one of them said in old time, when the Waves of the Sea did beat upon him, and he slept as one upon the Mast of a Ship, *When I awake I will seek it again.* You know when men talk in their Sleeps they say anything, but their words are not governed either by Faith or Reason. There is an incoherency in their words now, as there was before betwixt their going on Pilgrimage and sitting down here. This then is the mischief on't, when *heedless* ones go on Pilgrimage 'tis twenty to one but they are served thus. For this Inchanted Ground is one of the last Refuges that the Enemy to Pilgrims has; wherefore it is, as you see, placed almost at the end of the Way, and so it standeth against us with the more advantage. For when, thinks the Enemy, will these Fools be so desirous to sit down, as when they are weary? and when so like to be weary, as when almost at their Journey's end? therefore it is I say, that the Inchanted Ground is placed so nigh to the Land *Beulah,* and so near the end of their Race. Wherefore let Pilgrims look to themselves, lest it happen to them as it has done to these, that, as you see, are fallen asleep, and none can wake them.

Then the Pilgrims desired with trembling to go forward; only they prayed their Guide to strike a Light, that they might go the rest of their way by the help of the Light of a Lanthorn. So he struck a Light, and they went by the help of that through the rest of this way, tho' the Darkness was very great.

The light of the Word

But the Children began to be sorely weary, and they cried out unto him that loveth Pilgrims to make their way more comfortable. So by that they had gone a little further, a Wind arose that drove away the Fog, so the Air became more clear.

The children cry for weariness

Yet they were not off (by much) of the Inchanted Ground, only now they could see one another better, and the way wherein they should walk.

Now when they were almost at the end of this ground, they perceived that a little before them was a solemn Noise, as of one that was much concerned. So they went on and looked before them; and behold they saw, as they thought, a man upon his Knees, with Hands and Eyes lift up, and speaking, as they thought, earnestly to one that was above. They drew nigh, but could not tell what he said; so they went softly till he had done. When he had done, he got up and began to run towards the Cœlestial City. Then Mr *Great-heart* called after him, saying, Soho Friend, let us have your Company, if you go, as I suppose you do, to the Cœlestial City. So the man stopped, and they came up to him. But so soon as Mr *Honest* saw him, he said, I know this man. Then said Mr *Valiant-for-truth,* Prithee, who is it? 'Tis one, said he, who comes from whereabouts I dwelt, his name is *Stand-fast,* he is certainly a right good Pilgrim.

Stand-fast upon his knees in the Enchanted ground

The story of Stand-fast

So they came up one to another; and presently *Stand-fast* said to old *Honest,* Ho Father *Honest,* are you there? Ay, said he, that I am, as sure as you are there. Right glad am I, said Mr *Stand-*

Talk between him and Mr Honest

fast, that I have found you on this Road. And as glad am I, said the other, that I espied you upon your Knees. Then Mr *Stand-fast* blushed, and said, But why, did you see me? Yes, that I did, quoth the other, and with my heart was glad at the sight. Why, what did you think? said *Stand-fast*. Think, said old *Honest*, what should I think? I thought we had an honest man upon the Road, and therefore should have his Company by and by. If you thought not amiss [said *Stand-fast*] how happy am I, but if I be not as I should, I alone must bear it. That is true, said the other, but your fear doth further confirm me that things are right betwixt the Prince of Pilgrims and your Soul, for he saith, *Blessed is the man that feareth always.*

They found him at prayer

VALIANT. Well but Brother, I pray thee tell us what was it that was the cause of thy being upon thy Knees even now? Was it for that some special mercy laid obligations upon thee, or how?

What it was that fetched him upon his knees

STAND-FAST. Why we are, as you see, upon the Inchanted Ground, and as I was coming along, I was musing with myself of what a dangerous Road the Road in this place was, and how many that had come even thus far on Pilgrimage had here been stopt and been destroyed. I thought also of the manner of the Death with which this place destroyeth men. Those that die here, die of no violent Distemper. The Death which such die is not grievous to them, for he that goeth away in a *sleep* begins that Journey with Desire and Pleasure; yea, such acquiesce in the will of that Disease.

HON. Then Mr *Honest* interrupting of him said, Did you see the two men asleep in the Arbor?

Madam Bubble, or this vain world

STAND-FAST. Ay, ay, I saw *Heedless* and *Too-bold* there, and for ought I know, there they will lie till they rot. But let me go on in my Tale. As I was thus musing, as I said, there was one in very pleasant attire, but old, who presented herself unto me, and offered me three things, to wit, her Body her Purse and her Bed. Now the truth is, I was both a-weary and sleepy, I am also as poor as a *Howlet,* and that perhaps the Witch knew. Well I repulsed her once and twice, but she put by my repulses, and smiled. Then I began to be angry, but she mattered that nothing at all. Then she made offers again, and said, If I would be ruled by her, she would make me great and happy, for said she, I am the Mistress of the World, and men are made happy by me. Then I asked her name, and she told me it was Madam *Bubble.* This set me further from her, but she still followed me with Inticements. Then I betook me, as you see, to my Knees, and with hands lift up and cries, I pray'd to him that had said he would help. So just as you came up, the Gentlewoman went her way. Then I continued to give thanks for this my great Deliverance, for I verily believe she intended no good, but rather sought to make stop of me in my Journey.

HON. Without doubt her Designs were bad. But stay, now you talk of her, methinks I either have seen her, or have read some story of her.

STAND-FAST. Perhaps you have done both.

HON. Madam *Bubble,* is she not a tall comely Dame, something of a swarthy Complexion?

STAND-FAST. Right, you hit it, she is just such an one.

HON. Doth she not speak very smoothly, and give you a Smile at the end of a Sentence?

STAND-FAST. You fall right upon it again, for these are her very Actions.

HON. Doth she not wear a great Purse by her side, and is not her Hand often in it fingering her Mony, as if that was her heart's delight?

STAND-FAST. 'Tis just so; had she stood by all this while, you could not more amply have set her forth before me, nor have better described her Features.

HON. Then he that drew her picture was a good Limner, and he that wrote of her said true.

The World

GREAT-HEART. This woman is a Witch, and it is by vertue of her Sorceries that this ground is inchanted. Whoever doth lay their Head down in her Lap, had as good lay it down upon that Block over which the Ax doth hang; and whoever lay their Eyes upon her Beauty, are counted the Enemies of God. This is she that maintaineth in their splendor all those that are the Enemies of Pilgrims. Yea, this is she that hath bought off many a man from a Pilgrim's Life. She is a great Gossiper, she is always, both she and her Daughters, at one Pilgrim's heels or another, now commending and then preferring the excellencies of this Life. She is a bold and impudent Slut, she will talk with any man. She always laugheth *poor* Pilgrims to scorn, but highly commends the *rich*. If there be one cunning to get Mony in a place, she will speak well of him from house to house. She loveth Banqueting and Feasting mainly well, she is always at one full Table or another. She has given it out in some places that she is a Goddess, and therefore some do worship her. She has her times and open places of Cheating, and she will say and avow it that none can shew a good comparable to hers. She promiseth to dwell with Children's Children, if they will but love and make much of her. She will cast out of her Purse Gold like Dust, in some places, and to some persons. She loves to be sought after, spoken well of, and to lie in the Bosoms of Men. She is never weary of commending her Commodities, and she loves them most that think best of her. She will promise to some Crowns and Kingdoms if they will but take her advice, yet many has she brought to the Halter, and ten thousand times more to Hell.

STAND-FAST. Oh, said *Stand-fast,* what a mercy is it that I did resist her, for whither might she a drawn me?

GREAT-HEART. Whither, nay, none but God knows whither. But in general to be sure, she would a drawn thee *into many foolish and hurtful Lusts, which drown men in Destruction and Perdition.* 'Twas she that set *Absalom* against his Father, and *Jeroboam* against his Master. 'Twas she that persuaded *Judas* to sell his Lord, and that prevailed with *Demas* to forsake the godly Pilgrim's Life. None can tell of the Mischief that she doth. She makes variance betwixt Rulers and Subjects, betwixt Parents and Children, 'twixt Neighbor and Neighbor, 'twixt a Man and his Wife, 'twixt a Man and Himself, 'twixt the Flesh and the Heart.

Wherefore good Master *Stand-fast,* be as your name is, and when you have done all, *stand.*

At this Discourse there was among the Pilgrims a mixture of Joy and Trembling, but at length they brake out, and sang,

> What danger is the Pilgrim in,
> How many are his Foes,
> How many ways there are to sin,
> No living mortal knows.
>
> Some of the Ditch shy are, yet can
> Lie tumbling on the Mire;
> Some tho' they shun the Frying-pan,
> Do leap into the Fire.

After this I beheld until they were come unto the Land of *Beulah,* where the Sun shineth Night and Day. Here, because they was weary, they betook themselves a while to rest. And because this Country was common for Pilgrims, and because the Orchards and Vineyards that were here belonged to the King of the Cœlestial Country, therefore they were licensed to make bold with any of his things. But a little while soon refreshed them here; for the Bells did so ring, and the Trumpets continually sound so melodiously, that they could not sleep; and yet they received as much refreshing as if they had slept their sleep never so soundly. Here also all the noise of them that walked the Streets, was, *More Pilgrims are come to Town.* And

First Part, p. 158

another would answer, saying, And so many went over the Water, and were let in at the Golden Gates to-day. They would cry again, There is now a Legion of Shining Ones just come to Town, by which we know that there are more Pilgrims upon the road, for here they come to wait for them, and to comfort them after all their Sorrow. Then the Pilgrims got up and walked to and fro; but how were their Ears now filled with Heavenly Noises, and their eyes delighted with Cœlestial Visions! In this Land they heard nothing, saw nothing, felt nothing, smelt nothing, tasted nothing, that was offensive to their Stomach or Mind; only when they tasted of the Water of the River over which they were to go, they thought that tasted a little *bitterish* to the Palate, but it proved sweeter when 'twas down.

Death bitter to the flesh, but sweet to the soul

Death has its ebbings and flowings like the tide

In this place there was a Record kept of the names of them that had been Pilgrims of old, and a History of all the famous Acts that they had done. It was here also much discoursed how the River to some had had its *flowings,* and what *ebbings* it has had while others have gone over. It has been in a manner dry for some, while it has overflowed its banks for others.

In this place the Children of the Town would go into the King's Gardens and gather Nosegays for the Pilgrims, and bring them to them with much affection. Here also grew *Camphire* with *Spikenard* and *Saffron Calamus* and *Cinnamon,* with all its Trees of *Frankincense Myrrh* and *Aloes,* with all chief Spices. With these the Pilgrim's Chambers were perfumed while they stayed here, and with these were their Bodies anointed, to prepare them to go over the River when the time appointed was come.

A messenger of death sent to Christiana

Now while they lay here and waited for the good hour, there was a noise in the Town that there was a Post come from the Cœlestial City, with matter of great importance to one *Christiana* the Wife of *Christian* the Pilgrim. So enquiry was made for her, and the house was found out where she was. So the Post presented her with a Letter, the contents whereof was, *Hail, good Woman, I bring thee Tidings that the Master calleth for thee, and expecteth that thou shouldest stand in his presence in Cloaths of Immortality, within this ten days.*

His message

When he had read this Letter to her, he gave her therewith a sure token that he was a true Messenger, and was come to bid her make haste to be gone. The token was an *Arrow* with a point sharpened with Love, let easily into her heart, which by degrees wrought so effectually with her, that at the time appointed she must be gone.

How welcome is death to them that have nothing to do but to die

When *Christiana* saw that her time was come, and that she was the first of this Company that was to go over, she called for Mr *Great-heart* her Guide, and told him how matters were. So he told her he was heartily glad of the News, and could have been glad had the Post come for him. Then she bid that he should give advice how all things should be prepared for her Journey. So he told her, saying, Thus and thus it must be, and we that survive will accompany you to the River-side.

Her speech to her guide

Then she called for her Children, and gave them her Blessing, and told them that she yet read with comfort the Mark that was set in their Foreheads, and was glad to see them with her there, and that they had kept their Garments so white. Lastly, she bequeathed to the Poor that little she had, and commanded her Sons and her Daughters to be ready against the Messenger should come for them.

To her children

When she had spoken these words to her Guide and to her Children, she called for Mr *Valiant-for-truth,* and said unto him, Sir, you have in all places shewed yourself true-hearted, be faithful unto Death, and my King will give you a Crown of Life. I would also entreat you to have an eye to my Children, and if at any time you see them faint, speak comfortably to them. For my Daughters, my Sons'

To Mr Valiant

Wives, they have been faithful, and a fulfilling of the Promise upon them will be their end. But she gave Mr *Stand-fast* a Ring.

To Mr Stand-fast

To old Honest

Then she called for old Mr *Honest,* and said of him, Behold an *Israelite* indeed, in whom is no Guile. Then said he, I wish you a fair day when you set out for Mount *Sion,* and shall be glad to see that you go over the River dry-shod. But she answered, Come wet, come dry, I long to be gone, for however the Weather is in my Journey, I shall have time enough when I come there to sit down and rest me and dry me.

To Mr Ready-to-halt

Then came in that good man Mr *Ready-to-halt* to see her. So she said to him, Thy Travel hither has been with difficulty, but that will make thy Rest the sweeter. But watch and be ready, for at an hour when you think not, the Messenger may come.

To Dispondency and his daughter

After him came in Mr *Dispondency* and his Daughter *Much-afraid,* to whom she said, You ought with thankfulness for ever to remember your Deliverance from the hands of Giant *Despair* and out of *Doubting* Castle. The effect of that Mercy is, that you are brought with safety hither. Be ye watchful and cast away Fear, be sober and hope to the end.

To Feeble-mind

Then she said to Mr *Feeble-mind,* Thou wast delivered from the mouth of Giant *Slay-good,* that thou mightest live in the Light of the Living for ever, and see thy King with comfort. Only I advise thee to repent thee of thine aptness to fear and doubt of his goodness before he sends for thee, lest thou shouldest when he comes, be forced to stand before him for that fault with blushing.

Her last day, and manner of departure

Now the day drew on that *Christiana* must be gone. So the Road was full of People to see her take her Journey. But behold all the Banks beyond the River were full of Horses and Chariots, which were come down from above to accompany her to the City Gate. So she came forth and entered the River, with a beckon of Farewell to those that followed her to the River-side. The last word she was heard to say here was, *I come Lord, to be with thee and bless thee.*

So her Children and Friends returned to their place, for that those that waited for *Christiana* had carried her out of their sight. So she went and called, and entered in at the Gate with all the Ceremonies of Joy that her Husband *Christian* had done before her.

At her departure her Children wept, but Mr *Great-heart* and Mr *Valiant* played upon the well-tuned Cymbal and Harp for Joy. So all departed to their respective places.

Ready-to-halt summoned

In process of time there came a Post to the Town again, and his business was with Mr *Ready-to-halt.* So he enquired him out, and said to him, I am come to thee in the name of him whom thou hast loved and followed, tho' upon Crutches; and my Message is to tell thee that he expects thee at his Table to sup with him in his Kingdom the next day after *Easter,* wherefore prepare thyself for this Journey.

Then he also gave him a Token that he was a true Messenger, saying, *I have broken thy golden bowl, and loosed thy silver cord.*

Promises

After this Mr *Ready-to-halt* called for his fellow Pilgrims, and told them, saying, I am sent for, and God shall surely visit you also. So he desired Mr *Valiant* to make his Will. And because he had nothing to bequeath to them that should survive him but his Crutches and his good Wishes, therefore thus he said, *These Crutches I bequeath to my Son that shall tread in my steps, with a hundred warm wishes that he may prove better than I have done.*

His will

His last words

Then he thanked Mr *Great-heart* for his Conduct and Kindness, and so addressed himself to his Journey. When he came at the Brink of the River he said, *Now I shall have no more need of these*

Crutches, since yonder are Chariots and Horses for me to ride on. The last words he was heard to say was, *Welcome Life.* So he went his way.

Feeble-mind summoned

After this Mr *Feeble-mind* had Tidings brought him that the Post sounded his Horn at his Chamber-door. Then he came in and told him, saying, I am come to tell thee that thy Master has need of thee, and that in very little time thou must behold his Face in Brightness. And take this as a Token of the Truth of my Message, *Those that look out at the Windows shall be darkened.*

He makes no will

Then Mr *Feeble-mind* called for his Friends, and told them what Errand had been brought unto him, and what Token he had received of the Truth of the Message. Then he said, Since I have nothing to bequeath to any, to what purpose should I make a Will? As for my *feeble mind,* that I will leave behind me, for that I have no need of that in the place whither I go. Nor is it worth bestowing upon the poorest Pilgrim; wherefore when I am gone, I desire that you, Mr *Valiant,* would bury it in a Dunghill. This done, and the day being come in which he was to depart, he entered the River as the rest. His last words were, *Hold out Faith and Patience.* So he went over to the other side.

His last words

Mr Dispondency's summons

When days had many of them passed away, Mr *Dispondency* was sent for. For a Post was come, and brought this Message to him, *Trembling man, these are to summon thee to be ready with thy King by the next Lord's day, to shout for Joy for thy Deliverance from all thy Doubtings.*

His daughter goes too

And said the Messenger, That my Message is true take this for a Proof; so he gave him *The Grasshopper to be a Burden unto him.* Now Mr *Dispondency's* Daughter whose name was *Much-afraid* said when she heard what was done, that she would go with her Father. Then Mr *Dispondency* said to his Friends, Myself and my Daughter, you know what we have been, and how troublesomely we have behaved ourselves in every Company. My Will and my Daughter's is, that our Disponds and slavish Fears be by no man ever received from the day of our Departure for ever, for I know that after my Death they will offer themselves to others. For to be plain with you, they are Ghosts, the which we entertained when we first began to be Pilgrims, and could never shake them off after; and they will walk about and seek entertainment of the Pilgrims, but for our sakes shut ye the doors upon them. His will

When the time was come for them to depart, they went to the Brink of the River. The last words of Mr *Dispondency* were, *Farewell Night, welcome Day.* His Daughter went through the River singing, but none could understand what she said. His last words

Then it came to pass a while after, that there was a Post in the town that enquired for Mr *Honest*. So he came to his house where he was, and delivered to his hand these lines, *Thou art commanded to be ready against this day seven-night to present thyself before thy Lord at his Father's house.* And for a Token that my Message is true, *All thy Daughters of Musick shall be brought low.* Then Mr *Honest* called for his Friends, and said unto them, I die, but shall make no Will. As for my Honesty, it shall go with me; let him that comes after be told of this. When the day that he was to be gone was come, he addressed himself to go over the River. Now the River at that time overflowed the Banks in some places, but Mr *Honest* in his lifetime had spoken to one *Good-conscience* to meet him there, the which he also did, and lent him his hand, and so helped him over. The last words of Mr *Honest* were, *Grace reigns.* So he left the World. Mr Honest summoned He makes no will Good-conscience helps Mr Honest over the river

After this it was noised abroad that Mr *Valiant-for-truth* was taken with a Summons by the same Mr Valiant summoned

Post as the other, and had this for a Token that the Summons was true, *That his Pitcher was broken at the Fountain.* When he understood it, he called for his Friends, and told them of it. Then said he, I am going to my Fathers, and tho' with great difficulty I am got hither, yet now I do not repent me of all the Trouble I have been at to arrive where I am. My Sword I give to him that shall succeed me in my Pilgrimage, and my Courage and Skill to him that can get it. My Marks and Scars I carry with me, to be a witness for me that I have fought his Battles who now will be my Rewarder. When the day that he must go hence was come, many accompanied him to the River-side, into which as he went he said, *Death, where is thy Sting?* And as he went down deeper he said, *Grave, where is thy Victory?* So he passed over, and all the Trumpets sounded for him on the other side.

His will

His last words

Mr Stand-fast is summoned

Then there came forth a Summons for Mr *Stand-fast,* (This Mr *Stand-fast* was he that the rest of the Pilgrims found upon his Knees in the Inchanted Ground) for the Post brought it him open in his hands. The contents whereof, were, *that he must prepare for a Change of Life, for his Master was not willing that he should be so far from him any longer.* At this Mr *Stand-fast* was put into a muse. Nay, said the Messenger, you need not doubt of the truth of my Message, for here is a Token of the Truth thereof, *Thy Wheel is broken at the Cistern.* Then he called to him Mr *Great-heart* who was their Guide, and said, unto him, Sir, altho' it was not my hap to be much in your good Company in the days of my Pilgrimage, yet since the time I knew you, you have been profitable to me. When I came from home, I left behind me a Wife and five small Children, let me entreat you at your return, (for I know that you will go and return to your Master's house, in hopes that you may yet be a Conductor to more of the holy Pilgrims) that you send to my

He calls for Mr Great-heart

His speech to him

Family, and let them be acquainted with all that hath and shall happen unto me. Tell them moreover of my happy Arrival to this place, and of the present late blessed condition that I am in. Tell them also of *Christian* and *Christiana* his Wife, and how she and her Children came after her Husband. Tell them also of what a happy end she made, and whither she is gone. I have little or nothing to send to my Family, except it be Prayers and Tears for them; of which it will suffice if thou acquaint them, if peradventure they may prevail.

His errand to his family

When Mr *Stand-fast* had thus set things in order, and the time being come for him to haste him away, he also went down to the River. Now there was a great Calm at that time in the River; wherefore Mr *Stand-fast,* when he was about half-way in, he stood awhile, and talked to his Companions that had waited upon him thither. And he said,

His last words

This River has been a Terror to many, yea, the thoughts of it also have often frighted me. But now methinks I stand easy, my Foot is fixed upon that upon which the Feet of the Priests that bare the Ark of the Covenant stood, while *Israel* went over this *Jordan.* The Waters indeed are to the Palate bitter and to the Stomach cold, yet the thoughts of what I am going to and of the Conduct that waits for me on the other side, doth lie as a glowing Coal at my Heart.

I see myself now at the end of my Journey, my toilsome days are ended. I am going now to see that Head that was crowned with Thorns, and that Face that was spit upon for me.

I have formerly lived by Hear-say and Faith, but now I go where I shall live by sight, and shall be with him in whose Company I delight myself.

I have loved to hear my Lord spoken of, and wherever I have seen the print of his Shoe in the Earth, there I have coveted to set my Foot too.

His Name has been to me as a Civit-box, yea, sweeter than all Perfumes. His Voice to me has been most sweet, and his Countenance I have more desired than they that have most desired the Light of the Sun. His Word I did use to gather for my Food, and for Antidotes against my Faintings. He has held me, and I have kept me from mine iniquities, yea, my Steps hath he strengthened in his Way.

Now while he was thus in Discourse, his Countenance changed, his strong man bowed under him, and after he had said, *Take me, for I come unto thee,* he ceased to be seen of them.

But glorious it was to see how the open Region was filled with Horses and Chariots, with Trumpeters and Pipers, with Singers and Players on stringed Instruments, to welcome the Pilgrims as they went up, and followed one another in at the beautiful Gate of the City.

As for *Christian's* Children, the four Boys that *Christiana* brought with her, with their Wives and Children, I did not stay where I was till they were gone over. Also since I came away, I heard one say that they were yet alive, and so would be for the Increase of the Church in that place where they were for a time.

Shall it be my Lot to go that way again, I may give those that desire it an account of what I here am silent about; mean-time I bid my Reader *Adieu.*

THE AUTHOR'S VINDICATION

OF HIS PILGRIM

FOUND AT THE END OF HIS "HOLY WAR"

SOME say the Pilgrim's Progress *is not mine,*
Insinuating as if I would shine
In name and fame by the worth of another,
Like some made rich by robbing of their Brother.
Or that so fond I am of being Sire,
I'll father Bastards; or if need require,
I'll tell a lye in print to get applause.
I scorn it: John *such dirt-heap never was,*
Since God converted him. Let this suffice
To show why I my Pilgrim *patronize.*
It came from mine own heart, so to my head,
And thence into my fingers trickled;
Then to my pen, from whence immediately
On paper I did dribble it daintily.
Manner and matter too was all mine own,
Nor was it unto any mortal known,
Till I had done it. Nor did any then
By books, by wits, by tongues, or hand, or pen,
Add five words to it, or write half a line
Thereof: the whole and every whit is mine.
Also, for this thine eye is now upon,
The matter in this manner came from none
But the same heart and head, fingers and pen,
As did the other. Witness all good men;
For none in all the world, without a lye,
Can say that this is mine, *excepting I.*
I write not this of any ostentation,
Nor 'cause I seek of men their commendation;

I do it to keep them from such surmise,
As tempt them will my name to scandalize.
Witness my name, if anagram'd to thee,
The letters make, Nu hony in a B.

JOHN BUNYAN.

THE LIFE OF DR. DONNE

INTRODUCTORY NOTE

Izaak Walton *was born on August 9, 1593, in Staffordshire, England. He came to London where he served his apprenticeship as an ironmonger, and later seems to have been in business on his own account. He was a loyal member of the Church of England, and was on terms of friendship with a number of distinguished divines, notably Dr. John Donne, who, when he was vicar of Saint Dunstan's, was a near neighbor of Walton's. In politics he sympathized warmly with the Royalist party, and it has been supposed that it was the triumph of the Parliament in the Civil War that led him in 1644 to retire from business, and, for a time, from London. Most of his old age was spent with his friend, George Morley, Bishop of Winchester, and with his daughter Anne, the wife of William Hawkins, a prebendary of Winchester. In the house of the latter he died in December, 1683, and was buried in Winchester Cathedral. He was twice married.*

Walton's chief literary work, "The Compleat Angler, or the Contemplative Man's Recreation," was published when he was sixty, and he induced his friend, Charles Cotton, to supplement it with a treatise on fly-fishing, which was incorporated with Walton's fifth edition in 1676. Whatever may be the value of this work as a practical guide, it remains the literary classic of the gentle art of angling, and is remarkable for its success in conveying in delightful prose the charm of English meadows and streams.

"The Life of Dr. Donne" was written by Walton in 1640 as an introduction to a collection of Donne's sermons; and thirty years later was issued in a volume with lives of Sir Henry Wotton, Richard Hooker, and George Herbert. In 1678 he completed his biographical labors with a life of Robert Sanderson. These lives are in their way models of short biography. The charming personality of Walton himself, and the clarity and delicacy of a style of high artistic simplicity, set off a narrative in which facts are not allowed to obscure the outlines of a character drawn with loving admiration. Few bulky official lives succeed in giving the reader so vivid a picture of personality as these sketches from the hand of Izaak Walton.

THE LIFE OF DR. DONNE

MASTER JOHN DONNE was born in London, in the year 1573, of good and virtuous parents; and, though his own learning and other multiplied merits may justly appear sufficient to dignify both himself and his posterity, yet the reader may be pleased to know that his father was masculinely and lineally descended from a very ancient family in Wales, where many of his name now live, that deserve, and have great reputation in that country.

By his mother he was descended of the family of the famous and learned Sir Thomas More, sometime Lord Chancellor of England: as also, from that worthy and laborious judge Rastall, who left posterity the vast statutes of the law of this nation most exactly abridged.

He had his first breeding in his father's house, where a private tutor had the care of him, until the tenth year of his age; and, in his eleventh year, was sent to the University of Oxford; having at that time a good command both of the French and Latin tongue. This, and some other of his remarkable abilities, made one then give this censure of him: That this age had brought forth another Picus Mirandola; of whom story says that he was rather born than made wise by study.

There he remained for some years in Hart Hall, having for the advancement of his studies, tutors of several sciences to attend and instruct him, till time made him capable, and his learning expressed in public exercises declared him worthy, to receive his first degree in the schools, which he forbore by advice from his friends, who, being for their religion of the Romish persuasion, were conscionably averse to some parts of the oath that is always tendered at those times, and not to be refused by those that expect the titulary honour of their studies.

About the fourteenth year of his age he was transplanted from Oxford to Cambridge, where, that he might receive nourishment from both soils, he stayed till his seventeenth year; all which time he was a most laborious student, often changing his studies, but endeavouring to take no degree, for the reasons formerly mentioned.

About the seventeenth year of his age he was removed to London, and then admitted into Lincoln's Inn, with an intent to study the law; where he gave great testimonies of his wit, his learning, and of his improvement in that profession; which never served him for other use than an ornament and self-satisfaction.

His father died before his admission into this society, and, being a merchant, left him his portion in money. (It was £3000.) His mother, and those to whose care he was committed, were watchful to improve his knowledge, and to that end appointed him tutors, both in the mathematics and in all the other liberal sciences, to attend him. But with these arts they were advised to instil into him particular principles of the Romish Church, of which those tutors professed, though secretly, themselves to be members.

They had almost obliged him to their faith; having for their advantage, besides many opportunities, the example of his dear and pious parents, which was a most powerful persuasion, and did work much upon him, as he professeth in his Preface to his *Pseudo-Martyr,* a book of which the reader shall have some account in what follows.

He was now entered into the eighteenth year of his age, and at that time had betrothed himself to no religion that might give him any other denomination than a Christian. And reason and piety had both persuaded him that there could be no such sin as schism, if an adherence to some visible church were not necessary.

About the nineteenth year of his age, he, being then unresolved what religion to adhere to, and considering how much it concerned his soul to choose the most orthodox, did therefore,—though his youth and health promised him a long life, —to rectify all scruples that might concern that, presently laid aside all study of the law, and of all other sciences that might give him a denomination; and began seriously to survey and consider the body of divinity, as it was then controverted betwixt the reformed and the Roman Church. And as God's blessed Spirit did then awaken him to the search, and in that industry did never forsake him,—they be his own words,[1]—so he calls the same Holy Spirit to witness this protestation; that in that disquisition and search he proceeded with humility and diffidence in himself, and by that which he took to be the safest way, namely, frequent prayers, and an indifferent affection to both parties; and indeed, truth had too much light about her to be hid from so sharp an inquirer; and he had too much ingenuity not to acknowledge he had found her.

Being to undertake this search, he believed the Cardinal Bellarmine to be the best defender of the Roman cause, and therefore betook himself to the examination of his reasons. The cause was weighty, and wilful delays had been inexcusable both towards God and his own conscience: he therefore proceeded in this search with all moderate haste, and about the twentieth year of his age did show the then Dean of Gloucester—whose name my memory hath now lost—all the Cardinal's works marked with many weighty observations under his own hand; which works were bequeathed by him, at his death, as a legacy to a most dear friend.

About a year following he resolved to travel; and the Earl of Essex going first to Cales, and after the island voyages, the first anno 1596, the second 1597, he took the advantage of those opportunities, waited upon his lordship, and was an eye-witness of those happy and unhappy employments.

But he returned not back into England till he had stayed some years, first in Italy, and then in Spain, where he made many useful observations of those countries, their laws and manner of government, and returned perfect in their languages.

The time that he spent in Spain was, at his first going into Italy, designed for travelling to the Holy Land, and for viewing Jerusalem and the sepulchre of our Saviour. But at his being in the farthest parts of Italy, the disappointment of company, or of a safe convoy, or the uncertainty of returns of money into those remote parts, denied him that

[1] In his Preface to Pseudo-Martyr.

happiness, which he did often occasionally mention with a deploration.

Not long after his return into England, that exemplary pattern of gravity and wisdom, the Lord Ellesmere, then Keeper of the Great Seal, the Lord Chancellor of England, taking notice of his learning, languages, and other abilities, and much affecting his person and behaviour, took him to be his chief secretary; supposing and intending it to be an introduction to some more weighty employment in the State; for which, his Lordship did often protest, he thought him very fit.

Nor did his Lordship in this time of Master Donne's attendance upon him, account him to be so much his servant, as to forget he was his friend; and, to testify it, did always use him with much courtesy, appointing him a place at his own table, to which he esteemed his company and discourse to be a great ornament.

He continued that employment for the space of five years, being daily useful, and not mercenary to his friend. During which time, he—I dare not say unhappily—fell into such a liking, as—with her approbation—increased into a love, with a young gentlewoman that lived in that family, who was niece to the Lady Ellesmere, and daughter to Sir George More, then Chancellor of the Garter and Lieutenant of the Tower.

Sir George had some intimation of it, and, knowing prevention to be a great part of wisdom, did therefore remove her with much haste from that to his own house at Lothesley, in the County of Surrey; but too late, by reason of some faithful promises which were so interchangeably passed, as never to be violated by either party.

These promises were only known to themselves; and the friends of both parties used much diligence, and many arguments, to kill or cool their affections to each other: but in vain; for love is a flattering mischief, that hath denied aged and wise men a foresight of those evils that too often prove to be the children of that blind father; a passion, that carries us to commit errors with as much ease as whirlwinds move feathers, and begets in us an unwearied industry to the attainment of what we desire. And such an industry did, notwithstanding much watchfulness against it, bring them secretly together,—I forbear to tell the manner how,—and at last to a marriage too, without the allowance of those friends, whose approbation always was, and ever will be necessary, to make even a virtuous love become lawful.

And, that the knowledge of their marriage might not fall, like an unexpected tempest, on those that were unwilling to have it so; and that pre-apprehensions might make it the less enormous when it was known, it was purposely whispered into the ears of many that it was so, yet by none that could affirm it. But, to put a period to the jealousies of Sir George,—doubt often begetting more restless thoughts than the certain knowledge of what we fear,—the news was, in favour to Mr. Donne, and with his allowance, made known to Sir George by his honourable friend and neighbour, Henry, Earl of Northumberland; but it was to Sir George so immeasurably unwelcome, and so transported him, that, as though his passion of anger and inconsideration might exceed theirs of love and error, he presently engaged his sister, the Lady Ellesmere, to join with him to procure her lord to discharge Mr. Donne of the place he held under his Lordship. This request was followed with violence; and though Sir George was remembered that errors might be over-punished, and desired therefore to forbear till second considerations might clear some scruples, yet he became restless until his suit was granted, and the punishment executed. And though the Lord Chancellor did not, at Mr. Donne's dismission, give him such a commendation as the great Emperor Charles the Fifth did of his Secretary Eraso, when he parted with him to his son and successor, Philip the Second, saying, "That in his Eraso, he gave to him a greater gift than all his estate, and all the kingdoms which he then resigned to him;" yet the Lord Chancellor said, "He parted with a friend, and such a secretary as was fitter to serve a king than a subject."

Immediately after his dismission from his service he sent a sad letter to his wife, to acquaint her with it; and after the subscription of his name, writ,

John Donne, Anne Donne, Un-done;

And God knows it proved too true; for this bitter physic of Mr. Donne's dismission was not enough to purge out all Sir George's choler; for he was not satisfied till Mr. Donne and his sometime com-pupil in Cambridge, that married him, namely, Samuel Brooke, who was after Doctor in Divinity and Master of Trinity College, and his brother, Mr. Christopher Brooke, sometime Mr. Donne's chamber-fellow in Lincoln's Inn, who gave Mr. Donne his wife, and witnessed the marriage, were all committed to three several prisons.

Mr. Donne was first enlarged, who neither gave rest to his body or brain, nor to any friend in whom he might hope to have an interest, until he had procured an enlargement for his two imprisoned friends.

He was now at liberty, but his days were still cloudy: and being past these troubles, others did still multiply upon him; for his wife was—to her extreme sorrow—detained from him; and though with Jacob he endured not a hard service for her, yet he lost a good one, and was forced to make good his title, and to get possession of her by a long and restless suit in law; which proved troublesome and sadly chargeable to him, whose youth, and travel, and needless bounty had brought his estate into a narrow compass.

It is observed, and most truly, that silence and submission are charming qualities, and work most upon passionate men; and it proved so with Sir George; for these, and a general report of Mr. Donne's merits, together with his winning behaviour, which, when it would entice, had a strange kind of elegant irresistible art;—these and time had so dispassionated Sir George, that as the world approved his daughter's choice, so he also could not but see a more than ordinary merit in his new son; and this at last melted him into so much remorse,—for love and anger are so like agues, as to have hot and cold fits; and love in parents, though it may be quenched, yet is easily re-kindled, and expires not till death denies mankind a natural heat,—that he laboured his son's restoration to his place; using to that end both his own and his sister's power to her lord; but with no success, for his answer was, " That though he was unfeignedly sorry for what he had done, yet it was inconsistent with his place and credit to discharge and re-admit servants at the request of passionate petitioners."

Sir George's endeavour for Mr. Donne's re-admission was by all means to be kept secret: for men do more naturally reluct for errors than submit to put on those blemishes that attend their visible acknowledgment.—But, however, it was not long before Sir George appeared to be so far reconciled as to wish their happiness, and not to deny them his paternal blessing, but yet refused to contribute any means that might conduce to their livelihood.

Mr. Donne's estate was the greater part spent in many and chargeable travels, books, and dear-bought experience; he out of all employment that might yield a support for himself and wife, who had been curiously and plentifully educated; both their natures generous, and accustomed to confer, and not to receive, courtesies: these and other considerations, but chiefly that his wife was to bear a part in his sufferings, surrounded him with many sad thoughts, and some apparent apprehensions of want.

But his sorrows were lessened and his wants prevented by the seasonable courtesy of their noble kinsman, Sir Francis Wolly, of Pirford, in Surrey, who entreated them to a cohabitation with him, where they remained with much freedom to themselves, and equal content to him, for some years; and as their charge increased—she had yearly a child—so did his love and bounty.

It hath been observed by wise and considering men that wealth hath seldom been the portion, and never the mark to discover good people; but that Almighty God, who disposeth all things wisely, hath of his abundant goodness denied it—He only knows why—to many whose minds He hath enriched with the greater blessings of knowledge and virtue, as the fairer testimonies of his love to mankind: and this was the present condition of this man of so excellent erudition and endowments; whose necessary and daily expenses were hardly reconcilable with his uncertain and narrow estate. Which I mention, for that at this time there was a most generous offer made him for the moderating of his worldly cares; the declaration of which shall be the next employment of my pen.

God hath been so good to his church as to afford it in every age some such men to serve at his altar as have been piously ambitious of doing good to mankind; a disposition that is so like to God himself that it owes itself only to Him, who takes a pleasure to behold it in his creatures. These times[1] He did bless with many such; some of which still live to be patterns of apostolical charity, and of more than human patience. I have said this because I have occasion to mention one of them in my following discourse, namely, Dr. Morton, the most laborious and learned Bishop of Durham; one that God hath blessed with perfect intellectuals and a cheerful heart at the age of ninety-four years—and is yet living;—one that in his days of plenty had so large a heart as to use his large revenue to the encouragement of learning and virtue, and is now—be it spoken with sorrow—reduced to a narrow estate, which he embraces without repining; and still shows the beauty of his mind by so liberal a hand, as if this were an age in which to-morrow were to care for itself. I have taken a pleasure in giving the reader a short but true character of this good man, my friend, from whom I received this following relation.—He sent to Mr. Donne, and entreated to borrow an hour of his time for a conference the next day. After their meeting there was not many minutes passed before he spake to Mr. Donne to this purpose: "Mr. Donne, the occasion of sending for you is to propose to you what I have often revolved in my own thought since I last saw you: which, nevertheless, I will not declare but upon this condition, that you shall not return me a present answer, but forbear three days, and bestow some part of that time in fasting and prayer; and after a serious consideration of what I shall propose, then return to me with your answer. Deny me not, Mr. Donne; for it is the effect of a true love, which I would gladly pay as a debt due for yours to me."

This request being granted, the Doctor expressed himself thus:—

"Mr. Donne, I know your education and abilities; I know your expectation of a State employment; and I know your fitness for it; and I know, too, the many delays and contingencies that attend Court promises: and let me tell you

[1] 1648.

that my love, begot by our long friendship and your merits, hath prompted me to such an inquisition after your present temporal estate as makes me no stranger to your necessities, which I know to be such as your generous spirit could not bear if it were not supported with a pious patience. You know I have formerly persuaded you to waive your Court hopes, and enter into holy orders; which I now again persuade you to embrace, with this reason added to my former request: The King hath yesterday made me Dean of Gloucester, and I am also possessed of a benefice, the profits of which are equal to those of my deanery; I will think my deanery enough for my maintenance,—who am, and resolved to die, a single man,—and will quit my benefice, and estate you in it, which the patron is willing I shall do, if God shall incline your heart to embrace this motion. Remember, Mr. Donne, no man's education or parts make him too good for this employment, which is to be an ambassador for the God of glory; that God who by a vile death opened the gates of life to mankind. Make me no present answer; but remember your promise, and return to me the third day with your resolution."

At the hearing of this, Mr. Donne's faint breath and perplexed countenance give a visible testimony of an inward conflict; but he performed his promise, and departed without returning an answer till the third day, and then his answer was to this effect:—

"My most worthy and most dear friend, since I saw you I have been faithful to my promise, and have also meditated much of your great kindness, which hath been such as would exceed even my gratitude; but that it cannot do; and more I cannot return you; and I do that with an heart full of humility and thanks, though I may not accept of your offer: but, sir, my refusal is not for that I think myself too good for that calling, for which kings, if they think so, are not good enough; nor for that my education and learning, though not eminent, may not, being assisted with God's grace and humility, render me in some measure fit for it: but I dare make so dear a friend as you are my confessor. Some irregularities of my life have been so visible to some men, that though I have, I thank God, made my peace with Him by penitential resolutions against them, and by the assistance of his grace banished them my affections; yet this, which God knows to be so, is not so visible to man as to free me from their censures, and it may be that sacred calling from a dishonour. And besides, whereas it is determined by the best of casuists that God's glory should be the first end, and a maintenance the second motive to embrace that calling, and though each man may propose to himself both together, yet the first may not be put last without a violation of conscience, which he that searches the heart will judge. And truly my present condition is such that if I ask my own conscience whether it be reconcilable to that rule, it is at this time so perplexed about it, that I can neither give myself nor you an answer. You know, sir, who says, 'Happy is that man whose conscience doth not accuse him for that thing which he does.' To these I might add other reasons that dissuade me; but I crave your favour that I may forbear to express them, and thankfully decline your offer."

This was his present resolution, but the heart of man is not in his own keeping; and he was destined to this sacred service by an higher hand—a hand so powerful as at last forced him to a compliance: of which I shall give the reader an account before I shall give a rest to my pen.

Mr. Donne and his wife continued with Sir Francis Wolly till his death: a little before which time Sir Francis was so happy as to make a perfect reconciliation betwixt Sir George and his forsaken son and daughter; Sir George conditioning by bond to pay to Mr. Donne £800 at a certain day, as a portion with his wife, or £20 quarterly for their maintenance as the interest for it, till the said portion was paid.

Most of those years that he lived with Sir Francis he studied the Civil and Canon Laws; in which he acquired such a perfection, as was judged to hold proportion with many who had made that study the employment of their whole life.

Sir Francis being dead, and that happy family dissolved, Mr. Donne took for himself a house in Mitcham, near to Croydon in Surrey, a place noted for good air and choice company: there his wife and children remained; and for himself he took lodgings in London, near to Whitehall, whither his friends and occasions drew him very often, and where he was as often visited by many of the nobility and others of this nation, who used him in their counsels of greatest consideration, and with some rewards for his better subsistence.

Nor did our own nobility only value and favour him, but his acquaintance and friendship was sought for by most ambassadors of foreign nations, and by many other strangers, whose learning or business occasioned their stay in this nation.

He was much importuned by many friends to make his constant residence in London; but he still denied it, having settled his dear wife and children at Mitcham, and near some friends that were bountiful to them and him; for they, God knows, needed it: and that you may the better now judge of the then present condition of his mind and fortune, I shall present you with an extract collected out of some few of his many letters.

" . . . And the reason why I did not send an answer to your last week's letter was, because it then found me under too great a sadness; and at present 'tis thus with me: There is not one person, but myself, well of my family: I have already lost half a child, and, with that mischance of hers, my wife has fallen into such a discomposure as would afflict her too extremely, but that the sickness of all her other children stupefies her—of one of which, in good faith, I have not much hope; and these meet with a fortune so ill-provided for physic, and such relief, that if God should ease us with burials, I know not how to perform even that: but I flatter myself with this hope, that I am dying too; for I cannot waste faster than by such griefs. As for,—

From my Hospital at Mitcham,

Aug. 10. JOHN DONNE."

Thus he did bemoan himself; and thus in other letters—

" . . . For, we hardly discover a sin, when it is but an omission of some good, and no accusing act: with this or the former I have often suspected myself to be overtaken; which is, with an over-earnest desire of the next life: and, though I know it is not merely a weariness of this, because I had the same desire when I went with the tide, and enjoyed fairer hopes than I now do; yet I doubt worldly troubles have increased it: 'tis now spring, and all the pleasures of it displease me; every other tree blossoms, and I wither; I grow older, and not better; my strength diminisheth, and my load grows heavier; and yet I would fain be or do something; but that I cannot tell what, is no wonder in this time of my sadness; for to choose is to do: but to be no part of any body is as to be nothing: and so I am, and shall so judge myself, unless I could be so incorporated into a part of the world, as by business to contribute some sustentation to the whole. This I made account: I began early, when I understood the study of our laws; but was diverted by leaving that, and embracing the worst voluptuousness, an hydroptic immoderate desire of human learning and languages: beautiful ornaments indeed to men of great fortunes, but mine was grown so low as to need an occupation; which I thought I entered well into, when I subjected myself to such a service as I thought might exercise my poor abilities: and there I stumbled, and fell too; and now I am become so little, or such a nothing, that I am not a subject good enough for one of my own letters.—Sir, I fear my present discontent does not proceed from a good root, that I am so well content to be nothing, that is, dead. But, sir, though my fortune hath made me such, as that I am rather a sickness or a disease of the world, than any part of it, and therefore neither love it nor life, yet I would gladly live to become some such thing as you should not repent loving me. Sir, your own soul cannot be more zealous for your good than I am; and God, who loves that zeal in me, will not suffer you to doubt it. You would pity me now if you saw me write, for my pain hath drawn my head so much awry, and holds it so, that my eye cannot follow my pen. I therefore receive you into my prayers with mine own weary soul, and commend myself to yours. I doubt not but next week will bring you good news, for I have either mending or dying on my side; but if I do continue longer thus, I shall have comfort in this, that my blessed Saviour in exercising his justice upon my two worldly parts, my fortune and my body, reserves all his mercy for that which most needs it, my soul! which is, I doubt, too like a porter, that is very often near the gate, and yet goes not out. Sir, I profess to you truly that my loathness to give over writing now seems to myself a sign that I shall write no more.

Your poor friend, and
God's poor patient,
JOHN DONNE."

Sept. 7.

By this you have seen a part of the picture of his narrow fortune, and the perplexities of his generous mind: and thus it continued with him for about two years, all which time his family remained constantly at Mitcham; and to which place he often retired himself, and destined some days to a constant study of some points of controversy betwixt the English and Roman Church, and especially those of Supremacy and Allegiance: and to that place and such studies he could willingly have wedded himself during his life; but the earnest persuasion of friends became at last to be so powerful as to cause the removal of himself and family to London, where Sir Robert Drewry, a gentleman of a very noble estate, and a more liberal mind, assigned him and his wife an useful apartment in his own large house in Drury Lane, and not only rent free, but was also a cherisher of his studies, and such a friend as sympathised with him and his, in all their joy and sorrows.

At this time of Mr. Donne's and his wife's living in Sir Robert's house, the Lord Hay was, by King James, sent upon a glorious embassy to the then French king, Henry the Fourth; and Sir Robert put on a sudden resolution to accompany him to the French court, and to be present at his audience there. And Sir Robert put on a sudden resolution to solicit Mr. Donne to be his companion in that journey. And this desire was suddenly made known to his wife, who was then with child, and otherwise under so dangerous a habit of body, as to her health, that she professed an unwillingness to allow him any absence from her; saying, "Her divining soul boded her some ill in his absence;" and therefore desired him not to leave her. This made Mr.

Donne lay aside all thoughts of the journey, and really to resolve against it. But Sir Robert became restless in his persuasions for it, and Mr. Donne was so generous as to think he had sold his liberty, when he received so many charitable kindnesses from him; and told his wife so, who did therefore, with an unwilling-willingness, give a faint consent to the journey, which was proposed to be but for two months; for about that time they determined their return. Within a few days after this resolve, the Ambassador, Sir Robert, and Mr. Donne left London; and were the twelfth day got all safe to Paris. Two days after their arrival there, Mr. Donne was left alone in that room in which Sir Robert, and he, and some other friends had dined together. To this place Sir Robert returned within half-an-hour; and as he left, so he found, Mr. Donne alone, but in such an ecstasy, and so altered as to his looks, as amazed Sir Robert to behold him; insomuch that he earnestly desired Mr. Donne to declare what had befallen him in the short time of his absence. To which Mr. Donne was not able to make a present answer, but after a long and perplexed pause, did at last say, "I have seen a dreadful vision since I saw you: I have seen my dear wife pass twice by me through this room, with her hair hanging about her shoulders, and a dead child in her arms; this I have seen since I saw you." To which Sir Robert replied, "Sure, sir, you have slept since I saw you; and this is the result of some melancholy dream, which I desire you to forget, for you are now awake." To which Mr. Donne's reply was, "I cannot be surer that I now live than that I have not slept since I saw you; and am as sure that at her second appearing she stopped and looked me in the face, and vanished." Rest and sleep had not altered Mr. Donne's opinion the next day, for he then affirmed this opinion with a more deliberate, and so confirmed a confidence, that he inclined Sir Robert to a faint belief that the vision was true.—It is truly said that desire and doubt have no rest, and it proved so with Sir Robert; for he immediately sent a servant to Drewry House, with a charge to hasten back, and bring him word whether Mrs. Donne were alive; and, if alive, in what condition she was as to her health. The twelfth day the messenger returned with this account: That he found and left Mrs. Donne very sad, and sick in her bed; and that, after a long and dangerous labour, she had been delivered of a dead child. And, upon examination, the abortion proved to be the same day, and about the very hour, that Mr. Donne affirmed he saw her pass by him in his chamber.

This is a relation that will beget some wonder, and it well may; for most of our world are at present possessed with an opinion that visions and miracles are ceased. And, though it is most certain that two lutes being both strung and tuned to an equal pitch, and then one played upon, the other, that is not touched, being laid upon a table at a fit distance, will —like an echo to a trumpet—warble a faint audible harmony in answer to the same tune; yet many will not believe there is any such thing as a sympathy of souls; and I am well pleased that every reader do enjoy his own opinion. But if the unbelieving will not allow the believing reader of this story a liberty to believe that it may be true, then I wish him to consider, many wise men have believed that the ghost of Julius Cæsar did appear to Brutus, and that both St. Austin and Monica his mother had visions in order to his conversion. And though these, and many others—too many to name—have but the authority of human story, yet the incredible reader may find in the sacred story[1] that Samuel did appear to Saul even after his death—whether really or not, I undertake not to determine.—And Bildad, in the Book of Job, says these words: "A spirit passed before my face; the hair of my head stood up; fear and trembling came upon me, and made all my bones to shake."[2] Upon which words I will make no comment, but leave them to be considered by the incredulous reader; to whom I will also commend this following consideration: That there be many pious and learned men that believe our merciful God hath assigned to every man a particular guardian angel, to be his constant monitor, and to attend him in all his dangers, both of body and soul. And the opinion that every man hath his particular Angel may gain some authority by the relation of St. Peter's miraculous deliverance out of prison,[3] not by

[1] 1 Sam. xxviii. 14. [2] Job iv. 13-16
[3] Acts xii. 7-10; *ib.* 13-15.

many, but by one angel. And this belief may yet gain more credit by the reader's considering, that when Peter after his enlargement knocked at the door of Mary the mother of John, and Rhode, the maidservant, being surprised with joy that Peter was there, did not let him in, but ran in haste and told the disciples—who were then and there met together—that Peter was at the door; and they, not believing it, said she was mad; yet, when she again affirmed it, though they then believed it not, yet they concluded, and said, "It is his angel."

More observations of this nature, and inferences from them, might be made to gain the relation a firmer belief; but I forbear, lest I, that intended to be but a relator, may be thought to be an engaged person for the proving what was related to me; and yet I think myself bound to declare, that though it was not told me by Mr. Donne himself, it was told me—now long since—by a person of honour, and of such intimacy with him, that he knew more of the secrets of his soul than any person then living: and I think he told me the truth; for it was told with such circumstances, and such asseverations, that—to say nothing of my own thoughts—I verily believe he that told it me did himself believe it to be true.

I forbear the reader's further trouble, as to the relation, and what concerns it; and will conclude mine with commending to his view a copy of verses given by Mr. Donne to his wife at the time he then parted from her. And I beg leave to tell that I have heard some critics, learned both in languages and poetry, say that none of the Greek or Latin poets did ever equal them.

A VALEDICTION, FORBIDDING TO MOURN.

As virtuous men pass mildly away,
  And whisper to their souls to go,
Whilst some of their sad friends do say,
  The breath goes now, and some say No:

So let us melt, and make no noise,
  No tear-floods, nor sigh-tempests move;
'Twere profanation of our joys,
  To tell the laity our love.

Moving of th' earth brings harms and fears:
  Men reckon what it did or meant:
But trepidation of the spheres,
  Though greater far, is innocent.

Dull sublunary lovers' love—
  Whose soul is sense—can not admit
Absence, because that doth remove
  Those things which elemented it.

But we, by a love so far refined,
  That ourselves know not what it is,
Inter-assured of the mind,
  Care not hands, eyes, or lips to miss.

Our two souls therefore which are one,—
  Though I must go, endure not yet
A breach, but an expansion,
  Like gold to airy thinness beat.

If we be two? we are two so
  As stiff twin-compasses are two:
Thy soul, the fix'd foot, makes no show
  To move, but does if th' other do.

And though thine in the centre sit,
  Yet, when my other far does roam,
Thine leans and hearkens after it,
  And grows erect as mine comes home.

Such wilt thou be to me, who must,
  Like th' other foot, obliquely run:
Thy firmness makes my circle just,
  And me to end where I begun.

I return from my account of the vision, to tell the reader that both before Mr. Donne's going into France, at his being there, and after his return, many of the nobility and others that were powerful at Court, were watchful and solicitous to the King for some secular employment for him. The King had formerly both known and put a value upon his company, and had also given him some hopes of a State employment; being always much pleased when Mr. Donne attended him, especially at his meals, where there were usually many deep discourses of general learning, and very often friendly disputes, or debates of religion, betwixt his Majesty and those divines whose places required their attendance on him at those times, particularly the Dean of the Chapel, who then was Bishop Montague—the publisher of the learned and the eloquent works of his Majesty—and the most Reverend Doctor Andrews, the late learned Bishop of Winchester, who was then the King's almoner.

About this time there grew many disputes that concerned the oath of supremacy and allegiance, in which the King had appeared, and engaged himself by his public writings now extant; and his Majesty discoursing with Mr. Donne concerning many of the reasons which are usually urged against the taking of those oaths, apprehended such a validity and clearness in his stating the questions, and his answers to them, that his Majesty commanded him to bestow some time in drawing the arguments into a method, and then to write his answers to them; and, having done that, not to send, but be his own messenger, and bring them to him. To this he presently and diligently applied himself, and within six weeks brought them to him under his own handwriting, as they be now printed; the book bearing the name of *Pseudo-Martyr,* printed anno 1610.

When the King had read and considered that book, he persuaded Mr. Donne to enter into the ministry; to which, at that time, he was, and appeared, very unwilling, apprehending it—such was his mistaken modesty—to be too weighty for his abilities: and though his Majesty had promised him a favour, and many persons of worth mediated with his Majesty for some secular employment for him,—to which his education had adapted him,—and particularly the Earl of Somerset, when in his greatest height of favour; who being then at Theobald's with the King, where one of the clerks of the council died that night, the Earl posted a messenger for Mr. Donne to come to him immediately, and at Mr. Donne's coming said, "Mr. Donne, to testify the reality of my affection, and my purpose to prefer you, stay in this garden till I go up to the King and bring you word that you are clerk of the council: doubt not my doing this, for I know the King loves you, and know the King will not deny me." But the King gave a positive denial to all requests, and, having a discerning spirit, replied, "I know Mr. Donne is a learned man, has the abilities of a learned divine, and will prove a powerful preacher; and my desire is to prefer him that way, and in that way I will deny you nothing for him."

After that time, as he professeth,[1] "the King descended to a persuasion, almost to a solicitation, of him to enter into sacred orders;" which, though he then denied not, yet he deferred it for almost three years. All which time he applied himself to an incessant study of textual divinity, and to the attainment of a greater perfection in the learned languages, Greek and Hebrew.

In the first and most blessed times of Christianity, when the clergy were looked upon with reverence, and deserved it, when they overcame their opposers by high examples of virtue, by a blessed patience and long suffering, those only were then judged worthy the ministry whose quiet and meek spirits did make them look upon that sacred calling with an humble adoration and fear to undertake it; which indeed requires such great degrees of humility, and labour, and care, that none but such were then thought worthy of that celestial dignity. And such only were then sought out, and solicited to undertake it. This I have mentioned, because forwardness and inconsideration could not, in Mr. Donne, as in many others, be an argument of insufficiency or unfitness; for he had considered long, and had many strifes within himself concerning the strictness of life, and competency of learning, required in such as enter into sacred orders; and doubtless, considering his own demerits, did humbly ask God with St. Paul, "Lord, who is sufficient for these things?" and with meek Moses, "Lord, who am I?" And sure, if he had consulted with flesh and blood, he had not for these reasons put his hand to that holy plough. But God, who is able to prevail, wrestled with him, as the angel did with Jacob, and marked him; marked him for his own; marked him with a blessing, a blessing of obedience to the motions of his blessed Spirit. And then, as he had formerly asked God with Moses, "Who am I?" so now, being inspired with an apprehension of God's particular mercy to him, in the King's and others' solicitations of him he came to ask King David's thankful question, "Lord, who am I, that thou art so mindful of me?" So mindful of me, as to lead me for more than forty years through this wilderness of the many temptations and various turnings of a dan-

1 In his Book of Devotions.

gerous life; so merciful to me, as to move the learnedest of Kings to descend to move me to serve at the altar! So merciful to me, as at last to move my heart to embrace this holy motion! Thy motions I will and do embrace; and I now say with the blessed Virgin, "Be it with thy servant as seemeth best in thy sight"; and so, Blessed Jesus, I do take the cup of salvation, and will call upon thy name, and will preach thy gospel.

Such strifes as these St. Austin had, when St. Ambrose endeavoured his conversion to Christianity; with which he confesseth he acquainted his friend Alipius. Our learned author—a man fit to write after no mean copy—did the like. And declaring his intentions to his dear friend Dr. King, then Bishop of London, a man famous in his generation, and no stranger to Mr. Donne's abilities,—for he had been chaplain to the Lord Chancellor at the time of Mr. Donne's being his Lordship's secretary,—that reverend man did receive the news with much gladness; and, after some expressions of joy, and a persuasion to be constant in his pious purpose, he proceeded with all convenient speed to ordain him first deacon, and then priest not long after.

Now the English Church had gained a second St. Austin; for I think none was so like him before his conversion, none so like St. Ambrose after it: and if his youth had the infirmities of the one, his age had the excellencies of the other; the learning and holiness of both.

And now all his studies, which had been occasionally diffused, were all concentered in divinity. Now he had a new calling, new thoughts, and a new employment for his wit and eloquence. Now, all his earthly affections were changed into divine love; and all the faculties of his own soul were engaged in the conversion of others; in preaching the glad tidings of remission to repenting sinners, and peace to each troubled soul.

To these he applied himself with all care and diligence; and now such a change was wrought in him, that he could say with David, "O how amiable are thy tabernacles, O Lord God of Hosts!" Now he declared openly, "that when he required a temporal, God gave him a spiritual blessing." And that "he was now gladder to be a door-keeper in the house of God, than he could be to enjoy the noblest of all temporal employments."

Presently after he entered into his holy profession, the King sent for him, and made him his chaplain in ordinary, and promised to take a particular care for his preferment.

And though his long familiarity with scholars and persons of greatest quality was such as might have given some men boldness enough to have preached to any eminent auditory, yet his modesty in this employment was such that he could not be persuaded to it, but went usually accompanied with some one friend to preach privately in some village, not far from London, his first sermon being preached at Paddington. This he did, till his Majesty sent and appointed him a day to preach to him at Whitehall; and, though much were expected from him, both by his Majesty and others, yet he was so happy—which few are—as to satisfy and exceed their expectations: preaching the Word so, as showed his own heart was possessed with those very thoughts and joys that he laboured to distil into others; a preacher in earnest; weeping sometimes for his auditory, sometimes with them; always preaching to himself, like an angel from a cloud, but in none; carrying some, as St. Paul was, to heaven in holy raptures, and enticing others by a sacred art and courtship to amend their lives; here picturing a vice so as to make it ugly to those that practised it, and a virtue so as to make it beloved even by those that loved it not; and all this with a most particular grace and an unexpressible addition of comeliness.

There may be some that may incline to think—such indeed as have not heard him—that my affection to my friend hath transported me to an immoderate commendation of his preaching. If this meets with any such, let me entreat, though I will omit many, yet that they will receive a double witness for what I say; it being attested by a gentleman of worth,—Mr. Chidley, a frequent hearer of his sermons,—in part of a funeral elegy writ by him on Dr. Donne; and is a known truth, though it be in verse—

—Each altar had his fire—
He kept his love, but not his object; wit
He did not banish, but transplanted it:

Taught it both time and place, and brought it home
To piety which it doth best become.

. . . .

For say, had ever pleasure such a dress?
Have you seen crimes so shaped, or loveliness
Such as his lips did clothe religion in?
Had not reproof a beauty passing sin?
Corrupted Nature sorrow'd that she stood
So near the danger of becoming good.
And, when he preach'd, she wish'd her ears exempt
From piety, that had such power to tempt.
How did his sacred flattery beguile
Men to amend?—

More of this, and more witnesses, might be brought; but I forbear and return.

That summer, in the very same month in which he entered into sacred orders, and was made the King's chaplain, his Majesty then going his progress, was entreated to receive an entertainment in the University of Cambridge; and Mr. Donne attending his Majesty at that time, his Majesty was pleased to recommend him to the University, to be made doctor in divinity. Dr. Harsnett, after Archbishop of York, was then Vice-Chancellor, who, knowing him to be the author of that learned book, *The Pseudo-Martyr,* required no other proof of his abilities, but proposed it to the University, who presently assented, and expressed a gladness that they had such an occasion to entitle him to be theirs.

His abilities and industry in his profession were so eminent, and he so known and so beloved by persons of quality, that within the first year of his entering into sacred orders he had fourteen advowsons of several benefices presented to him; but they were in the country, and he could not leave his beloved London, to which place he had a natural inclination, having received both his birth and education in it, and there contracted a friendship with many, whose conversation multiplied the joys of his life: but an employment that might affix him that place would be welcome, for he needed it.

Immediately after his return from Cambridge his wife died, leaving him a man of a narrow, unsettled state, and—having buried five—the careful father of seven children then living, to whom he gave a voluntary assurance never to bring them under the subjection of a step-mother; which promise he kept most faithfully, burying with his tears all his earthly joys in his most dear and deserving wife's grave, and betook himself to a most retired and solitary life.

In this retiredness, which was often from the sight of his dearest friends, he became crucified to the world, and all those vanities, those imaginary pleasures, that are daily acted on that restless stage; and they were as perfectly crucified to him. Nor is it hard to think—being, passions may be both changed and heightened by accidents—but that *that* abundant affection which once was betwixt him and her, who had long been the delight of his eyes and the companion of his youth; her, with whom he had divided so many pleasant sorrows and contented fears, as common people are not capable of;—not hard to think but that she being now removed by death, a commensurable grief took as full a possession of him as joy had done; and so indeed it did; for now his very soul was elemented of nothing but sadness; now grief took so full a possession of his heart, as to leave no place for joy: if it did, it was a joy to be alone, where, like a pelican in the wilderness, he might bemoan himself without witness or restraint, and pour forth his passions like Job in the days of his affliction: "Oh that I might have the desire of my heart! Oh that God would grant the thing that I long for!" For then, as the grave is become her house, so I would hasten to make it mine also; that we two might there make our beds together in the dark. Thus, as the Israelites sat mourning by the rivers of Babylon, when they remembered Sion, so he gave some ease to his oppressed heart by thus venting his sorrows: thus he began the day, and ended the night; ended the restless night and began the weary day in lamentations. And thus he continued, till a consideration of his new engagements to God, and St. Paul's "Woe is me, if I preach not the gospel!" dispersed those sad clouds that had then benighted his hopes, and now forced him to behold the light.

His first motion from his house was to preach where his beloved wife lay buried,—in St. Clement's Church, near Temple Bar, London,—and his text was a part of the Prophet Jeremy's Lamentation: "Lo, I am the man that have seen affliction."

And indeed his very words and looks testified him to be truly such a man; and they, with the addition of his sighs and tears, expressed in his sermon, did so work upon the affections of his hearers, as melted and moulded them into a companionable sadness; and so they left the congregation; but then their houses presented them with objects of diversion, and his presented him with nothing but fresh objects of sorrow, in beholding many helpless children, a narrow fortune, and a consideration of the many cares and casualties that attend their education.

In this time of sadness he was importuned by the grave Benchers of Lincoln's Inn—who were once his companions and friends of his youth—to accept of their lecture, which, by reason of Dr. Gataker's removal from thence, was then void; of which he accepted, being most glad to renew his intermitted friendship with those whom he so much loved, and where he had been a Saul,—though not to persecute Christianity, or to deride it, yet in his irregular youth to neglect the visible practice of it,—there to become a Paul, and preach salvation to his beloved brethren.

And now his life was a shining light among his old friends; now he gave an ocular testimony of the strictness and regularity of it; now he might say, as St. Paul adviseth his Corinthians, "Be ye followers of me, as I follow Christ, and walk as ye have me for an example;" not the example of a busy body, but of a contemplative, a harmless, an humble and an holy life and conversation.

The love of that noble society was expressed to him many ways; for, besides fair lodgings that were set apart, and newly furnished for him with all necessaries, other courtesies were also daily added; indeed so many, and so freely, as if they meant their gratitude should exceed his merits: and in this love-strife of desert and liberality, they continued for the space of two years, he preaching faithfully and constantly to them, and they liberally requiting him. About which time the Emperor of Germany died, and the Palsgrave, who had lately married the Lady Elizabeth, the king's only daughter, was elected and crowned King of Bohemia, the unhappy beginning of many miseries in that nation.

King James, whose motto—*Beati pacifici*—did truly speak

the very thoughts of his heart, endeavoured first to prevent, and after to compose, the discords of that discomposed State: and, amongst other his endeavours, did then send the Lord Hay, Earl of Doncaster, his ambassador to those unsettled Princes; and, by a special command from his Majesty, Dr. Donne was appointed to assist and attend that employment to the princes of the union; for which the Earl was most glad, who had always put a great value on him, and taken a great pleasure in his conversation and discourse: and his friends at Lincoln's Inn were as glad, for they feared that his immoderate study and sadness for his wife's death would, as Jacob said, "make his days few," and, respecting his bodily health, "evil" too; and of this there were many visible signs.

At his going he left his friends of Lincoln's Inn, and they him, with many reluctations; for, though he could not say as St. Paul to his Ephesians, "Behold, you, to whom I have preached the kingdom of God, shall from henceforth see my face no more," yet he, believing himself to be in a consumption, questioned, and they feared it: all concluding that his troubled mind, with the help of his unintermitted studies, hastened the decays of his weak body. But God, who is the God of all wisdom and goodness, turned it to the best; for this employment—to say nothing of the event of it—did not only divert him from those too serious studies and sad thoughts, but seemed to give him a new life, by a true occasion of joy, to be an eye-witness of the health of his most dear and most honoured mistress, the Queen of Bohemia, in a foreign nation; and to be a witness of that gladness which she expressed to see him: who, having formerly known him a courtier, was much joyed to see him in a canonical habit, and more glad to be an ear-witness of his excellent and powerful preaching.

About fourteen months after his departure out of England, he returned to his friends of Lincoln's Inn, with his sorrows moderated, and his health improved; and there betook himself to his constant course of preaching.

About a year after his return out of Germany, Dr. Carey was made Bishop of Exeter, and by his removal the Deanery of St. Paul's being vacant, the King sent to Dr. Donne, and appointed him to attend him at dinner the next day. When his Majesty sat down, before he had eat any meat, he said after his pleasant manner, "Dr. Donne, I have invited you to dinner; and, though you sit not down with me, yet I will carve to you of a dish that I know you love well; for, knowing you love London, I do therefore make you Dean of St. Paul's; and, when I have dined, then do you take your beloved dish home to your study, say grace there to yourself, and much good may it do you."

Immediately after he came to his deanery he employed workmen to repair and beautify the chapel; suffering, as holy David once vowed, "his eyes and temples to take no rest till he had first beautified the house of God."

The next quarter following, when his father-in-law, Sir George More—whom time had made a lover and admirer of him—came to pay to him the conditioned sum of twenty pounds, he refused to receive it; and said, as good Jacob did when he heard his beloved son Joseph was alive, "'It is enough;' you have been kind to me and mine. I know your present condition is such as not to abound, and I hope mine is, or will be such as not to need it: I will therefore receive no more from you upon that contract;" and in testimony of it freely gave him up his bond.

Immediately after his admission into his deanery, the vicarage of St. Dunstan in the West, London, fell to him by the death of Dr. White, the advowson of it having been given to him long before by his honourable friend, Richard, Earl of Dorset, then the patron, and confirmed by his brother, the late deceased Edward, both of them men of much honour.

By these, and another ecclesiastical endowment which fell to him about the same time, given to him formerly by the Earl of Kent, he was enabled to become charitable to the poor, and kind to his friends, and to make such provision for his children that they were not left scandalous, as relating to their or his profession and quality.

The next Parliament, which was within that present year, he was chosen Prolocutor to the Convocation, and about that time was appointed by his Majesty, his most gracious master, to preach very many occasional sermons, as at St. Paul's

Cross, and other places. All which employments he performed to the admiration of the representative body of the whole clergy of this nation.

He was once, and but once, clouded with the King's displeasure, and it was about this time; which was occasioned by some malicious whisperer, who had told his Majesty that Dr. Donne had put on the general humours of the pulpits, and was become busy in insinuating a fear of the King's inclining to Popery, and a dislike of his government; and particularly for the King's then turning the evening lectures into catechising, and expounding the Prayer of our Lord, and of the Belief and Commandments. His Majesty was the more inclinable to believe this, for that a person of nobility and great note, betwixt whom and Dr. Donne there had been a great friendship, was at this very time discarded the court—I shall forbear his name, unless I had a fairer occasion—and justly committed to prison; which begot many rumours in the common people, who in this nation think they are not wise unless they be busy about what they understand not, and especially about religion.

The King received this news with so much discontent and restlessness, that he would not suffer the sun to set and leave him under this doubt; but sent for Dr. Donne, and required his answer to the accusation; which was so clear and satisfactory, that the King said "he was right glad he rested no longer under the suspicion." When the King had said this, Dr. Donne kneeled down and thanked his Majesty, and protested his answer was faithful, and free from all collusion, and therefore, "desired that he might not rise till, as in like cases, he always had from God, so he might have from his Majesty, some assurance that he stood clear and fair in his opinion." At which the King raised him from his knees with his own hands, and "protested he believed him; and that he knew he was an honest man, and doubted not but that he loved him truly." And, having thus dismissed him, he called some lords of his council into his chamber, and said with much earnestness, "My doctor is an honest man; and, my lords, I was never better satisfied with an answer than he hath now made me; and I always rejoice when I think that by my means he became a divine."

He was made dean in the fiftieth year of his age; and in his fifty-fourth year a dangerous sickness seized him, which inclined him to a consumption: but God, as Job thankfully acknowledged, preserved his spirit, and kept his intellectuals as clear and perfect as when that sickness first seized his body; but it continued long, and threatened him with death, which he dreaded not.

In this distemper of body, his dear friend, Dr. Henry King,—then chief residentiary of that church, and late Bishop of Chichester,—a man generally known by the clergy of this nation, and as generally noted for his obliging nature, visited him daily; and observing that his sickness rendered his recovery doubtful, he chose a seasonable time to speak to him to this purpose:

"Mr. Dean, I am, by your favour, no stranger to your temporal estate, and you are no stranger to the offer lately made us, for the renewing a lease of the best Prebend's corps belonging to our church; and you know 'twas denied, for that our tenant being very rich, offered to fine at so low a rate as held not proportion with his advantages: but I will either raise him to a higher sum, or procure that the other residentiaries shall join to accept of what was offered; one of these I can and will by your favour do without delay, and without any trouble either to your body or mind: I beseech you to accept of my offer, for I know it will be a considerable addition to your present estate, which I know needs it."

To this, after a short pause, and raising himself upon his bed, he made this reply:

"My most dear friend, I most humbly thank you for your many favours, and this in particular; but in my present condition I shall not accept of your proposal; for doubtless there is such a sin as sacrilege; if there were not, it could not have a name in Scripture; and the primitive clergy were watchful against all appearances of that evil; and indeed then all Christians looked upon it with horror and detestation, judging it to be even an open defiance of the power and providence of Almighty God, and a sad presage of a declining religion. But instead of such Christians, who had selected times set apart to fast and pray to God, for a pious clergy, which they then did obey, our times abound with men that are busy and litigious about trifles and church ceremonies, and yet so far from scrupling sacrilege, that they make not so much as a quære what it is: but I thank God I have; and dare not now upon my sick-bed, when Almighty God hath made me useless to the service of the Church, make any advantages out of it. But if He shall again restore me to such a degree of health, as again to serve at his altar, I shall then gladly take the reward which the bountiful benefactors of this church have designed me; for God knows my children and relations will need it. In which number, my mother—whose credulity and charity has contracted a very plentiful to a very narrow estate—must not be forgotten. But, Dr. King, if I recover not, that little worldly estate that I shall leave behind me—that very little, when divided into eight parts—must, if you deny me not so charitable a favour, fall into your hands, as my most faithful friend and executor, of whose care and justice I make no more doubt than of God's blessing, on that which I have conscientiously collected for them; but it shall not be augmented on my sick-bed; and this I declare to be my unalterable resolution."

The reply to this was only a promise to observe his request.

Within a few days his distempers abated; and as his strength increased, so did his thankfulness to Almighty God, testified in his most excellent Book of Devotions, which he published at his recovery; in which the reader may see the most secret thoughts that then possessed his soul, paraphrased and made public: a book that may not unfitly be called a sacred picture of spiritual ecstasies, occasioned and appliable to the emergencies of that sickness; which book, being a composition of meditations, disquisitions, and prayers, he writ on his sick-bed; herein imitating the holy patriarchs, who were wont to build their altars in that place where they had received their blessings.

This sickness brought him so near to the gates of death, and he saw the grave so ready to devour him, that he would often say his recovery was supernatural: but that God that then restored his health continued it to him till the fifty-ninth year of his life; and then, in August 1630, being with his eldest daughter, Mrs. Harvey, at Abury Hatch, in Essex, he there fell into a fever, which with the help of his constant infirmity—vapours from the spleen—hastened him into so visible a consumption that his beholders might say, as St. Paul of himself, "He dies daily;" and he might say with Job, "My welfare passeth away as a cloud, the days of my affliction have taken hold of me, and weary nights are appointed for me."

Reader, this sickness continued long, not only weakening, but wearying him so much, that my desire is he may now take some rest; and that before I speak of his death, thou wilt not think it an impertinent digression to look back with me upon some observations of his life, which, whilst a gentle slumber give rest to his spirits, may, I hope, not unfitly exercise thy consideration.

His marriage was the remarkable error of his life—an error which, though he had a wit able and very apt to maintain paradoxes, yet he was very far from justifying it; and though his wife's competent years, and other reasons, might be justly urged to moderate severe censures, yet he would occasionally condemn himself for it; and doubtless it had been attended with an heavy repentance, if God had not blessed them with so mutual and cordial affections, as in the midst of their sufferings made their bread of sorrow taste more pleasantly than the banquets of dull and low-spirited people.

The recreations of his youth were poetry, in which he was so happy, as if nature and all her varieties had been made only to exercise his sharp wit and high fancy; and in those pieces which were facetiously composed and carelessly scattered—most of them being written before the twentieth year of his age—it may appear by his choice metaphors that both nature and all the arts joined to assist him with their utmost skill.

It is a truth, that in his penitential years, viewing some of those pieces that had been loosely—God knows, too loosely—scattered in his youth, he wished they had been abortive, or so short-lived that his own eyes had witnessed their funerals: but, though he was no friend to them, he was not so fallen out with heavenly poetry as to forsake that; no, not in his declining age; witnessed then by many divine sonnets, and other high, holy, and harmonious composures. Yea, even, on his former sick-bed he wrote this heavenly hymn, expressing the great joy that then possessed his soul in the assurance of God's favour to him when he composed it—

AN HYMN

TO GOD THE FATHER.

Wilt thou forgive that sin where I begun,
  Which was my sin, though it were done before?
Wilt thou forgive that sin through which I run,
  And do run still, though still I do deplore?
When thou hast done, thou hast not done,
  For I have more.

Wilt thou forgive that sin, which I have won
  Others to sin, and made my sin their door?
Wilt thou forgive that sin which I did shun
  A year or two;—but wallow'd in a score?
When thou hast done, thou hast not done,
  For I have more.

I have a sin of fear, that when I've spun
  My last thread, I shall perish on the shore;
But swear by thyself, that at my death thy Son
  Shall shine as he shines now, and heretofore;
And having done that, thou hast done,
  I fear no more.

I have the rather mentioned this hymn, for that he caused it to be set to a most grave and solemn tune, and to be often sung to the organ by the choristers of St. Paul's Church, in his own hearing, especially at the evening service; and at his return from his customary devotions in that place, did occasionally say to a friend, "The words of this hymn have restored to me the same thoughts of joy that possessed my soul in my sickness, when I composed it. And, O the power of church-music! that harmony added to this hymn has raised the affections of my heart, and quickened my graces of zeal and gratitude; and I observe that I always return from paying this public duty of prayer and praise to God, with an unexpressible tranquillity of mind, and a willingness to leave the world."

After this manner the disciples of our Saviour, and the best of Christians in those ages of the church nearest to his time, offer their praises to Almighty God. And the reader of St. Augustine's life may there find that towards his dissolution he wept abundantly, that the enemies of Christianity had broke in upon them, and profaned and ruined their sanctuaries, and because their public hymns and lauds were lost out of their churches. And after this manner have many devout souls lifted up their hands and offered acceptable sacrifices unto Almighty God, where Dr. Donne offered his, and now lies buried.

But now, O Lord! how is that place become desolate![1]

Before I proceed further, I think fit to inform the reader, that not long before his death he caused to be drawn a figure of the body of Christ extended upon an anchor, like those which painters draw when they would present us with the picture of Christ crucified on the cross: his varying no otherwise, than to affix him not to a cross, but to an anchor—the emblem of hope;—this he caused to be drawn in little, and then many of those figures thus drawn to be engraven very small in Heliotropium stones, and set in gold; and of these he sent to many of his dearest friends, to be used as seals, or rings, and kept as memorials of him, and of his affection to them.

His dear friends and benefactors, Sir Henry Goodier and Sir Robert Drewry, could not be of that number; nor could the Lady Magdalen Herbert, the mother of George Herbert, for they had put off mortality, and taken possession of the grave before him: but Sir Henry Wotton, and Dr. Hall, the then late deceased Bishop of Norwich, were; and so were Dr. Duppa, Bishop of Salisbury, and Dr. Henry King, Bishop of Chichester—lately deceased,—men in whom there was such a commixture of general learning, of natural eloquence, and Christian humility, that they deserve a commemoration by a pen equal to their own, which none have exceeded.

And in this enumeration of his friends, though many must be omitted; yet that man of primitive piety, Mr. George Herbert, may not; I mean that George Herbert who was the author of *The Temple, or Sacred Poems and Ejaculations.* A book in which, by declaring his own spiritual conflicts, he hath comforted and raised many a dejected and discomposed soul and charmed them into sweet and quiet thoughts; a book, by the frequent reading whereof, and the assistance of that spirit that seemed to inspire the author, the reader may attain

[1] 1656

habits of peace and piety, and all the gifts of the Holy Ghost and heaven; and may, by still reading, still keep those sacred fires burning upon the altar of so pure a heart, as shall free it from the anxieties of this world, and keep it fixed upon things that are above. Betwixt this George Herbert and Dr. Donne there was a long and dear friendship, made up by such a sympathy of inclinations, that they coveted and joyed to be in each other's company; and this happy friendship was still maintained by many sacred endearments; of which that which followeth may be some testimony.

TO MR. GEORGE HERBERT

SENT HIM WITH ONE OF MY SEALS OF THE ANCHOR AND CHRIST

A Sheaf of Snakes used heretofore to be my Seal, which is the Crest of our poor family

Qui priùs assuetus serpentum falce tabellas
  Signare, hæc nostræ symbola parva domûs,
Adscitus domui Domini—

Adopted in God's family, and so
My old coat lost, into new Arms I go.
The Cross, my Seal in Baptism, spread below,
Does by that form into an Anchor grow.
Crosses grow Anchors, bear as thou shouldst do
Thy Cross, and that Cross grows an Anchor too.
But he that makes our Crosses Anchors thus,
Is Christ, who there is crucified for us.
Yet with this I may my first Serpents hold;—
God gives new blessings, and yet leaves the old—
The Serpent, may, as wise, my pattern be;
My poison, as he feeds on dust, that's me.
And, as he rounds the earth to murder, sure
He is my death; but on the Cross, my cure,
Crucify nature then; and then implore
All grace from him, crucified there before.
When all is Cross, and that Cross Anchor grown
This Seal's a Catechism, not a Seal alone.
Under that little Seal great gifts I send,
Both works and prayers, pawns and fruits of a friend.
Oh! may that Saint that rides on our Great Seal,
To you that bear his name, large bounty deal.

JOHN DONNE.

IN SACRAM ANCHORAM PISCATORIS

GEORGE HERBERT

Quòd Crux nequibat fixa clavique additi,—
Tenere Christum scilicet ne ascenderet,
Tuive Christum—

Although the Cross could not here Christ detain,
When nail'd unto 't, but he ascends again;
Nor yet thy eloquence here keep him still,
But only whilst thou speak'st—this Anchor will:
Nor canst thou be content, unless thou to
This certain Anchor add a Seal; and so
The water and the earth both unto thee
Do owe the symbol of their certainty.
Let the world reel, we and all our's stand sure,
This holy cable's from all storms secure.

George Herbert.

I return to tell the reader that, besides these verses to his dear Mr. Herbert, and that hymn that I mentioned to be sung in the choir of St. Paul's Church, he did also shorten and beguile many sad hours by composing other sacred ditties; and he writ an hymn on his death-bed which bears this title:

AN HYMN TO GOD, MY GOD, IN MY SICKNESS

March 23, 1630

Since I am coming to that holy room,
  Where, with thy Choir of Saints, for evermore
I shall be made thy music, as I come
  I tune my instrument here at the door,
  And, what I must do then, think here before.
Since my Physicians by their loves are grown
  Cosmographers; and I their map, who lye
Flat on this bed—

So, in his purple wrapt, receive my Lord!
  By these his thorns, give me his other Crown:
And, as to other souls I preach'd thy word,
  Be this my text, my sermon to mine own,
  "That he may raise; therefore the Lord throws down."

If these fall under the censure of a soul whose too much mixture with earth makes it unfit to judge of these high raptures and illuminations, let him know, that many holy and devout men have thought the soul of Prudentius to be most refined, when, not many days before his death, "he charged it to present his God each morning and evening with a new and spiritual song;" justified by the example of King David and the good King Hezekiah, who, upon the renovation of his years paid his thankful vows to Almighty God in a royal hymn, which he concludes in these words: "The Lord was ready to save; therefore I will sing my songs to the stringed instruments all the days of my life in the temple of my God."

The latter part of his life may be said to be a continued study; for as he usually preached once a week, if not oftener, so after his sermon he never gave his eyes a rest, till he had chosen out a new text, and that night cast his sermon into a form, and his text into divisions; and the next day betook himself to consult the fathers, and so commit his meditations to his memory, which was excellent. But upon Saturday he usually gave himself and his mind a rest from the weary burthen of his week's meditations, and usually spent that day in visitation of friends, or some other diversions of his thoughts; and would say, "that he gave both his body and mind that refreshment, that he might be enabled to do the work of the day following, not faintly, but with courage and cheerfulness."

Nor was his age only so industrious, but in the most unsettled days of his youth his bed was not able to detain him beyond the hour of four in the morning; and it was no common business that drew him out of his chamber till past ten; all which time was employed in study; though he took great liberty after it. And if this seem strange, it may gain a belief by the visible fruits of his labours; some of which remain as testimonies of what is here written: for he left the resultance of 1400 authors, most of them abridged and analysed with his own hand; he left also six score of his sermons, all written with his own hand; also an exact and laborious treatise concerning self-murder, called Biathanatos; wherein all the laws violated by that act are diligently surveyed, and judiciously censured: a treatise written in his younger days, which alone might declare him then not only perfect in the civil and canon law but in many other such studies and arguments as enter not into the consideration of many that labour to be thought great clerks, and pretend to know all things.

Nor were these only found in his study, but all businesses that passed of any public consequence, either in this or any of our neighbour nations, he abbreviated either in Latin, or in the language of that nation, and kept them by him for useful memorials. So he did the copies of divers letters and cases of conscience that had concerned his friends, with his observations and solutions of them; and divers other businesses of importance, all particularly and methodically digested by himself.

He did prepare to leave the world before life left him, making his will when no faculty of his soul was damped or made defective by pain or sickness, or he surprised by a sudden apprehension of death: but it was made with mature deliberation, expressing himself an impartial father, by making his children's portions equal; and a lover of his friends, whom he remembered with legacies fitly and discreetly chosen and bequeathed. I cannot forbear a nomination of some of them; for methinks they be persons that seem to challenge a recordation in this place; as namely, to his brother-in-law, Sir Thomas Grimes, he gave that striking clock, which he had long worn in his pocket; to his dear friend and executor, Dr. King,—late Bishop of Chichester—that model of gold of the Synod of Dort, with which the States presented him at his last being at the Hague; and the two pictures of Padre Paolo and Fulgentio, men of his acquaintance when he travelled Italy, and of great note in that nation for their remarkable learning.—To his ancient friend Dr. Brook,—that married him—Master of Trinity College in Cambridge, he gave the picture of the Blessed Virgin and Joseph.—To Dr. Winniff, who succeeded him in the Deanery, he gave a picture called the Skeleton.—To the succeeding Dean, who was not then known, he gave many necessaries of worth, and useful for his house; and also several pictures and ornaments for the chapel, with a desire that they might be registered, and remain as a legacy to his successors.—To the Earls of Dorset and Carlisle he gave several pictures; and so he did to many other friends; legacies, given rather to express his affection, than to make any addition to their estates: but unto the poor he was full of charity, and unto many others, who, by his constant and long-continued bounty, might entitle themselves to be his alms-people: for all these he made provision, and so largely, as, having then six children living, might to some appear more than proportionable to his estate. I forbear to mention any more, lest the reader may think I trespass upon his patience: but I will beg his favour, to present him with the beginning and end of his will.

"In the name of the blessed and glorious Trinity, Amen, I, John Donne, by the mercy of Christ Jesus, and by the calling of the Church of England, priest, being at this time in good health and perfect understanding,—praised be God therefore—do hereby make my last will and testament in manner and form following.

"First, I give my gracious God an entire sacrifice of body and soul, with my most humble thanks for that assurance which his blessed Spirit imprints in me now of the salvation of the one, and the resurrection of the other; and for that constant and cheerful resolution, which the same Spirit hath established in me, to live and die in the religion now professed in the Church of England. In expectation of that resurrection, I desire my body may be buried—in the most private manner that may be—in that place of St. Paul's Church, London, that the now residentiaries have at my request designed for that purpose, etc.—And this my last will and testament, made in the fear of God,—whose mercy I humbly beg, and constantly rely upon in Jesus Christ—and in perfect love and charity with all the world—whose pardon I ask, from the lowest of my servants, to the highest of my superiors—written all with my own hand, and my name subscribed to every page, of which there are five in number.

"Sealed *December* 13, 1630."

Nor was this blessed sacrifice of charity expressed only at his death, but in his life also, by a cheerful and frequent visitation of any friend whose mind was dejected, or his fortune necessitous; he was inquisitive after the wants of prisoners, and redeemed many from prison that lay for their fees or small debts: he was a continual giver to poor scholars, both of this and foreign nations. Besides what he gave with his own hand, he usually sent a servant, or a discreet and trusty friend, to distribute his charity to all the prisons in London, at all the festival times of the year, especially at the birth and resurrection of our Saviour. He gave an hundred pounds at one time to an old friend, whom he had known live plentifully, and by a too liberal heart and carelessness became decayed in his estate; and when the receiving of it was denied by the gentleman's saying, "He wanted not;" for the reader may note, that as there be some spirits so generous as to labour to conceal and endure a sad poverty, rather than expose themselves to those blushes that attend the confession of it; so there be others, to whom nature and grace have afforded such sweet and compassionate souls, as to pity and prevent the distresses of mankind;—which I have mentioned because of Dr. Donne's reply, whose answer was: "I know you want not what will sustain nature; for a little will do that; but my desire is, that you, who in the days of your plenty have cheered and raised the hearts of so many of your dejected friends, would now receive from me, and use it as a cordial for the cheering of your own:" and upon these terms it was received. He was an happy reconciler of many differences in the families of his friends and kindred,—which he never undertook faintly; for such undertakings have usually faint effects—and they had such a faith in his judgment and impartiality, that he never advised them to any thing in vain. He was, even to her death, a most dutiful son to his mother, careful to provide for her supportation, of which she had been destitute, but that God raised him up to prevent her necessities; who having sucked in the religion of the Roman Church with the mother's milk, spent her estate in foreign countries, to enjoy a liberty in it, and died in his house but three months before him.

And to the end it may appear how just a steward he was of his lord and master's revenue, I have thought fit to let the reader know, that after his entrance into his Deanery, as he numbered his years, he at the foot of a private account, to which God and his angels were only witnesses with him,—computed first his revenue, then what was given to the poor, and other pious uses; and lastly, what rested for him and his; and having done that, he then blessed each year's poor remainder with a thankful prayer; which, for that they discover a more than common devotion, the reader shall partake some of them in his own words:

So all is that remains this year—[1624-5].

Deo Opt. Max. benigno largitori, à me, et ab iis quibus hæc à me reservantur, Gloria et gratia in æternum. Amen.

TRANSLATED THUS.

To God all Good, all Great, the benevolent Bestower, by me and by them, for whom by me these sums are laid up, be glory and grace ascribed for ever. Amen.

So that this year [1626] God hath blessed me and mine with:—

Multiplicatæ sunt super nos misericordiæ tuæ, Domine.

TRANSLATED THUS.

Thy mercies, O Lord! are multiplied upon us.

Da, Domine, ut quæ ex immensâ bonitate tuâ nobis elargiri dignatus sis, in quorumcunque manus devenerint, in tuam semper cedant gloriam. Amen.

TRANSLATED THUS.

Grant, O Lord! that what out of thine infinite bounty thou hast vouchsafed to lavish upon us, into whosoever hands it may devolve, may always be improved to thy glory. Amen.

In fine horum sex annorum manet:—[1628-9].

Quid habeo quod non accepi à Domino? Largitur etiam ut quæ largitus est sua iterum fiant, bono eorum usu; ut quemadmodum nec officiis hujus mundi, nec loci in quo me posuit dignitati, nec servis, nec egenis, in toto hujus anni curriculo mihi conscius sum me defuisse; ita et liberi, quibus quæ supersunt, supersunt, grato animo ea accipiant, et beneficum authorem recognoscant. Amen.

TRANSLATED THUS.

At the end of these six years remains:—

What have I, which I have not received from the Lord? He bestows, also, to the intent that what he hath bestowed may revert to him by the proper use of it: that, as I have not consciously been wanting to myself during the whole course of the past year, either in discharging my secular duties, in retaining the dignity of my station, or in my conduct towards my servants and the poor,—so my children for whom remains whatever is remaining, may receive it with gratitude, and acknowledge the beneficent Giver. Amen.

But I return from my long digression.

We left the author sick in Essex, where he was forced to spend much of that winter, by reason of his disability to remove from that place; and having never, for almost twenty years, omitted his personal attendance on his Majesty in that month, in which he was to attend and preach to him; nor having ever been left out of the roll and number of Lent preachers, and there being then—in January 1630—a report brought to London, or raised there, that Dr. Donne was dead; that report gave him occasion to write the following letter to a dear friend:

"Sir,—This advantage you and my other friends have by my frequent fevers, that I am so much the oftener at the gates of heaven; and this advantage by the solitude and close imprisonment that they reduce me to after, that I am so much the oftener at my prayers, in which I shall never leave out your happiness; and I doubt not, among his other blessings, God will add some one to you for my prayers. A man would almost be content to die,—if there were no other benefit in death,—to hear of so much sorrow, and so much good testimony from good men, as I—God be blessed for it—did upon the report of my death: yet I perceive it went not through all; for one writ to me, that some—and he said of my friends—conceived that I was not so ill as I pretended, but withdrew myself to live at ease, discharged of preaching. It is an unfriendly, and, God knows, an ill-grounded interpretation;

for I have always been sorrier when I could not preach than any could be they could not hear me. It hath been my desire, and God may be pleased to grant it, that I might die in the pulpit; if not that, yet that I might take my death in the pulpit; that is, die the sooner by occasion of those labours. Sir, I hope to see you presently after Candlemas; about which time will fall my Lent sermon at court, except my Lord Chamberlain believe me to be dead, and so leave me out of the roll: but as long as I live, and am not speechless, I would not willingly decline that service. I have better leisure to write, than you to read; yet I would not willingly oppress you with too much letter. God so bless you and your son, as I wish to

Your poor friend and servant
in Christ Jesus,
J. DONNE."

Before that month ended, he was appointed to preach upon his old constant day, the first Friday in Lent: he had notice of it, and had in his sickness so prepared for that employment, that as he had long thirsted for it, so he resolved his weakness should not hinder his journey; he came therefore to London some few days before his appointed day of preaching. At his coming thither, many of his friends—who with sorrow saw his sickness had left him but so much flesh as did only cover his bones—doubted his strength to perform that task, and did thereof persuade him from undertaking it, assuring him however, it was like to shorten his life: but he passionately denied their requests, saying "he would not doubt that that God, who in so many weaknesses had assisted him with an unexpected strength, would now withdraw it in his last employment; professing an holy ambition to perform that sacred work." And when, to the amazement of some of the beholders, he appeared in the pulpit, many of them thought he presented himself not to preach mortification by a living voice, but mortality by a decayed body and a dying face. And doubtless many did secretly ask that question in Ezekiel, —"Do these bones live? or, can that soul organise that tongue, to speak so long time as the sand in that glass will move towards its centre, and measure out an hour of this dying man's unspent life? Doubtless it cannot." And yet, after some faint pauses in his zealous prayer, his strong desires enabled his weak body to discharge his memory of his preconceived meditations, which were of dying; the text being, "To God the Lord belong the issues from death." Many that then saw his tears, and heard his faint and hollow voice, professing they thought the text prophetically chosen, and that Dr. Donne had preached his own funeral sermon.

Being full of joy that God had enabled him to perform this desired duty, he hastened to his house; out of which he never moved, till, like St. Stephen, "he was carried by devout men to his grave."

The next day after his sermon, his strength being much wasted, and his spirits so spent as indisposed him to business or to talk, a friend that had often been a witness of his free and facetious discourse asked him, "Why are you sad?" To whom he replied, with a countenance so full of cheerful gravity, as gave testimony of an inward tranquillity of mind, and of a soul willing to take a farewell of this world; and said,—

"I am not sad; but most of the night past I have entertained myself with many thoughts of several friends that have left me here, and are gone to that place from which they shall not return; and that within a few days I also shall go hence, and be no more seen. And my preparation for this change is become my nightly meditation upon my bed, which my infirmities have now made restless to me. But at this present time, I was in a serious contemplation of the providence and goodness of God to me; to me, who am less than the least of his mercies: and looking back upon my life past, I now plainly see it was his hand that prevented me from all temporal employment; and that it was his will I should never settle nor thrive till I entered into the ministry; in which I have now lived almost twenty years—I hope to his glory,—and by which, I most humbly thank him, I have been enabled to requite most of those friends which showed me kindness when my fortune was very low, as God knows it was: and—as it hath occasioned the expression of my gratitude I thank God most of them have stood in need of my requital. I have lived to be useful and comfortable to my good father-in-law, Sir George More, whose patience God hath been pleased to exercise with many temporal crosses; I have maintained my own mother, whom it hath pleased God, after a plentiful fortune in her younger days, to bring to great decay in her very old age. I have quieted the consciences of many that have groaned under the burthen of a wounded spirit, whose prayers I hope are available for me. I cannot plead innocency of life, especially of my youth; but I am to be judged by a merciful God, who is not willing to see what I have done amiss. And though of myself I have nothing to present to him but sins and misery, yet I know he looks not upon me now as I am of myself, but as I am in my Saviour, and hath given me, even at this present time, some testimonies by his Holy Spirit, that I am of the number of his elect: I am therefore full of inexpressible joy, and shall die in peace."

I must here look so far back, as to tell the reader that at his first return out of Essex, to preach his last sermon, his old friend and physician, Dr. Fox—a man of great worth—came to him to consult his health; and that after a sight of him, and some queries concerning his distempers, he told him, "That by cordials, and drinking milk twenty days together, there was a probability of his restoration to health;" but he passionately denied to drink it. Nevertheless, Dr. Fox, who loved him most entirely, wearied him with solicitations, till he yielded to take it for ten days; at the end of which time he told Dr. Fox, "He had drunk it more to satisfy him, than to recover his health; and that he would not drink it ten days longer, upon the best moral assurance of having twenty years added to his life; for he loved it not; and was so far from fearing death, which to others is the King of Terrors, that he longed for the day of dissolution."

It is observed that a desire of glory or commendation is rooted in the very nature of man; and that those of the severest and most mortified lives, though they may become so humble as to banish self-flattery, and such weeds as naturally grow there; yet they have not been able to kill this desire of glory, but that like our radical heat, it will both live and die with us; and many think it should do so; and we want not sacred examples to justify the desire of having our memory to outlive our lives; which I mention, because Dr. Donne, by the persuasion of Dr. Fox, easily yielded at this very time to have a monument made for him; but Dr. Fox undertook not to persuade him how, or what monument it should be; that was left to Dr. Donne himself.

A monument being resolved upon, Dr. Donne sent for a Carver to make for him in wood the figure of an urn, giving him directions for the compass and height of it; and to bring with it a board, of just the height of his body. "These being got, then without delay a choice painter was got to be in readiness to draw his picture, which was taken as followeth.—Several charcoal fires being first made in his large study, he brought with him into that place his winding-sheet in his hand, and having put off all his clothes, had this sheet put on him, and so tied with knots at his head and feet, and his hands so placed as dead bodies are usually fitted, to be shrouded and put into their coffin, or grave. Upon this urn he thus stood, with his eyes shut, and with so much of the sheet turned aside as might show his lean, pale, and death-like face, which was purposely turned towards the east, from whence he expected the second coming of his and our Saviour Jesus." In this posture he was drawn at his just height; and when the picture was fully finished, he caused it to be set by his bed-side, where it continued and became his hourly object till his death, and was then given to his dearest friend and executor Dr. Henry King, then chief residentiary of St. Paul's, who caused him to be thus carved in one entire piece of white marble, as it now stands in that church; and by Dr. Donne's own appointment, these words were to be affixed to it as an epitaph:

JOHANNES DONNE,

SAC. THEOL. PROFESS.
POST VARIA STVDIA, QVIBUS AB ANNIS
TENERRIMIS FIDELITER, NEC INFELICITER
INCVBVIT;
INSTINCTV ET IMPVLSV SP. SANCTI, MONITV
ET HORTATV
REGIS JACOBI, ORDINES SACROS AMPLEXVS,
ANN SVI JESV, MDCXIV. ET SVÆ ÆTATIS XLII.
DECANATV HVJVS ECCLESIÆ INDVTVS,
XXVII. NOVEMBRIS, MDCXXI.
EXVTVS MORTE VLTIMO DIE MARTII, MDCXXXI.
HIC LICET IN OCCIDVO CINERE, ASPICIT EVM
CVJVS NOMEN EST ORIENS.

And now, having brought him through the many labyrinths and perplexities of a various life, even to the gates of death and the grave; my desire is, he may rest till I have told my reader that I have seen many pictures of him, in several habits, and at several ages, and in several postures: and I now mention this, because I have seen one picture of him, drawn by a curious hand, at his age of eighteen, with his sword, and what other adornments might then suit with the present fashions of youth and the giddy gaieties of that age; and his motto then was—

How much shall I be changed,
Before I am changed!

And if that young and his now dying picture were at this time set together every beholder might say, Lord! how much is Dr. Donne already changed, before he is changed! And the view of them might give my reader occasion to ask himself with some amazement, "Lord! how much may I also, that am now in health, be changed before I am changed; before this vile, this changeable body shall put off mortality!" and therefore to prepare for it.—But this is not writ so much for my reader's memento, as to tell him that Dr. Donne would often in his private discourses, and often publicly in his sermons, mention the many changes both of his body and mind; especially of his mind from a vertiginous giddiness; and would as often say, "His great and most blessed change was from a temporal to a spiritual employment;" in which he was so happy, that he accounted the former part of his life to be lost; and the beginning of it to be from his first entering into sacred orders, and serving his most merciful God at his altar.

Upon Monday, after the drawing this picture, he took his last leave of his beloved study; and, being sensible of his hourly decay, retired himself to his bed-chamber; and that week sent at several times for many of his most considerable friends, with whom he took a solemn and deliberate farewell, commending to their considerations some sentences useful for the regulation of their lives; and then dismissed them, as good Jacob did his sons, with a spiritual benediction. The Sunday following, he appointed his servants, that if there were any business yet undone that concerned him or themselves, it should be prepared against Saturday next; for after that day he would not mix his thoughts with anything that concerned this world; nor ever did; but, as Job, so he "waited for the appointed day of his dissolution."

And now he was so happy as to have nothing to do but to die, to do which, he stood in need of no longer time; for he had studied it long, and to so happy a perfection, that in a former sickness he called God to witness[1] "He was that minute ready to deliver his soul into his hands if that minute God would determine his dissolution." In that sickness he begged of God the constancy to be preserved in that estate for ever; and his patient expectation to have his immortal soul disrobed from her garment of mortality, makes me confident that he now had a modest assurance that his prayers were then heard, and his petition granted. He lay fifteen days earnestly expecting his hourly change; and in the last hour of his last day, as his body melted away, and vapoured into spirit, his soul having, I verily believe some revelation of the beatifical vision, he said, "I were miserable if I might not die;" and after those words, closed many periods of his faint breath by saying often, "Thy kingdom come, thy will be done." His speech, which had long been his ready and faithful servant, left him not till the last minute of his life, and then forsook him, not to serve another master—for who speaks like him, —but died before him; for that it was then become useless to him, that now conversed with God on earth, as angels are said to do in heaven, only by thoughts and looks. Being speechless, and seeing heaven by that illumination by which he saw it, he did, as St. Stephen, "look steadfastly into it, till he saw the Son of Man standing at the right hand of God his Father;" and being satisfied with this blessed sight, as his soul ascended, and his last breath departed from him, he closed his own eyes, and then disposed his hands and body into such a posture as required not the least alteration by those that came to shroud him.

Thus variable, thus virtuous was the life: thus excellent, thus exemplary was the death of this memorable man.

[1] In his Book of Devotions written then.

He was buried in that place of St. Paul's Church, which he had appointed for that use some years before his death; and by which he passed daily to pay his public devotions to Almighty God—who was then served twice a day by a public form of prayer and praises in that place:—but he was not buried privately, though he desired it; for, beside an unnumbered number of others, many persons of nobility, and of eminence for learning, who did love and honour him in his life, did show it at his death, by a voluntary and sad attendance of his body to the grave, where nothing was so remarkable as a public sorrow.

To which place of his burial some mournful friends repaired, and, as Alexander the Great did to the grave of the famous Achilles, so they strewed his with an abundance of curious and costly flowers; which course, they—who were never yet known—continued morning and evening for many days, not ceasing, till the stones, that were taken up in that church, to give his body admission into the cold earth—now his bed of rest,—were again by the mason's art so levelled and firmed as they had been formerly, and his place of burial undistinguishable to common view.

The next day after his burial, some unknown friend, some one of the many lovers and admirers of his virtue and learning, writ this epitaph with a coal on the wall over his grave:—

Reader! I am to let thee know.
Donne's Body only lies below;
For, could the grave his Soul comprise,
Earth would be richer than the Skies!

Nor was this all the honour done to his reverend ashes; for, as there be some persons that will not receive a reward for that for which God accounts himself a debtor; persons that dare trust God with their charity, and without a witness; so there was by some grateful unknown friend, that thought Dr. Donne's memory ought to be perpetuated, an hundred marks sent to his faithful friends[1] and executors, towards the making of his monument. It was not for many years known by whom; but, after the death of Dr. Fox, it was known that it was he that sent it; and he lived to see as lively a representa-

[1] Dr. King and Dr. Montford.

tion of his dead friend as marble can express: a statue indeed so like Dr. Donne, that—as his friend Sir Henry Wotton hath expressed himself—" It seems to breathe faintly, and posterity shall look upon it as a kind of artificial miracle."

He was of stature moderately tall; of a straight and equally-proportioned body, to which all his words and actions gave an unexpressible addition of comeliness.

The melancholy and pleasant humour were in him so contempered, that each gave advantage to the other, and made his company one of the delights of mankind.

His fancy was unimitably high, equalled only by his great wit; both being made useful by a commanding judgment.

His aspect was cheerful, and such as gave a silent testimony of a clear knowing soul, and of a conscience at peace with itself.

His melting eye showed that he had a soft heart, full of noble compassion; of too brave a soul to offer injuries, and too much a Christian not to pardon them in others.

He did much contemplate—especially after he entered into his sacred calling—the mercies of Almighty God, the immortality of the soul, and the joys of heaven: and would often say in a kind of sacred ecstasy,—"Blessed be God that he is God, only and divinely like himself."

He was by nature highly passionate, but more apt to reluct at the excesses of it. A great lover of the offices of humanity, and of so merciful a spirit, that he never beheld the miseries of mankind without pity and relief.

He was earnest and unwearied in the search of knowledge, with which his vigorous soul is now satisfied, and employed in a continual praise of that God that first breathed it into his active body: that body, which once was a temple of the Holy Ghost, and is now become a small quantity of Christian dust:—

But I shall see it re-animated.

Feb. 15, 1639. I. W.

THE LIFE OF
MR. GEORGE HERBERT

INTRODUCTORY NOTE

"For *the life of that great example of holiness, Mr. George Herbert, I profess it to be so far a free-will offering, that it was writ chiefly to please myself, but yet not without some respect to posterity: for though he was not a man that the next age can forget, yet many of his particular acts and virtues might have been neglected, or lost, if I had not collected and presented them to the imitation of those that shall succeed us: for I humbly conceive writing to be both a safer and truer preserver of men's virtuous actions than tradition; especially as it is managed in this age. And I am also to tell the Reader, that though this Life of Mr. Herbert was not by me writ in haste, yet I intended it a review before it should be made public; but that was not allowed me, by reason of my absence from London when it was printing; so that the Reader may find in it some mistakes, some double expressions, and some not very proper, and some that might have been contracted, and some faults that are not justly chargeable upon me, but the printer; and yet I hope none so great, as may not, by this confession, purchase pardon from a good-natured Reader."—From Izaak Walton's Introduction to the "Lives."*

THE LIFE OF MR. GEORGE HERBERT

GEORGE HERBERT was born the third day of April, in the year of our redemption 1593. The place of his birth was near to the town of Montgomery, and in that castle that did then bear the name of that town and county; that castle was then a place of state and strength, and had been successively happy in the family of the Herberts, who had long possessed it; and with it, a plentiful estate, and hearts as liberal to their poor neighbours. A family that hath been blessed with men of remarkable wisdom, and a willingness to serve their country, and, indeed, to do good to all mankind; for which they are eminent: But alas! this family did in the late rebellion suffer extremely in their estates; and the heirs of that castle saw it laid level with that earth that was too good to bury those wretches that were the cause of it.

The father of our George was Richard Herbert, the son of Edward Herbert, Knight, the son of Richard Herbert, Knight, the son of the famous Sir Richard Herbert of Colebrook, in the county of Monmouth, Banneret, who was the youngest brother of that memorable William Herbert, Earl of Pembroke, that lived in the reign of our King Edward the Fourth.

His mother was Magdalen Newport, the youngest daughter of Sir Richard, and sister to Sir Francis Newport of High Arkall, in the county of Salop, Knight, and grandfather of Francis Lord Newport, now Controller of his Majesty's Household. A family that for their loyalty have suffered much in their estates, and seen the ruin of that excellent structure where their ancestors have long lived, and been memorable for their hospitality.

This mother of George Herbert—of whose person, and wisdom, and virtue, I intend to give a true account in a seasonable place—was the happy mother of seven sons and three daughters, which she would often say was Job's number, and Job's distribution; and as often bless God, that they were neither defective in their shapes nor in their reason; and very often reprove them that did not praise God for so great a blessing. I shall give the reader a short account of their names, and not say much of their fortunes.

Edward, the eldest, was first made Knight of the Bath, at that glorious time of our late Prince Henry's being installed Knight of the Garter; and after many years' useful travel, and the attainment of many languages, he was by King James sent ambassador resident to the then French king, Lewis the Thirteenth. There he continued about two years; but he could not subject himself to a compliance with the humours of the Duke de Luisens, who was then the great and powerful favourite at court: so that upon a complaint to our King, he was called back into England in some displeasure; but at his return he gave such an honourable account of his employment, and so justified his comportment to the Duke and all the court, that he was suddenly sent back upon the same embassy, from which he returned in the beginning of the reign of our good King Charles the First, who made him first Baron of Castleisland, and not long after of Cherbury in the county of Salop. He was a man of great learning and reason, as appears by his printed book *De Veritate,* and by his *History of the Reign of King Henry the Eighth,* and by several other tracts.

The second and third brothers were Richard and William, who ventured their lives to purchase honour in the wars of the Low Countries, and died officers in that employment. Charles was the fourth, and died fellow of New College in Oxford. Henry was the sixth, who became a menial servant to the crown in the days of King James, and hath continued to be so for fifty years; during all which time he hath been Master of the Revels, a place that requires a diligent wisdom, with which God hath blessed him. The seventh son was Thomas, who, being made captain of a ship in that fleet with which Sir Robert Mansell was sent against Algiers, did there show a fortunate and true English valour. Of the three sisters I need not say more than that they were all married to persons of worth and plentiful fortunes; and lived to be examples of virtue, and to do good in their generations.

I now come to give my intended account of George, who was the fifth of those seven brothers.

George Herbert spent much of his childhood in a sweet content under the eye and care of his prudent mother, and the tuition of a chaplain, or tutor to him and two of his brothers, in her own family,—for she was then a widow,—where he continued till about the age of twelve years; and being at that time well instructed in the rules of grammar, he was not long after commended to the care of Dr. Neale, who was then Dean of Westminster; and by him to the care of Mr. Ireland, who was then chief master of that school; where the beauties of his pretty behaviour and wit shined, and became so eminent and lovely in this his innocent age, that he seemed to be marked out for piety, and to become the care of heaven, and of a particular good angel to guard and guide him. And thus he continued in that school, till he came to be perfect in the learned languages, and especially in the Greek tongue, in which he after proved an excellent critic.

About the age of fifteen—he being then a King's scholar—he was elected out of that school for Trinity College in Cambridge, to which place he was transplanted about the year 1608; and his prudent mother, well knowing that he might easily lose or lessen that virtue and innocence which her advice and example had planted in his mind, did therefore procure the generous and liberal Dr. Nevil, who was then Dean of Canterbury, and master of that College, to take him into his particular care, and provide him a tutor; which he did most gladly undertake, for he knew the excellencies of his mother, and how to value such a friendship.

This was the method of his education, till he was settled in Cambridge; where we will leave him in his study, till I have paid my promised account of his excellent mother; and I will endeavour to make it short.

I have told her birth, her marriage, and the number of her children, and have given some short account of them. I shall next tell the reader that her husband died when our George was about the age of four years: I am next to tell, that she continued twelve years a widow; that she then married happily to a noble gentleman, the brother and heir of the Lord Danvers, Earl of Danby, who did highly value both her person and the most excellent endowments of her mind.

In this time of her widowhood, she being desirous to give Edward, her eldest son, such advantages of learning, and other education, as might suit his birth and fortune, and thereby make him the more fit for the service of his country, did, at his being of a fit age, remove from Montgomery Castle with him, and some of her younger sons, to Oxford; and having entered Edward into Queen's College, and provided him a fit tutor, she commended him to his care, yet she continued there with him, and still kept him in a moderate awe of herself, and so much under her own eye, as to see and converse with him daily: but she managed this power over him without any such rigid sourness as might make her company a torment to her child; but with such a sweetness and compliance with the recreations and pleasures of youth, as did incline him willingly to spend much of his time in the company of his dear and careful mother; which was to her great content: for she would often say, "That as our bodies take a nourishment suitable to the meat on which we feed; so our souls do as insensibly take in vice by the example or conversation with wicked company:" and would therefore as often say, "That ignorance of vice was the best preservation of virtue; and that the very knowledge of wickedness was as tinder to inflame and kindle sin and keep it burning." For these reasons she endeared him to her own company, and continued with him in Oxford four years; in which time her great and harmless wit, her cheerful gravity, and her obliging behaviour, gained her an acquaintance and friendship with most of any eminent worth or learning that were at that time in or near that university; and particularly with Mr. John Donne, who then came accidentally to that place, in this time of her being there. It was that John Donne, who was after Dr. Donne, and Dean of St. Paul's, London: and he, at his leaving Oxford, writ and left there, in verse, a character of the beauties of her body and mind: of the first he says,

> No spring nor summer-beauty has such grace,
> As I have seen in an autumnal face.

Of the latter he says,

> In all her words to every hearer fit,
> You may at revels, or at council sit.

The rest of her character may be read in his printed poems, in that elegy which bears the name of "The Autumnal Beauty." For both he and she were then past the meridian of man's life.

This amity, begun at this time and place, was not an amity that polluted their souls; but an amity made up of a chain of suitable inclinations and virtues; an amity like that of St. Chrysostom's to his dear and virtuous Olympias; whom, in his letters, he calls his saint: or an amity, indeed, more like that of St. Hierome to his Paula; whose affection to her was such, that he turned poet in his old age, and then made her epitaph; wishing all his body were turned into tongues that he might declare her just praises to posterity. And this amity betwixt her and Mr. Donne was begun in a happy time for him, he being then near to the fortieth year of his age,—which was some years before he entered into sacred orders;—a time when his necessities needed a daily supply for the support of his wife, seven children, and a family. And in this time she proved one of his most bountiful benefactors; and he as grateful an acknowledger of it. You may take one testimony for what I have said of these two worthy persons, from this following letter and sonnet:—

"Madam,

"Your favours to me are everywhere: I use them and have them. I enjoy them at London, and leave them there; and yet find them at Mitcham. Such riddles as these become things inexpressible; and such is your goodness. I was almost sorry to find your servant here this day, because I was loth to have any witness of my not coming home last night, and indeed of my coming this morning. But my not coming was excusable, because earnest business detained me; and my coming this day is by the example of your St. Mary Magdalen, who rose early upon Sunday to seek that which she loved most; and so did I. And, from her and myself, I return such thanks as are due to one to whom we owe all the good opinion that they, whom we need most, have of us. By this messenger, and on this good day, I commit the enclosed holy hymns and sonnets—which for the matter, not the workmanship, have yet escaped the fire—to your judgment, and to your protection too, if you think them worthy of it; and I have appointed this inclosed sonnet to usher them to your happy hand.

Your unworthiest servant,
Unless your accepting him to be so
have mended him,
JO. DONNE."

MITCHAM,
July 11, 1607.

To the Lady Magdalen Herbert:
Of St. Mary Magdalen

Her of your name, whose fair inheritance
Bethina was, and jointure Magdalo,
An active faith so highly did advance,
That she once knew more than the Church did know,
The Resurrection! so much good there is
Delivered of her, that some Fathers be
Loth to believe one woman could do this,
But think these Magdalens were two or three.
Increase their number, Lady, and their fame:
To their devotion add your innocence:
Take so much of th' example, as of the name;
The latter half; and in some recompense
That they did harbour Christ himself, a guest,
Harbour these Hymns, to his dear name addrest.

J. D.

These hymns are now lost to us; but doubtless they were such as they two now sing in heaven.

There might be more demonstrations of the friendship, and the many sacred endearments betwixt these two excellent persons,—for I have many of their letters in my hand,—and much more might be said of her great prudence and piety; but my design was not to write hers, but the life of her son; and therefore I shall only tell my reader, that about that very day twenty years that this letter was dated, and sent her, I saw and heard this Mr. John Donne—who was then Dean of St. Paul's—weep, and preach her funeral sermon, in the Parish Church of Chelsea, near London, where she now rests in her quiet grave: and where we must now leave her, and return to her son George, whom we left in his study in Cambridge.

And in Cambridge we may find our George Herbert's behaviour to be such, that we may conclude he consecrated the first-fruits of his early age to virtue, and a serious study of learning. And that he did so, this following letter and sonnet, which were, in the first year of his going to Cambridge, sent his dear mother for a New Year's gift, may appear to be some testimony:—

". . . But I fear the heat of my late ague hath dried up those springs by which scholars say the Muses use to take up their habitations. However, I need not their help to reprove the vanity of those many love-poems that are daily writ and consecrated to Venus; nor to bewail that so few are writ that look towards God and heaven. For my own part, my meaning—dear mother—is, in these sonnets, to declare my resolution to be, that my poor abilities in poetry shall be all and ever consecrated to God's glory: and I beg you to receive this as one testimony."

My God, where is that ancient heat towards thee,
  Wherewith whole shoals of Martyrs once did burn,
  Besides their other flames? Doth Poetry
Wear Venus' livery? only serve her turn?
Why are not Sonnets made of thee? and lays
  Upon thine altar burnt? Cannot thy love
  Heighten a spirit to sound out thy praise
As well as any she? Cannot thy Dove
Outstrip their Cupid easily in flight?
  Or, since thy ways are deep, and still the same,
  Will not a verse run smooth that bears thy name?
Why doth that fire, which by thy power and might
  Each breast does feel, no braver fuel choose
  Than that, which one day, worms may chance refuse?
Sure, Lord, there is enough in thee to dry
  Oceans of ink; for as the Deluge did
  Cover the Earth, so doth thy Majesty;
Each cloud distils thy praise, and doth forbid

Poets to turn it to another use.
Roses and lilies speak Thee; and to make
A pair of cheeks of them, is thy abuse.
Why should I women's eyes for crystal take?
Such poor invention burns in their low mind
Whose fire is wild, and doth not upward go
To praise, and on thee, Lord, some ink bestow.
Open the bones, and you shall nothing find
In the best face but filth; when Lord, in Thee
The beauty lies in the discovery.

G. H.

This was his resolution at the sending this letter to his dear mother, about which time he was in the seventeenth year of his age; and as he grew older, so he grew in learning, and more and more in favour both with God and man: insomuch that, in this morning of that short day of his life, he seemed to be marked out for virtue, and to become the care of Heaven; for God still kept his soul in so holy a frame, that he may, and ought to be a pattern of virtue to all posterity, and especially to his brethren of the clergy, of which the reader may expect a more exact account in what will follow.

I need not declare that he was a strict student, because, that he was so, there will be many testimonies in the future part of his life. I shall therefore only tell, that he was made Minor Fellow in the year 1609, Bachelor of Arts in the year 1611; Major Fellow of the College, March 15th, 1615: and that in that year he was also made Master of Arts, he being then in the twenty-second year of his age; during all which time, all, or the greatest diversion from his study, was the practice of music, in which he became a great master; and of which he would say, "That it did relieve his drooping spirits, compose his distracted thoughts, and raised his weary soul so far above earth, that it gave him an earnest of the joys of heaven, before he possessed them." And it may be noted, that from his first entrance into the college, the generous Dr. Nevil was a cherisher of his studies, and such a lover of his person, his behaviour, and the excellent endowments of his mind, that he took him often into his own company; by which he confirmed his native gentleness: and if during his time he expressed any error, it was that he kept himself too much retired, and at too great a distance with all his inferiors; and his clothes seemed to prove that he put too great a value on his parts and parentage.

This may be some account of his disposition, and of the employment of his time till he was Master of Arts, which was anno 1615, and in the year 1619 he was chosen Orator for the University. His two precedent Orators were Sir Robert Naunton and Sir Francis Nethersole. The first was not long after made Secretary of State, and Sir Francis, not very long after his being Orator, was made secretary to the Lady Elizabeth, Queen of Bohemia. In this place of Orator our George Herbert continued eight years; and managed it with as becoming and grave a gaiety as any had ever before or since his time. For "he had acquired great learning, and was blessed with a high fancy, a civil and sharp wit; and with a natural elegance, both in his behaviour, his tongue, and his pen." Of all which there might be very many particular evidences; but I will limit myself to the mention of but three.

And the first notable occasion of showing his fitness for this employment of Orator was manifested in a letter to King James, upon the occasion of his sending that university his book called *Basilicon Doron;* and their Orator was to acknowledge this great honour, and return their gratitude to his Majesty for such a condescension; at the close of which letter he writ,

Quid Vaticanam Bodleianamque objicis, hospes!
Unicus est nobis Bibliotheca Liber.

This letter was writ in such excellent Latin, was so full of conceits, and all the expressions so suited to the genius of the King, that he inquired the Orator's name, and then asked William, Earl of Pembroke, if he knew him? whose answer was, "That he knew him very well, and that he was his kinsman; but he loved him more for his learning and virtue than for that he was of his name and family." At which answer the King smiled, and asked the Earl leave that he might love him too, for he took him to be the jewel of that university.

The next occasion he had and took to show his great abilities was, with them, to show also his great affection to that Church in which he received his baptism, and of which he professed himself a member; and the occasion was this: There was one Andrew Melvin, a minister of the Scotch Church, and Rector of St. Andrew's; who, by a long and constant converse with a discontented part of that clergy which opposed episcopacy, became at last to be a chief leader of that faction; and had proudly appeared to be so to King James, when he was but King of that nation, who, the second year after his coronation in England, convened a part of the bishops, and other learned divines of his Church, to attend him at Hampton Court, in order to a friendly conference with some dissenting brethren, both of this and the Church of Scotland: of which Scotch party Andrew Melvin was one; and he being a man of learning, and inclined to satirical poetry, had scattered many malicious, bitter verses against our Liturgy, our ceremonies, and our Church government; which were by some of that party so magnified for the wit, that they were therefore brought into Westminster School, where Mr. George Herbert, then, and often after, made such answers to them, and such reflections on him and his Kirk, as might unbeguile any man that was not too deeply pre-engaged in such a quarrel. But to return to Mr. Melvin at Hampton Court conference: he there appeared to be a man of an unruly wit, of a strange confidence, of so furious a zeal, and of so ungoverned passions, that his insolence to the King, and others at this conference, lost him both his Rectorship of St. Andrew's and his liberty too; for his former verses, and his present reproaches there used against the Church and State, caused him to be committed prisoner to the Tower of London; where he remained very angry for three years. At which time of his commitment he found the Lady Arabella an innocent prisoner there; and he pleased himself much in sending, the next day after his commitment, these two verses to the good lady; which I will underwrite, because they may give the reader a taste of his others, which were like these:

Casua tibi mecum est communis, carceris, Ara-
Bella, tibi causa est, Araque sacra mihi.

I shall not trouble my reader with an account of his enlargement from that prison, or his death; but tell him Mr.

Herbert's verses were thought so worthy to be preserved, that Dr. Duport, the learned Dean of Peterborough, hath lately collected and caused many of them to be printed, as an honourable memorial of his friend Mr. George Herbert, and the cause he undertook.

And in order to my third and last observation of his great abilities, it will be needful to declare, that about this time King James came very often to hunt at Newmarket and Royston, and was almost as often invited to Cambridge, where his entertainment was comedies, suited to his pleasant humour; and where Mr. George Herbert was to welcome him with gratulations, and the applauses of an Orator; which he always performed so well, that he still grew more into the King's favour, insomuch that he had a particular appointment to attend his Majesty at Royston; where, after a discourse with him, his Majesty declared to his kinsman, the Earl of Pembroke, that he found the Orator's learning and wisdom much above his age or wit. The year following, the King appointed to end his progress at Cambridge, and to stay there certain days; at which time he was attended by the great secretary of nature and all learning, Sir Francis Bacon, Lord Verulam, and by the ever-memorable and learned Dr. Andrews, Bishop of Winchester, both which did at that time begin a desired friendship with our Orator. Upon whom, the first put such a value on his judgment, that he usually desired his approbation before he would expose any of his books to be printed; and thought him so worthy of his friendship, that having translated many of the Prophet David's Psalms into English verse, he made George Herbert his patron, by a public dedication of them to him, as the best judge of divine poetry. And for the learned Bishop, it is observable, that at that time there fell to be a modest debate betwixt them two about predestination, and sanctity of life; of both of which the Orator did, not long after, send the Bishop some safe and useful aphorisms, in a long letter, written in Greek; which letter was so remarkable for the language and reason of it, that, after the reading of it, the Bishop put it into his bosom, and did often show it to many scholars, both of this and foreign nations; but did always return it back to the place where he first lodged it, and continued it so near his heart till the last day of his life.

To this I might add the long and entire friendship betwixt him and Sir Henry Wotton, and Dr. Donne; but I have promised to contract myself, and shall therefore only add one testimony to what is also mentioned in the life of Dr. Donne; namely, that a little before his death he caused many seals to be made, and in them to be engraven the figure of Christ, crucified on an anchor,—the emblem of hope,—and of which Dr. Donne would often say, "*Crux mihi anchora.*"—These seals he gave or sent to most of those friends on which he put a value; and, at Mr. Herbert's death, these verses were found wrapt up with that seal, which was by the Doctor given to him:

> When my dear friend could write no more,
> He gave this Seal and so gave o'er.
>
> When winds and waves rise highest I am sure,
> This Anchor keeps my faith, that me, secure.

At this time of being Orator, he had learned to understand the Italian, Spanish, and French tongues very perfectly: hoping that as his predecessors, so he might in time attain the place of a Secretary of State, he being at that time very high in the King's favour, and not meanly valued and loved by the most eminent and most powerful of the court nobility. This, and the love of a court conversation, mixed with a laudable ambition to be something more than he then was, drew him often from Cambridge, to attend the King wheresoever the court was, who then gave him a sinecure, which fell into his Majesty's disposal, I think, by the death of the Bishop of St. Asaph. It was the same that Queen Elizabeth had formerly given to her favourite Sir Philip Sidney, and valued to be worth an hundred and twenty pounds per annum. With this, and his annuity, and the advantage of his college, and of his Oratorship, he enjoyed his genteel humour for clothes, and court-like company, and seldom looked towards Cambridge, unless the King were there, but then he never failed; and, at other times, left the manage of his Orator's place to his learned friend.

Mr. Herbert Thorndike, who is now Prebend of Westminster.

I may not omit to tell, that he had often designed to leave the university, and decline all study, which he thought did impair his health; for he had a body apt to a consumption, and to fevers, and other infirmities, which he judged were increased by his studies; for he would often say, "He had too thoughtful a wit; a wit like a penknife in too narrow a sheath, too sharp for his body." But his mother would by no means allow him to leave the university, or to travel; and though he inclined very much to both, yet he would by no means satisfy his own desires at so dear a rate, as to prove an undutiful son to so affectionate a mother; but did always submit to her wisdom. And what I have now said may partly appear in a copy of verses in his printed poems; 'tis one of those that bear the title of Affliction; and it appears to be a pious reflection on God's providence, and some passages of his life, in which he says,—

Whereas my birth and spirit rather took
    The way that takes the town:
Thou didst betray me to a lingering book,
    And wrapt me in a gown:
I was entangled in a world of strife,
Before I had the power to change my life.

Yet, for I threaten'd oft the siege to raise,
    Not simpering all mine age;
Thou often didst with academic praise
    Melt and dissolve my rage:
I took the sweeten'd pill, till I came where
I could not go away, nor persevere.

Yet, lest perchance I should too happy be
    In my unhappiness,
Turning my purge to food, thou throwest me
    Into more sicknesses.
Thus doth thy power cross-bias me, not making
Thine own gifts good, yet me from my ways taking.

Now I am here, what thou wilt do with me
    None of my books will show.
I read, and sigh, and wish I were a tree,
    For then sure I should grow
To fruit or shade, at least some bird would trust
Her household with me, and I would be just.

Yet, though thou troublest me, I must be meek,
    In weakness must be stout,
Well, I will change my service, and go seek
    Some other master out;
Ah, my dear God! though I am clean forgot,
Let me not love thee, if I love thee not.

G. H.

In this time of Mr. Herbert's attendance and expectation of some good occcasion to remove from Cambridge to court, God, in whom there is an unseen chain of causes, did in a short time put an end to the lives of two of his most obliging and most powerful friends, Lodowick Duke of Richmond, and James Marquis of Hamilton; and not long after him King James died also, and with them all Mr. Herbert's court hopes: so that he presently betook himself to a retreat from London, to a friend in Kent, where he lived very privately, and was such a lover of solitariness, as was judged to impair his health more than his study had done. In this time of retirement he had many conflicts with himself, whether he should return to the painted pleasures of a court life, or betake himself to a study of divinity, and enter into sacred orders, to which his mother had often persuaded him. These were such conflicts as they only can know that have endured them; for ambitious desires, and the outward glory of this world, are not easily laid aside; but at last God inclined him to put on a resolution to serve at his altar.

He did, at his return to London, acquaint a court-friend with his resolution to enter into sacred orders, who persuaded him to alter it, as too mean an employment, and too much below his birth, and the excellent abilities and endowments of his mind. To whom he replied, "It hath been formerly judged that the domestic servants of the King of Heaven should be of the noblest families on earth. And though the iniquity of the late times have made clergymen meanly valued, and the sacred name of priest contemptible; yet I will labour to make it honourable, by consecrating all my learning, and all my poor abilities to advance the glory of that God that gave them; knowing that I can never do too much for him, that hath done so much for me as to make me a Christian. And I will labour to be like my

Saviour, by making humility lovely in the eyes of all men, and by following the merciful and meek example of my dear Jesus."

This was then his resolution; and the God of constancy, who intended him for a great example of virtue, continued him in it, for within that year he was made deacon, but the day when, or by whom, I cannot learn; but that he was about that time made deacon is most certain; for I find by the records of Lincoln, that he was made Prebend of Layton Ecclesia, in the diocese of Lincoln, July 15th, 1626, and that this Prebend was given him by John, then Lord Bishop of that see. And now he had a fit occasion to show that piety and bounty that was derived from his generous mother, and his other memorable ancestors, and the occasion was this.

This Layton Ecclesia is a village near to Spalden, in the county of Huntingdon, and the greatest part of the parish church was fallen down, and that of it which stood was so decayed, so little, and so useless, that the parishioners could not meet to perform their duty to God in public prayer and praises; and thus it had been for almost twenty years, in which time there had been some faint endeavours for a public collection to enable the parishioners to rebuild it; but with no success, till Mr. Herbert undertook it; and he, by his own, and the contribution of many of his kindred, and other noble friends, undertook the re-edification of it; and made it so much his whole business, that he became restless till he saw it finished as it now stands; being for the workmanship, a costly mosaic; for the form, an exact cross; and for the decency and beauty, I am assured, it is the most remarkable parish church that this nation affords. He lived to see it so wainscotted as to be exceeded by none, and, by his order, the reading pew and pulpit were a little distance from each other, and both of an equal height; for he would often say, "They should neither have a precedency or priority of the other; but that prayer and preaching, being equally useful, might agree like brethren, and have an equal honour and estimation."

Before I proceed further, I must look back to the time of Mr. Herbert's being made Prebend, and tell the reader, that not long after, his mother being informed of his intentions to rebuild that church, and apprehending the great trouble and charge that he was like to draw upon himself, his relations and friends, before it could be finished, sent for him from London to Chelsea,—where she then dwelt,—and at his coming, said, "George, I sent for you, to persuade you to commit simony, by giving your patron as good a gift as he has given to you; namely, that you give him back his prebend; for, George, it is not for your weak body, and empty purse, to undertake to build churches." Of which, he desired he might have a day's time to consider, and then make her an answer. And at his return to her the next day, when he had first desired her blessing, and she given it him, his next request was, "That she would, at the age of thirty-three years, allow him to become an undutiful son; for he had made a vow to God, that, if he were able, he would rebuild that church." And then showed her such reasons for his resolution, that she presently subscribed to be one of his benefactors; and undertook to solicit William Earl of Pembroke to become another, who subscribed for fifty pounds; and not long after, by a witty and persuasive letter from Mr. Herbert, made it fifty pounds more. And in this nomination of some of his benefactors, James Duke of Lenox, and his brother, Sir Henry Herbert, ought to be remembered; as also the bounty of Mr. Nicholas Farrer, and Mr. Arthur Woodnot: the one a gentleman in the neighbourhood of Layton, and the other a goldsmith in Foster Lane, London, ought not to be forgotten: for the memory of such men ought to outlive their lives. Of Mr. Farrer I shall hereafter give an account in a more seasonable place; but before I proceed further, I will give this short account of Mr. Arthur Woodnot.

He was a man that had considered overgrown estates do often require more care and watchfulness to preserve than get them, and considered that there be many discontents that riches cure not; and did therefore set limits to himself, as to desire of wealth. And having attained so much as to be able to show some mercy to the poor, and preserve a competence for himself, he dedicated the remaining part of his life to the service of God, and to be useful to his friends; and he proved to be so to Mr. Herbert; for besides his own bounty, he collected and returned most of the money that was paid for the rebuilding of that church; he kept all the account of the charges, and would often go down to state them, and see all the workmen paid. When I have said that this good man was a useful friend to Mr. Herbert's father, and to his mother, and continued to be so to him, till he closed his eyes on his death-bed, I will forbear to say more, till I have the next fair occasion to mention the holy friendship that was betwixt him and Mr. Herbert. From whom Mr. Woodnot carried to his mother this following letter, and delivered it to her in a sickness, which was not long before that which proved to be her last:—

A Letter of MR. GEORGE HERBERT *to his mother, in her sickness.*

"MADAM,

"At my last parting from you, I was the better content, because I was in hope I should myself carry all sickness out of your family: but since I know I did not, and that your share continues, or rather increaseth, I wish earnestly that I were again with you; and would quickly make good my wish, but that my employment does fix me here, it being now but a month to our commencement: wherein my absence, by how much it naturally augmenteth suspicion, by so much shall it make my prayers the more constant and the more earnest for you to the God of all consolation. In the meantime, I beseech you to be cheerful, and comfort yourself in the God of all comfort, who is not willing to behold any sorrow but for sin.—What hath affliction grievous in it more than for a moment? or why should our afflictions here have so much power or boldness as to oppose the hope of our joys hereafter? Madam, as the earth is but a point in respect of the heavens, so are earthly troubles compared to heavenly joys; therefore, if either age or sickness lead you to those joys, consider what advantage you have over youth and health, who are now so near those true comforts. Your last letter gave me earthly preferment, and I hope kept heavenly for yourself: but would you divide and choose too? Our college customs allow not that: and I should account myself most happy, if I might change with you; for I have always observed the thread of life to be like other threads or skeins of silk, full of snarles and incumbrances. Happy is he whose bottom is wound up, and laid ready for work in the New Jerusalem. For myself, dear mother, I always feared sickness more than death, because sickness hath made me unable to perform those offices for which I came into the world, and must yet be kept in it; but you are freed from that fear, who have already abundantly discharged that part, having both ordered your family and so brought up your children, that they have attained to the years of discretion, and competent maintenance. So that now, if they do not well, the fault cannot be charged on you, whose example and care of them will justify you both to the world and your own conscience; insomuch that, whether you turn your thoughts on the life past, or on the joys that are to come, you have strong preservatives against all disquiet. And for temporal afflictions, I beseech you consider, all that can happen to you are either afflictions of estate, or body, or mind. For those of estate, of what poor regard ought they to be? since, if we had riches, we are commanded to give them away: so that the best use of them is having, not to have them. But perhaps, being above the common people, our credit and estimation calls on us to live in a more splendid fashion: but, O God! how easily is that answered, when we consider that the blessings in the holy scripture are never given to the rich, but to the poor. I never find 'Blessed be the rich,' or 'Blessed be the noble'; but 'Blessed be the meek,' and 'Blessed be the poor,' and 'Blessed be the mourners, for they shall be comforted.' And yet, O God! most carry themselves so as if they not only not desired, but even feared to be blessed. And for afflictions of the body, dear madam, remember the holy martyrs of God, how they have been burned by thousands, and have endured such other tortures, as the very mention of them might beget amazement; but their fiery trials have had an end; and yours—which, praised be God, are less—are not like to continue long. I beseech you, let such thoughts as these moderate your present fear and sorrow; and know that if any of yours should prove a Goliah-like trouble, yet you may say with David, 'That God, who hath delivered me out of the paws of the lion and bear, will also deliver me out of the hands of this uncircumcised Philistine.' Lastly, for those afflictions of the soul; consider that God intends that to be as a sacred temple for himself to dwell in, and will not allow any room there for such an inmate as grief; or allow that any sadness shall be his competitor. And, above all, if any care of future things molest you, remember those admirable words of the Psalmist: 'Cast thy care on the Lord, and he shall nourish thee.'[1] To which join that of St. Peter, 'Casting all your care on the Lord, for he careth for you.'[2] What an admirable thing is this, that God puts his shoulder to our burden, and entertains our care for us, that we may the more quietly intend his service! To conclude, let me commend only one place more to you: Philipp. iv. 4. St. Paul saith there, 'Rejoice in the Lord always: and again I say, Rejoice.' He doubles it, to take away the scruple of those that might say, What, shall we rejoice in afflictions? Yes, I say again, rejoice; so that it is not left to us to rejoice, or not rejoice; but, whatsoever befalls us, we must always, at all times, rejoice in the Lord, who taketh care for us. And it follows in the next verses: 'Let your moderation appear to all men: The Lord is at hand: Be careful for nothing.' What can be said more comfortably? Trouble not yourselves; God is at hand to deliver us from all, or in all. Dear madam, pardon my boldness, and accept the good meaning of

Your most obedient son,

GEORGE HERBERT."

TRIN. COLL.,
May 25th, 1622.

About the year 1629, and the thirty-fourth of his age, Mr. Herbert was seized with a sharp quotidian ague, and thought to remove it by the change of air; to which end he went to Woodford in Essex, but thither more chiefly to enjoy the company of his beloved brother, Sir Henry Herbert, and other friends then of that family. In his house he remained about twelve months, and there became his own physician, and cured himself of his ague, by forbearing to drink, and not eating any meat, no not mutton, nor a hen, or pigeon, unless they were salted; and by such a constant diet he re-

[1] Psalm lv. 22. [2] 1 Peter v. 7.

moved his ague, but with inconveniences that were worse; for he brought upon himself a disposition to rheums, and other weaknesses, and a supposed consumption. And it is to be noted that in the sharpest of his extreme fits he would often say, "Lord, abate my great affliction, or increase my patience: but Lord, I repine not; I am dumb, Lord, before thee, because thou doest it." By which, and a sanctified submission to the will of God, he showed he was inclinable to bear the sweet yoke of Christian discipline, both then and in the latter part of his life, of which there will be many true testimonies.

And now his care was to recover from his consumption, by a change from Woodford into such an air as was most proper to that end. And his remove was to Dauntsey in Wiltshire, a noble house, which stands in a choice air; the owner of it then was the Lord Danvers, Earl of Danby, who loved Mr. Herbert so very much, that he allowed him such an apartment in it as might best suit with his accommodation and liking. And in this place, by a spare diet, declining all perplexing studies, moderate exercise, and a cheerful conversation, his health was apparently improved to a good degree of strength and cheerfulness. And then he declared his resolution both to marry and to enter into the sacred orders of priesthood. These had long been the desire of his mother and his other relations; but she lived not to see either, for she died in the year 1627. And though he was disobedient to her about Layton Church, yet, in conformity to her will, he kept his Orator's place till after her death, and then presently declined it; and the more willingly that he might be succeeded by his friend Robert Creighton, who now is Dr. Creighton, and the worthy Bishop of Wells.

I shall now proceed to his marriage; in order to which, it will be convenient that I first give the reader a short view of his person, and then an account of his wife, and of some circumstances concerning both. He was for his person of a stature inclining towards tallness; his body was very straight, and so far from being cumbered with too much flesh, that he was lean to an extremity. His aspect was cheerful, and his speech and motion did both declare him a gentleman; for they were all so meek and obliging, that they purchased love and respect from all that knew him.

These, and his other visible virtues, begot him much love from a gentleman of a noble fortune, and a near kinsman to his friend the Earl of Danby; namely, from Mr. Charles Danvers of Bainton, in the county of Wilts, Esq. This Mr. Danvers, having known him long, and familiarly, did so much affect him, that he often and publicly declared a desire that Mr. Herbert would marry any of his nine daughters,—for he had so many,—but rather his daughter Jane than any other, because Jane was his beloved daughter. And he had often said the same to Mr. Herbert himself; and that if he could like her for a wife, and she him for a husband, Jane should have a double blessing: and Mr. Danvers had so often said the like to Jane, and so much commended Mr. Herbert to her, that Jane became so much a platonic as to fall in love with Mr. Herbert unseen.

This was a fair preparation for a marriage; but, alas! her father died before Mr. Herbert's retirement to Dauntsey: yet some friends to both parties procured their meeting; at which time a mutual affection entered into both their hearts, as a conqueror enters into a surprised city; and love having got such possession, governed, and made there such laws and resolutions as neither party was able to resist; insomuch, that she changed her name into Herbert the third day after this first interview.

This haste might in others be thought a love-frenzy, or worse; but it was not, for they had wooed so like princes, as to have select proxies; such as were true friends to both parties, such as well understood Mr. Herbert's and her temper of mind, and also their estates, so well before this interview, that the suddenness was justifiable by the strictest rules of prudence; and the more, because it proved so happy to both parties; for the eternal lover of mankind made them happy in each other's mutual and equal affections, and compliance; indeed, so happy, that there never was any opposition betwixt them, unless it were a contest which should most incline to a compliance with the other's desires. And though this begot, and continued in them, such a mutual love, and joy, and content, as was no way defective; yet this mutual content, and love, and joy, did receive a daily augmentation, by such daily obligingness to each other, as still added such new affluences to the former fulness of these divine souls, as was only improvable in heaven, where they now enjoy it.

About three months after this marriage, Dr. Curle, who was then Rector of Bemerton, in Wiltshire, was made Bishop of Bath and Wells, and not long after translated to Winchester, and by that means the presentation of a clerk to Bemerton did not fall to the Earl of Pembroke,—who was the undoubted patron of it,—but to the King, by reason of Dr. Curle's advancement: but Philip, then Earl of Pembroke, —for William was lately dead—requested the King to bestow it upon his kinsman George Herbert; and the King said, "Most willingly to Mr. Herbert, if it be worth his acceptance;" and the Earl as willingly and suddenly sent it him, without seeking. But though Mr. Herbert had formerly put on a resolution for the clergy; yet, at receiving this presentation, the apprehension of the last great account, that he was to make for the cure of so many souls, made him fast and pray often, and consider for not less than a month: in which time he had some resolutions to decline both the priesthood and that living. And in this time of considering, "he endured," as he would often say, "such spiritual conflicts as none can think, but only those that have endured them."

In the midst of these conflicts, his old and dear friend, Mr. Arthur Woodnot, took a journey to salute him at Bainton,—where he then was with his wife's friends and relations—and was joyful to be an eye-witness of his health and happy marriage. And after they had rejoiced together some few days, they took a journey to Wilton, the famous seat of the Earls of Pembroke; at which time the King, the Earl, and the whole court were there, or at Salisbury, which is near to it. And at this time Mr. Herbert presented his thanks to the Earl for his presentation to Bemerton, but had not yet resolved to accept it, and told him the reason why: but that night, the Earl acquainted Dr. Laud, then Bishop of London, and after Archbishop of Canterbury, with his kinsman's irresolution. And the Bishop did the next day so convince Mr. Herbert that the refusal of it was sin, that a tailor was sent for to come speedily from Salisbury to Wilton, to make measure, and make him canonical clothes against next day; which the tailor did: and Mr. Herbert being so habited, went with his presentation to the learned Dr. Davenant, who was then Bishop of Salisbury, and he gave him institution immediately,—for Mr. Herbert had been made deacon some years before,—and he was also the same day—which was April 26th, 1630—inducted into the good, and more pleasant than healthful, parsonage of Bemerton, which is a mile from Salisbury.

I have now brought him to the parsonage of Bemerton, and to the thirty-sixth year of his age, and must stop here, and bespeak the reader to prepare for an almost incredible story, of the great sanctity of the short remainder of his holy life; a life so full of charity, humility, and all Christian virtues, that it deserves the eloquence of St. Chrysostom to commend and declare it: a life, that if it were related by a pen like his, there would then be no need for this age to look back into times past for the examples of primitive piety; for they might be all found in the life of George Herbert. But now, alas! who is fit to undertake it? I confess I am not; and am not pleased with myself that I must; and profess myself amazed when I consider how few of the clergy lived like him then, and how many live so unlike him now. But it becomes not me to censure: my design is rather to assure the reader that I have used very great diligence to inform myself, that I might inform him of the truth of what follows; and though I cannot adorn it with eloquence, yet I will do it with sincerity.

When at his induction he was shut into Bemerton Church, being left there alone to toll the bell,—as the law requires him,—he stayed so much longer than an ordinary time, before he returned to those friends that stayed expecting him at the church door, that his friend Mr. Woodnot looked in at the church window, and saw him lie prostrate on the ground before the altar; at which time and place—as he after told Mr. Woodnot—he set some rules to himself, for the future manage of his life; and then and there made a vow to labour to keep them.

And the same night that he had his induction, he said to Mr. Woodnot, "I now look back upon my aspiring thoughts, and think myself more happy than if I had attained what then I so ambitiously thirsted for. And I now can behold the court with an impartial eye, and see plainly that it is made up of fraud and titles, and flattery, and many other such empty, imaginary, painted pleasures; pleasures that are so empty as not to satisfy when they are enjoyed. But in God, and his service, is a fulness of all joy and pleasure, and no satiety. And I will now use all my endeavours to bring my relations and dependants to a love and reliance on him, who never fails those that trust him. But above all, I will be sure to live well, because the virtuous life of a clergyman is the most powerful eloquence to persuade all that see it to reverence and love, and at least to desire to live like him. And this I will do, because I know we live in an age that hath more need of good examples than precepts. And I beseech that God, who hath honoured me so much as to call me to serve him at his altar, that as by his special grace he hath put into my heart these good desires and resolutions; so he will, by his assisting grace, give me ghostly strength to bring the same to good effect. And I beseech him, that my humble and charitable life may so win upon others, as to bring glory to my Jesus, whom I have this day taken to be my master and governor; and I am so proud of his service, that I will always observe, and obey, and do his will; and always call him, Jesus my Master; and I will always contemn my birth, or any title or dignity that can be conferred upon me, when I shall compare them with my title of being a priest, and serving at the altar of Jesus my Master."

And that he did so may appear in many parts of his book of *Sacred Poems:* especially in that which he calls "The Odour." In which he seems to rejoice in the thoughts of that word Jesus, and say, that the adding these words, my master, to it, and the often repetition of them, seemed to perfume his mind, and leave an oriental fragrancy in his very breath. And for his unforced choice to serve at God's altar, he seems in another place of his poems, "The Pearl" (Matt. xiii. 45, 46), to rejoice and say: "He knew the ways of learning; knew what nature does willingly, and what, when it is forced by fire; knew the ways of honour, and when glory inclines the soul to noble expressions: knew the court: knew the ways of pleasure, of love, of wit, of music, and upon what terms he declined all these for the service of his master Jesus": and then concludes, saying:

> That, through these labyrinths, not my grovelling wit,
> But thy silk twist, let down from Heaven to me,
> Did both conduct, and teach me, how by it
> To climb to thee.

The third day after he was made Rector of Bemerton, and had changed his sword and silk clothes into a canonical coat, he returned so habited with his friend Mr. Woodnot to Bainton; and immediately after he had seen and saluted his wife, he said to her—"You are now a minister's wife, and must now so far forget your father's house as not to claim a precedence of any of your parishioners; for you are to know, that a priest's wife can challenge no precedence or place, but that which she purchases by her obliging humility; and I am sure, places so purchased do best become them. And let me tell you, that I am so good a herald, as to assure you that this is truth." And she was so meek a wife, as to assure him, "it was no vexing news to her, and that he should see her observe it with a cheerful willingness." And, indeed, her unforced humility, that humility that was in her so original, as to be born with her, made her so happy as to do so; and her doing so begot her an unfeigned love, and a serviceable respect from all that conversed with her; and this love followed her in all places, as inseparably as shadows follow substances in sunshine.

It was not many days before he returned back to Bemerton, to view the church and repair the chancel: and indeed to rebuild almost three parts of his house, which was fallen down, or decayed by reason of his predecessor's living at a better parsonage-house; namely, at Minal, sixteen or twenty miles from this place. At which time of Mr. Herbert's coming alone to Bemerton, there came to him a poor old woman, with an intent to acquaint him with her necessitous condition, as also with some troubles of her mind: but after she had spoke some few words to him, she was surprised with a fear, and that begot a shortness of breath, so that her spirits and speech failed her; which he perceiving, did so compassionate her, and was so humble, that he took her by the hand, and said, "Speak, good mother; be not afraid to speak to me; for I am a man that will hear you with patience; and will relieve your necessities too, if I be able: and this I will do willingly; and therefore, mother, be not afraid to acquaint me with what you desire." After which comfortable speech, he again took her by the hand, made her sit down by him, and understanding she was of his parish, he told her "He would be acquainted with her, and take her into his care." And having with patience heard and understood her wants,—and it is some relief for a poor body to be but heard with patience,—he, like a Christian clergyman, comforted her by his meek behaviour and counsel; but because that cost him nothing, he relieved her with money too, and so sent her home with a cheerful heart, praising God, and praying for him. Thus worthy, and—like David's blessed man—thus lowly, was Mr. George Herbert in his own eyes, and thus lovely in the eyes of others.

At his return that night to his wife at Bainton, he gave her an account of the passages betwixt him and the poor woman; with which she was so affected, that she went next day to Salisbury, and there bought a pair of blankets, and sent them as a token of her love to the poor woman; and with them a message, "that she would see and be acquainted with her, when her house was built at Bemerton."

There be many such passages both of him and his wife, of which some few will be related: but I shall first tell, that he hasted to get the parish church repaired; then to beautify the chapel,—which stands near his house,—and that at his own great charge. He then proceeded to rebuild the greatest part of the parsonage-house, which he did also very completely, and at his own charge; and having done this good work, he caused these verses to be writ upon, or engraven in, the mantel of the chimney in his hall.

TO MY SUCCESSOR

If thou chance for to find
A new house to thy mind,
And built without thy cost;
Be good to the poor,
As God gives thee store,
And then my labour's not lost.

We will now, by the reader's favour, suppose him fixed at Bemerton, and grant him to have seen the church repaired, and the chapel belonging to it very decently adorned at his own great charge,—which is a real truth;—and having now fixed him there, I shall proceed to give an account of the rest of his behaviour, both to his parishioners, and those many others that knew and conversed with him.

Doubtless Mr. Herbert had considered, and given rules to himself for his Christian carriage both to God and man, before he entered into holy orders. And 'tis not unlike, but that he renewed those resolutions at his prostration before the holy altar, at his induction into the church of Bemerton: but as yet he was but a deacon, and therefore longed for the next ember-week, that he might be ordained priest, and make capable of administering both the sacraments. At which time the Reverend Dr. Humphrey Henchman, now Lord Bishop of London,—who does not mention him but with some veneration for his life and excellent learning,—tells me, "He laid his hand on Mr. Herbert's head, and, alas! within less than three years lent his shoulder to carry his dear friend to his grave."

And that Mr. Herbert might the better preserve those holy rules which such a priest as he intended to be ought to observe; and that time might not insensibly blot them out of his memory, but that the next year might show him his variations from this year's resolutions; he therefore did set down his rules, then resolved upon, in that order as the world now sees them printed in a little book, called *The Country Parson;* in which some of his rules are:

The Parson's knowledge.
The Parson on Sundays.
The Parson praying.
The Parson preaching.
The Parson's charity.
The Parson comforting the sick.
The Parson arguing.
The Parson condescending.
The Parson in his journey.
The Parson in his mirth.
The Parson with his Church-wardens.
The Parson blessing the people.

And his behaviour towards God and man may be said to be a practical comment on these, and the other holy rules set down in that useful book: a book so full of plain, prudent, and useful rules, that that country parson that can spare twelve pence, and yet wants it, is scarce excusable; because it will both direct him what he ought to do, and convince him for not having done it.

At the death of Mr. Herbert this book fell into the hands of his friend Mr. Woodnot; and he commended it into the trusty hands of Mr. Barnabas Oley, who published it with a most conscientious and excellent preface; from which I have had some of those truths, that are related in this life of Mr. Herbert. The text of his first sermon was taken out of Solomon's Proverbs, chap. iv. 23, and the words were, "Keep thy heart with all diligence." In which first sermon he gave his parishioners many necessary, holy, safe rules for the discharge of a good conscience, both to God and man; and delivered his sermon after a most florid manner, both with great learning and eloquence; but, at the close of this sermon, told them, "That should not be his constant way of preaching; for since Almighty God does not intend to lead men to heaven by hard questions, he would not therefore fill their heads with unnecessary notions; but that, for their sakes, his language and his expressions should be more plain and practical in his future sermons." And he then made it his humble request, "That they would be constant to the afternoon's service, and catechising;" and showed them convincing reasons why he desired it; and his obliging example and persuasions brought them to a willing conformity to his desires.

The texts for all his future sermons—which God knows were not many—were constantly taken out of the gospel for the day; and he did as constantly declare why the Church did appoint that portion of scripture to be that day read; and in what manner the collect for every Sunday does refer to the gospel, or to the epistle then read to them; and, that they might pray with understanding, he did usually take occasion to explain, not only the collect for every particular Sunday, but the reasons of all the other collects and responses in our Church service; and made it appear to them that the whole service of the Church was a reasonable, and therefore an acceptable sacrifice to God: as namely, that we begin with "Confession of ourselves to be vile, miserable sinners;" and that we begin so, because, till we have confessed ourselves to be such, we are not capable of that mercy which we acknowledge we need, and pray for: but having, in the prayer of our Lord, begged pardon for those sins which we have confessed; and hoping, that as the priest hath declared our absolution, so by our public confession, and real repentance, we have obtained that pardon; then we dare and do proceed to beg of the Lord, "to open our lips, that our mouth may show forth his praise;" for till then we are neither able nor worthy to praise him. But this being supposed, we are then fit to say, "Glory be to the Father, and to the Son, and to the Holy Ghost;" and fit to proceed to a further service of our God, in the collects, and psalms, and lauds, that follow in the service.

And as to the psalms and lauds, he proceeded to inform them why they were so often, and some of them daily, repeated in our Church service; namely, the psalms every month, because they be an historical and thankful repetition of mercies past, and such a composition of prayers and praises, as ought to be repeated often, and publicly; for with such sacrifice God is honoured and well-pleased. This for the psalms.

And for the hymns and lauds appointed to be daily repeated or sung after the first and second lessons are read to the congregation; he proceeded to inform them, that it was most reasonable, after they have heard the will and goodness of God declared or preached by the priest in his reading the two chapters, that it was then a seasonable duty to rise up, and express their gratitude to Almighty God for those his mercies to them, and to all mankind; and then to say with the Blessed Virgin, "that their souls do magnify the Lord, and that their spirits do also rejoice in God their Saviour:" and that it was their duty also to rejoice with Simeon in his song, and say with him, "That their eyes have" also "seen their salvation;" for they have seen that salvation which was but prophesied till his time: and he then broke out into these expressions of joy that he did see it; but they live to see it daily in the history of it, and therefore ought daily to rejoice, and daily to offer up their sacrifices of praise to their God, for that particular mercy. A service, which is now the constant employment of that

Blessed Virgin and Simeon, and all those blessed saints that are possessed of heaven: and where they are at this time interchangeably and constantly singing, "Holy, holy, holy, Lord God; glory be to God on high, and on earth peace." And he taught them that to do this was an acceptable service to God, because the Prophet David says in his Psalms, "He that praiseth the Lord honoureth him."

He made them to understand how happy they be that are freed from the encumbrances of that law which our forefathers groaned under: namely, from the legal sacrifices, and from the many ceremonies of the Levitical law; freed from circumcision, and from the strict observation of the Jewish Sabbath, and the like. And he made them know, that having received so many and great blessings, by being born since the days of our Saviour, it must be an acceptable sacrifice to Almighty God, for them to acknowledge those blessings daily, and stand up and worship, and say as Zacharias did, "Blessed be the Lord God of Israel, for he hath—in our days—visited and redeemed his people; and—he hath in our days—remembered, and showed that mercy, which by the mouth of the prophets he promised to our forefathers; and this he has done according to his holy covenant made with them." And he made them to understand that we live to see and enjoy the benefit of it, in his birth, in his life, his passion, his resurrection, and ascension into heaven, where he now sits sensible of all our temptations and infirmities; and where he is at this present time making intercession for us, to his and our Father: and therefore they ought daily to express their public gratulations, and say daily with Zacharias, "Blessed be the Lord God of Israel, that hath thus visited and thus redeemed his people." These were some of the reasons by which Mr. Herbert instructed his congregation for the use of the psalms and hymns appointed to be daily sung or said in the Church service.

He informed them also when the priest did pray only for the congregation, and not for himself; and when they did only pray for him; as namely, after the repetition of the creed before he proceeds to pray the Lord's Prayer, or any of the appointed collects, the priest is directed to kneel down and pray for them, saying, "The Lord be with you;" and when they pray for him, saying, "And with thy spirit;" and then they join together in the following collects: and he assured them, that when there is such mutual love, and such joint prayers offered for each other, then the holy angels look down from heaven, and are ready to carry such charitable desires to God Almighty, and he is ready to receive them; and that a Christian congregation calling thus upon God with one heart, and one voice, and in one reverent and humble posture, looks as beautifully as Jerusalem, that is at peace with itself.

He instructed them also why the prayer of our Lord is prayed often in every full service of the Church; namely, at the conclusion of the several parts of that service; and prayed then, not only because it was composed and commanded by our Jesus that made it, but as a perfect pattern for our less perfect forms of prayer, and therefore fittest to sum up and conclude all our imperfect petitions.

He instructed them also, that as by the second commandment we are required not to bow down, or worship an idol, or false God; so, by the contrary rule, we are to bow down and kneel, or stand up and worship the true God. And he instructed them why the Church required the congregation to stand up at the repetition of the creeds; namely, because they thereby declare both their obedience to the Church, and an assent to that faith into which they had been baptized. And he taught them, that in that shorter creed or doxology, so often repeated daily, they also stood up to testify their belief to be, that "the God that they trusted in was one God, and three persons; the Father, the Son, and the Holy Ghost; to whom they and the priest gave glory." And because there had been heretics that had denied some of those three persons to be God, therefore the congregation stood up and honoured him, by confessing and saying, "It was so in the beginning, is now so, and shall ever be so, world without end." And all gave their assent to this belief, by standing up and saying Amen.

He instructed them also what benefit they had by the Church's appointing the celebration of holy-days and the excellent use of them, namely, that they were set apart for particular commemorations of particular mercies received from Almighty God; and—as Reverend Mr. Hooker says—to be the landmarks to distinguish times; for by them we are taught to take notice how time passes by us, and that we ought not to let the years pass without a celebration of praise for those mercies which those days give us occasion to remember, and therefore they were to note that the year is appointed to begin the 25th day of March; a day in which we commemorate the angel's appearing to the Blessed Virgin, with the joyful tidings that "she should conceive and bear a son, that should be the redeemer of mankind." And she did so forty weeks after this joyful salutation; namely, at our Christmas; a day in which we commemorate his birth with joy and praise: and that eight days after this happy birth we celebrate his circumcision; namely, in that which we call New Year's day. And that, upon that day which we call Twelfth day, we commemorate the manifestation of the unsearchable riches of Jesus to the Gentiles: and that that day we also celebrate the memory of his goodness in sending a star to guide the three wise men from the east to Bethlehem, that they might there worship, and present him with their oblation of gold, frankincense, and myrrh. And he—Mr. Herbert—instructed them that Jesus was forty days after his birth presented by his blessed mother in the temple; namely, on that day which we call "The Purification or the Blessed Virgin, Saint Mary." And he instructed them that by the Lent-fast we imitate and commemorate our Saviour's humiliation in fasting forty days; and that we ought to endeavour to be like him in purity: and that on Good Friday we commemorate and condole his crucifixion; and on Easter commemorate his glorious resurrection. And he taught them that after Jesus had manifested himself to his disciples to be "that Christ that was crucified, dead and buried;" and by his appearing and conversing with his disciples for the space of forty days after his resurrection, he then, and not till then, ascended into heaven in the sight of those disciples; namely, on that day which we call the ascension, or Holy Thursday. And that we then celebrate the performance of the promise which he made to his disciples at or before his ascension; namely, "that though he left them, yet he would send them the Holy Ghost to be their comforter;" and that he did so on that day which the Church calls Whitsunday. Thus the Church keeps an historical and circular commemoration of times, as they pass by us; of such times as ought to incline us to occasional praises, for the particular blessings which we do, or might receive, by those holy commemorations.

He made them know also why the Church hath appointed ember-weeks; and to know the reason why the commandments, and the epistles and gospels, were to be read at the altar or communion table: why the priest was to pray the Litany kneeling; and why to pray some collects standing: and he gave them many other observations, fit for his plain congregation, but not fit for me now to mention; for I must set limits to my pen, and not make that a treatise which I intended to be a much shorter account than I have made it; but I have done, when I have told the reader that he was constant in catechising every Sunday in the afternoon, and that his catechising was after his second lesson, and in the pulpit; and that he never exceeded his half-hour, and was always so happy as to have an obedient and full congregation.

And to this I must add, that if he were at any time too zealous in his sermons, it was in reproving the indecencies of the people's behaviour in the time of divine service; and of those ministers that huddle up the Church prayers, without a visible reverence and affection; namely, such as seemed to say the Lord's Prayer or a collect in a breath. But for himself, his custom was to stop betwixt every collect, and give the people time to consider what they had prayed, and to force their desires affectionately to God, before he engaged them into new petitions.

And by this account of his diligence to make his parishioners understand what they prayed, and why they praised and adored their Creator, I hope I shall the more easily obtain the reader's belief to the following account of Mr. Herbert's own practice; which was to appear constantly with his wife and three nieces—the daughters of a deceased sister—and his whole family, twice every day at the Church prayers in the chapel, which does almost join his parsonage-house. And for the time of his appearing, it was strictly at the canonical hours of ten and four: and then and there he lifted up pure and charitable hands to God in the midst of the congregation. And he would joy to have spent that time in that place, where the honour of his master Jesus dwelleth; and there, by that inward devotion which he testified constantly by an humble behaviour and visible adoration, he, like Joshua, brought not only "his own household thus to serve the Lord;" but brought most of his parishioners, and many gentlemen in the neighbourhood, constantly to make a part of his congregation twice a day: and some of the meaner sort of his parish did so love and reverence Mr. Herbert, that they would let their plough rest when Mr. Herbert's saint's-bell rung to prayers, that they might also offer their devotions to God with him; and would then return back to their plough. And his most holy life was such, that it begot such reverence to God, and to him, that they thought themselves the happier when they carried Mr. Herbert's blessing back with them to their labour. Thus powerful was his reason and example to persuade others to a practical piety and devotion.

And his constant public prayers did never make him to neglect his own private devotions, nor those prayers that he thought himself bound to perform with his family, which always were a set form, and not long; and he did always conclude them with a collect which the Church hath appointed for the day or week. Thus he made every day's sanctity a step towards that kingdom, where impurity cannot enter.

His chiefest recreation was music, in which heavenly art he was a most excellent master, and did himself compose many divine hymns and anthems, which he set and sung to his lute or viol: and though he was a lover of retiredness, yet his love to music was such, that he went usually twice every week, on certain appointed days, to the Cathedral Church in Salisbury; and at his return would say, "That his time spent in prayer, and cathedral-music, elevated his soul, and was his heaven upon earth." But before his return thence to Bemerton, he would usually sing and play his part at an appointed private music-meeting; and, to justify this practice, he would often say, "Religion does not banish mirth, but only moderates and sets rules to it."

And as his desire to enjoy his heaven upon earth drew him twice every week to Salisbury, so his walks thither were the occasion of many happy accidents to others; of which I will mention some few.

In one of his walks to Salisbury, he overtook a gentleman, that is still living in that city; and in their walk together, Mr. Herbert took a fair occasion to talk with him, and humbly begged to be excused, if he asked him some account of his faith; and said, "I do this the rather because though you are not of my parish, yet I receive tithe from you by the hand of your tenant; and, sir, I am the bolder to do it, because I know there be some sermon-bearers that be like those fishes that always live in salt water, and yet are always fresh."

After which expression, Mr. Herbert asked him some needful questions, and having received his answer, gave him such rules for the trial of his sincerity, and for a practical piety, and in so loving and meek a manner, that the gentleman did so fall in love with him, and his discourse, that he would often contrive to meet him in his walk to Salisbury, or to attend him back to Bemerton; and still mentions the name of Mr. George Herbert with veneration, and still praiseth God for the occasion of knowing him.

In another of his Salisbury walks he met with a neighbour minister; and after some friendly discourse betwixt them, and some condolement for the decay of piety, and too general contempt of the clergy, Mr. Herbert took occasion to say:

"One cure for these distempers would be for the clergy themselves to keep the ember-weeks strictly, and beg of their parishioners to join with them in fasting and prayers for a more religious clergy.

"And another cure would be for themselves to restore the great and neglected duty of catechising, on which the salvation of so many of the poor and ignorant lay-people does depend; but principally, that the clergy themselves would be sure to live unblamably; and that the dignified clergy especially which preach temperance would avoid surfeiting and take all occasions to express a visible humility and charity in their lives; for this would force a love and an imitation, and an unfeigned reverence from all that knew them to be such." (And for proof of this, we need no other testimony than the life and death of Dr. Lake, late Lord Bishop of Bath and Wells.) "This," said Mr. Herbert, "would be a cure for the wickedness and growing atheism of our age. And, my dear brother, till this be done by us, and done in earnest, let no man expect a reformation of the manners of the laity; for 'tis not learning, but this, this only that must do it; and, till then, the fault must lie at our doors."

In another walk to Salisbury he saw a poor man with a poorer horse, that was fallen under his load: they were both in distress, and needed present help; which Mr. Herbert perceiving, put off his canonical coat, and helped the poor man to unload, and after to load, his horse. The poor man blessed him for it, and he blessed the poor man; and was so like the good Samaritan, that he gave him money to refresh both himself and his horse; and told him, "That if he loved himself he should be merciful to his beast." Thus he left the poor man: and at his coming to his musical friends at Salisbury, they began to wonder that Mr. George Herbert, which used to be so trim and clean, came into that company so soiled and discomposed: but he told them the occasion. And when one of the company told him "He had disparaged himself by so dirty an employment," his answer was, "That the thought of what he had done would prove music to him at midnight; and that the omission of it would have upbraided and made discord in his conscience, whensoever he should pass by that place: for if I be bound to pray for all that be in distress, I am sure that I am bound, so far as it is in my power, to practise what I pray for. And though I do not wish for the like occasion every day, yet let me tell you, I would not willingly pass one day of my life without comforting a sad soul, or showing mercy; and I praise God for this occasion. And now let's tune our instruments."

Thus, as our blessed Saviour, after his resurrection, did take occasion to interpret scripture to Cleopas, and that other disciple, which he met with and accompanied in their journey to Emmaus; so Mr. Herbert, in his path toward heaven, did daily take any fair occasion to instruct the ignorant, or comfort any that were in affliction; and did always confirm his precepts by showing humility and mercy, and ministering grace to the hearers.

And he was most happy in his wife's unforced compliance with his acts of charity, whom he made his almoner, and paid constantly into her hand a tenth penny of what money he received for tithe, and gave her power to dispose that to the poor of his parish, and with it a power to dispose a tenth part of the corn that came yearly into his barn: which trust she did most faithfully perform, and would often offer to him an account of her stewardship, and as often beg an enlargement of his bounty; for she rejoiced in the employment: and this was usually laid out by her in blankets and shoes for some such poor people as she knew to stand in most need of them. This as to her charity.—And for his own, he set no limits to it: nor did ever turn his face from any that he saw in want, but would relieve them; especially his poor neighbours; to the meanest of whose houses he would go, and inform himself of their wants, and relieve them cheerfully, if they were in distress; and would always praise God, as much for being willing, as for being able to do it. And when he was advised by a friend to be more frugal, because he might have children, his answer was, "He would not see the danger of want so far off: but being the scripture does so commend charity, as to tell us that charity is the top of Christian virtues, the covering of sins, the fulfilling of the law, the life of faith; and that charity hath a promise of the blessings of this life, and of a reward in that life which is to come: being these, and more excellent things are in scripture spoken of thee, O charity! and that, being all my tithes and Church dues are a deodate from thee, O my God! make me, O my God! so far to trust thy promise, as to return them back to thee; and by thy grace I will do so, in distributing them to any of thy poor members that are in distress, or do but bear the image of Jesus my master." "Sir," said he to his friend, "my wife hath a competent maintenance secured her after my death; and therefore, as this is my prayer, so this my resolution shall, by God's grace, be unalterable."

This may be some account of the excellencies of the active part of his life; and thus he continued, till a consumption so weakened him as to confine him to his house, or to the chapel, which does almost join to it; in which he continued to read prayers constantly twice every day, though he were very weak: in one of which times of his reading his wife observed him to read in pain, and told him so, and that it wasted his spirits, and weakened him; and he confessed it did, but said, his "life could not be better spent than in the service of his master Jesus, who had done and suffered so much for him. But," said he, "I will not be wilful; for though my spirit be willing, yet I find my flesh is weak; and therefore Mr. Bostock shall be appointed to read prayers for me to-morrow; and I will now be only a hearer of them, till this mortal shall put on immortality." And Mr. Bostock did the next day undertake and continue this happy employment till Mr. Herbert's death. This Mr. Bostock was a learned and virtuous man, an old friend of Mr. Herbert's, and then his curate to the church of Fulston, which is a mile from Bemerton, to which church Bemerton is but a chapel of ease. And this Mr. Bostock did also constantly supply the Church service for Mr. Herbert in that chapel, when the music-meeting at Salisbury caused his absence from it.

About one month before his death, his friend Mr. Farrer, —for an account of whom I am by promise indebted to the reader, and intend to make him sudden payment,—hearing of Mr. Herbert's sickness, sent Mr. Edmund Duncon—who is now rector of Friar Barnet in the county of Middlesex— from his house of Gidden Hall, which is near to Huntingdon, to see Mr. Herbert, and to assure him he wanted not his daily prayers for his recovery; and Mr. Duncon was to return back to Gidden, with an account of Mr. Herbert's condition. Mr. Duncon found him weak, and at that time lying on his bed, or on a pallet; but at his seeing Mr. Duncon he raised himself vigorously, saluted him, and with some earnestness inquired the health of his brother Farrer; of which Mr. Duncon satisfied him, and after some discourse of Mr. Farrer's holy life, and the manner of his constant serving God, he said to Mr. Duncon,—"Sir, I see by your habit that you are a priest, and I desire you to pray with me:" which being granted, Mr. Duncon asked him, "What prayers?" To which Mr. Herbert's answer was, "O sir! the prayers of my mother, the Church of England: no other prayers are equal to them! But at this time I beg of you to pray only the Litany, for I am weak and faint:" and Mr. Duncon did so. After which, and some other discourse of Mr. Farrer, Mrs. Herbert provided Mr. Duncon a plain supper, and a clean lodging, and he betook himself to rest. This Mr. Duncon tells me; and he tells me that, at his first view of Mr. Herbert, he saw majesty and humility so reconciled in his looks and behaviour, as begot in him an awful reverence for his person; and says, "his discourse was so pious, and his motion so genteel and meek, that after almost forty years, yet they remain still fresh in his memory."

The next morning Mr. Duncon left him, and betook himself to a journey to Bath, but with a promise to return back to him within five days; and he did so: but before I shall say anything of what discourse then fell betwixt them two, I will pay my promised account of Mr. Farrer.

Mr. Nicholas Farrer—who got the reputation of being called St. Nicholas at the age of six years—was born in London, and doubtless had good education in his youth; but certainly was, at an early age, made Fellow of Clare Hall in Cambridge; where he continued to be eminent for his piety, temperance, and learning. About the twenty-sixth year of his age he betook himself to travel: in which he added to his Latin and Greek a perfect knowledge of all the languages spoken in the western parts of our Christian world; and understood well the principles of their religion, and of their manner, and the reasons of their worship. In this his travel he met with many persuasions to come into a communion with that Church which calls itself Catholic; but he returned from his travels as he went, eminent for his obedience to his mother, the Church of England. In his absence from England, Mr. Farrer's father—who was a merchant—allowed him a liberal maintenance; and, not long after his return into England, Mr. Farrer had, by the death of his father, or an elder brother, or both, an estate left him that enabled him to purchase land to the value of four or five hundred pounds a year; the greatest part of which land was at Little Gidden, four or six miles from Huntingdon, and about eighteen from Cambridge; which place he chose for the privacy of it, and for the hall, which had the parish church or chapel belonging and adjoining near to it; for Mr. Farrer, having seen the manners and vanities of the world, and found them to be, as Mr. Herbert says, "a nothing between two dishes," did so contemn it, that he resolved to spend the remainder of his life in mortifications, and in devotion, and charity, and to be always prepared for death. And his life was spent thus:

He and his family, which were like a little college, and about thirty in number, did most of them keep Lent and all ember-weeks strictly, both in fasting and using all those mortifications and prayers that the Church hath appointed to be then used: and he and they did the like constantly on Fridays, and on the vigils or eves to be fasted before the saints' days: and this frugality and abstinence turned to the relief of the poor: but this was but a part of his charity; none but God and he knew the rest.

This family, which I have said to be in number about thirty, were a part of them his kindred, and the rest chosen to be of a temper fit to be moulded into a devout life; and all of them were for their dispositions serviceable, and quiet, and humble, and free from scandal. Having thus fitted himself for his family, he did, about the year 1630, betake himself to a constant and methodical service of God; and it was in this manner:—He, being accompanied with most of his family, did himself use to read the common prayers—for he was a deacon—every day, at the appointed hours of ten and four, in the parish church, which was very near his house, and which he had both repaired and adorned; for it was fallen into a great ruin, by reason of a depopulation of the village before Mr. Farrer bought the manor. And he did also constantly read the matins every morning at the hour of six, either in the church, or in an oratory, which was within his own house. And many of the family did there continue with him after the prayers were ended, and there they spent some hours in singing hymns, or anthems, sometimes in the church, and often to an organ in the oratory. And there they sometimes betook themselves to meditate, or to pray privately, or to read a part of the New Testament to themselves, or to continue their praying or reading the psalms; and in case the psalms were not always read in the day, then Mr. Farrer and others of the congregation did at night, at the ringing of a watch-bell, repair to the church or oratory, and there betake themselves to prayer and lauding God, and reading the psalms that had not been read in the day: and when these, or any part of the congregation, grew weary or faint, the watch-bell was rung, sometimes before, and sometimes after midnight; and then another part of the family rose, and maintained the watch, sometimes by praying, or singing lauds to God, or reading the psalms; and when, after some hours, they aslo grew weary or faint, then they rung the watch-bell and were also relieved by some of the former, or by a new part of the society, which continued their devotions—as hath been mentioned—until morning. And it is to be noted, that in this continued serving of God, the psalter or the whole book of psalms, was in every four and twenty hours sung or read over, from the first to the last verse: and this was done as constantly as the sun runs his circle every day about the world, and then begins again the same instant that it ended.

Thus did Mr. Farrer and his happy family serve God day and night; thus did they always behave themselves as in his presence. And they did always eat and drink by the strictest rules of temperance; eat and drink so as to be ready to rise at midnight, or at the call of the watch-bell, and perform their devotions to God. And it is fit to tell the reader, that many of the clergy, that were more inclined to practical piety and devotion than to doubtful and needless disputations, did often come to Gidden Hall, and make themselves a part of that happy society, and stay a week or more, and then join with Mr. Farrer and the family in these devotions, and assist and ease him or them in their watch by night. And these various devotions had never less than two of the domestic family in the night; and the watch was always kept in the church or oratory, unless in extreme cold winter nights, and then it was maintained in a parlour, which had a fire in it; and the parlour was fitted for that purpose. And this course of piety, and great liberality to his poor neighbours, Mr. Farrer maintained till his death, which was in the year 1639.

Mr. Farrer's and Mr. Herbert's devout lives were both so noted, that the general report of their sanctity gave them occasion to renew that slight acquaintance which was begun at their being contemporaries in Cambridge; and this new holy friendship was long maintained without any interview, but only by loving and endearing letters. And one testimony of their friendship and pious designs may appear by Mr. Farrer's commending the *Considerations of John Valdesso*—a book which he had met with in his travels, and translated out of Spanish into English—to be examined and censored by Mr. Herbert before it was made public: which excellent book Mr. Herbert did read, and return back with many marginal notes, as they be now printed with it; and with them, Mr. Herbert's affectionate letter to Mr. Farrer.

This John Valdesso was a Spaniard, and was for his learning and virtue much valued and loved by the great Emperor Charles the Fifth, whom Valdesso had followed as a cavalier all the time of his long and dangerous wars: and when Valdesso grew old, and grew weary both of war and the world, he took his fair opportunity to declare to the Emperor that his resolution was to decline his Majesty's service, and betake himself to a quiet and contemplative life, "because there ought to be a vacancy of time betwixt fighting and dying." The Emperor had himself, for the same, or other like reasons, put on the same resolution: but God and himself did, till then, only know them; and he did therefore desire Valdesso to consider well of what he had said, and to keep his purpose within his own breast, till they two might have a second opportunity of a friendly discourse; which Valdesso promised to do.

In the meantime the Emperor appoints privately a day for him and Valdesso to meet again; and after a pious and free discourse, they both agreed on a certain day to receive the blessed sacrament publicly; and appointed an eloquent and devout friar to preach a sermon of contempt of the world, and of the happiness and benefit of a quiet and contemplative life; which the friar did most affectionately. After which sermon, the Emperor took occasion to declare openly, "That the preacher had begot in him a resolution to lay down his dignities, and to forsake the world, and betake himself to a monastical life." And he pretended he had persuaded John Valdesso to do the like: but this is most certain, that after the Emperor had called his son Philip out of England, and resigned to him all his kingdoms, that then the Emperor and John Valdesso did perform their resolutions.

This account of John Valdesso I received from a friend, that had it from the mouth of Mr. Farrer. And the reader may note that in this retirement John Valdesso writ his *Hundred and Ten Considerations,* and many other treatises of worth, which want a second Mr. Farrer to procure and translate them.

After this account of Mr. Farrer and John Valdesso, I proceed to my account of Mr. Herbert and Mr. Duncon, who according to his promise returned from Bath the fifth day, and then found Mr. Herbert much weaker than he left him; and therefore their discourse could not be long: but at Mr. Duncon's parting with him, Mr. Herbert spoke to this purpose: "Sir, I pray you give my brother Farrer an account of the decaying condition of my body, and tell him I beg him to continue his daily prayers for me; and let him know that I have considered, that God only is what he would be; and that I am, by his grace, become now so like him, as to be pleased with what pleaseth him; and tell him, that I do not repine but am pleased with my want of health: and tell him, my heart is fixed on that place where true joy is only to be found; and that I long to be there, and do wait for my appointed change with hope and patience." Having said this, he did, with so sweet a humility as seemed to exalt him, bow down to Mr. Duncon, and with a thoughtful and contented look, say to him, "Sir, I pray deliver this little book to my dear brother Farrer, and tell him he shall find in it a picture of the many spiritual conflicts that have passed betwixt God and my soul, before I could subject mine to the will of Jesus my master: in whose service I have now found perfect freedom. Desire him to read it; and then, if he can think it may turn to the advantage of any dejected poor soul, let it be made public; if not, let him burn it; for I and it are less than the least of God's mercies." Thus meanly did this humble man think of this excellent book, which now bears the name of *The Temple; or, Sacred*

Poems and Private Ejaculations; of which Mr. Farrer would say, "There was in it the picture of a divine soul in every page: and that the whole book was such a harmony of holy passions, as would enrich the world with pleasure and piety." And it appears to have done so; for there have been more than twenty thousand of them sold since the first impression.

And this ought to be noted, that when Mr. Farrer sent this book to Cambridge to be licensed for the press, the Vice-Chancellor would by no means allow the two so much noted verses,

> Religion stands a tiptoe in our land,
> Ready to pass to the American strand,

to be printed; and Mr. Farrer would by no means allow the book to be printed and want them. But after some time, and some arguments for and against their being made public, the Vice-Chancellor said, "I knew Mr. Herbert well, and know that he had many heavenly speculations, and was a divine poet: but I hope the world will not take him to be an inspired prophet, and therefore I license the whole book." So that it came to be printed without the diminution or addition of a syllable, since it was delivered into the hands of Mr. Duncon, save only that Mr. Farrer hath added that excellent preface that is printed before it.

At the time of Mr. Duncon's leaving Mr. Herbert,—which was about three weeks before his death,—his old and dear friend Mr. Woodnot came from London to Bemerton, and never left him till he had seen him draw his last breath, and closed his eyes on his death-bed. In this time of his decay, he was often visited and prayed for by all the clergy that lived near to him, especially by his friends the Bishop and Prebends of the Cathedral Church in Salisbury; but by none more devoutly than his wife, his three nieces,—then a part of his family,—and Mr. Woodnot, who were the sad witnesses of his daily decay; to whom he would often speak to this purpose: "I now look back upon the pleasures of my life past, and see the content I have taken in beauty, in wit, in music, and pleasant conversation, are now all past by me like a dream, or as a shadow that returns not, and are now all become dead to me, or I to them; and I see, that as my father and generation hath done before me, so I also shall now suddenly (with Job) make my bed also in the dark; and I praise God I am prepared for it; and I praise him that I am not to learn patience now I stand in such need of it; and that I have practised mortification, and endeavoured to die daily, that I might not die eternally; and my hope is, that I shall shortly leave this valley of tears, and be free from all fevers and pain; and, which will be a more happy condition, I shall be free from sin, and all the temptations and anxieties that attend it: and this being past, I shall dwell in the New Jerusalem; dwell there with men made perfect; dwell where these eyes shall see my master and Saviour Jesus; and with him see my dear mother, and all my relations and friends. But I must die, or not come to that happy place. And this is my content, that I am going daily towards it: and that every day which I have lived, hath taken a part of my appointed time from me; and that I shall live the less time, for having lived this and the day past." These, and the like expressions, which he uttered often, may be said to be his enjoyment of heaven before he enjoyed it. The Sunday before his death, he rose suddenly from his bed or couch, called for one of his instruments, took it into his hand, and said,—

My God, my God,
My music shall find thee,
  And every string
Shall have his attribute to sing.

And having tuned it, he played and sung—

  The Sundays of man's life,
Threaded together on time's string,
Make bracelets to adorn the wife
Of the eternal glorious King:
On Sundays Heaven's door stands ope;
Blessings are plentiful and rife,
  More plentiful than hope.

Thus he sung on earth such hymns and anthems as the angels, and he, and Mr. Farrer now sing in heaven.

Thus he continued meditating, and praying, and rejoicing, till the day of his death; and on that day said to Mr. Woodnot, "My dear friend, I am sorry I have nothing to present to my merciful God but sin and misery; but the first is pardoned, and a few hours will now put a period to the latter; for I shall suddenly go hence, and be no more seen." Upon which expression Mr. Woodnot took occasion to remember him of the re-edifying Layton Church, and his many acts of mercy. To which he made answer, saying, "They be good works, if they be sprinkled with the blood of Christ, and not otherwise." After this discourse he became more restless, and his soul seemed to be weary of her earthly tabernacle; and this uneasiness became so visible, that his wife, his three nieces, and Mr. Woodnot stood constantly about his bed, beholding him with sorrow, and an unwillingness to lose the sight of him, whom they could not hope to see much longer. As they stood thus beholding him, his wife observed him to breathe faintly, and with much trouble, and observed him to fall into a sudden agony; which so surprised her, that she fell into a sudden passion, and required of him to know how he did. To which his answer was, "that he had passed a conflict with his last enemy, and had overcome him by the merits of his master Jesus." After which answer he looked up, and saw his wife and nieces weeping to an extremity, and charged them, if they loved him, to withdraw into the next room, and there pray every one alone for him; for nothing but their lamentations could make his death uncomfortable. To which request their sighs and tears would not suffer them to make any reply; but they yielded him a sad obedience, leaving only with him Mr. Woodnot and Mr. Bostock. Immediately after they had left him, he said to Mr. Bostock, "Pray, sir, open that door, then look into that cabinet, in which you may easily find my last will, and give it into my hand": which being done, Mr. Herbert delivered it into the hand of Mr. Woodnot, and said, "My old friend, I here deliver you my last will, in which you will find that I have made you my sole executor for the good of my wife and nieces; and I desire you to show kindness to them, as they shall need it: I do not desire you to be just; for I know you will be so for your own sake; but I charge you, by the religion of our friendship, to be careful of them." And having obtained Mr. Woodnot's promise to be so, he said, "I am now ready to die." After which words he said, "Lord, forsake me not now my strength faileth me: but grant me mercy for the merits of my Jesus. And now, Lord —Lord, now receive my soul." And with those words he breathed forth his divine soul, without any apparent disturbance, Mr. Woodnot and Mr. Bostock attending his last breath, and closing his eyes.

Thus he lived, and thus he died, like a saint, unspotted of the world, full of alms-deeds, full of humility, and all the examples of a virtuous life; which I cannot conclude better, than with this borrowed observation:

—All must to their cold graves:
But the religious actions of the just
Smell sweet in death, and blossom in the dust.

Mr. George Herbert's have done so to this, and will doubtless do so to succeeding generations. I have but this to say more of him: that if Andrew Melvin died before him, then George Herbert died without an enemy. I wish—if God shall be so pleased—that I may be so happy as to die like him.

Iz. Wa.

There is a debt justly due to the memory of Mr. Herbert's virtuous wife; a part of which I will endeavour to pay, by a very short account of the remainder of her life, which shall follow.

She continued his disconsolate widow about six years, bemoaning herself, and complaining, that she had lost the delight of her eyes; but more that she had lost the spiritual guide for her poor soul; and would often say, "O that I had, like holy Mary, the mother of Jesus, treasured up all his sayings in my heart! But since I have not been able to do that, I will labour to live like him, that where he now is I may be also." And she would often say,—as the prophet David for his son Absalom,—"O that I had died for him!" Thus she continued mourning till time and conversation had so moderated her sorrows, that she became the happy wife of Sir Robert Cook, of Highnam, in the county of Gloucester, Knight. And though he put a high value on the excellent accomplishments of her mind and body, and was so like Mr. Herbert, as not to govern like a master, but as an affectionate husband; yet she would even to him often take occasion to mention the name of Mr. George Herbert, and say, that name must live in her memory till she put off mortality. By Sir Robert she had only one child, a daughter, whose parts and plentiful estate make her happy in this world, and her well using of them gives a fair testimony that she will be so in that which is to come.

Mrs. Herbert was the wife of Sir Robert eight years, and lived his widow about fifteen; all which time she took a pleasure in mentioning and commending the excellencies of Mr. George Herbert. She died in the year 1663, and lies buried at Highnam: Mr. Herbert in his own church, under the altar, and covered with a gravestone without any inscription.

This Lady Cook had preserved many of Mr. Herbert's private writings, which she intended to make public; but they and Highnam House were burnt together by the late rebels, and so lost to posterity. I. W.